CO-ORDINATED SCIENCE

GCSE BOOK 2

Ann Daniels, Colin Davies, Ken Dobson, Clive Griffin, Robin Pote, Richard Shewry, Peter Smith and Jim Stather

EDITED BY KEN DOBSON

CollinsEducational

An imprint of HarperCollinsPublishers

Collins Educational, an imprint of HarperCollins*Publishers*
77–85 Fulham Palace Road, Hammersmith, London W6 8JB

© Suffolk County Council 1993

First published 1993

ISBN 0 00 327826 3

Reprinted 1993

Designed by Derek Lee

Picture research by Marilyn Rawlings

Artwork by Pantek Arts, John Booth, Ray Burrows, Tom Cross, Gay Galsworthy, Jeremy Gower, Archie Plumb and Rodney Sutton

Cartoons by Martin Shovel

Index by Laurence Errington

Typeset by Dorchester Typesetting Group Ltd, Dorchester, Dorset DT1 1UA

Printed and bound in Hong Kong

Acknowledgements

The author and publishers are grateful to the following for permission to reproduce the copyright material on the pages indicated:

(T, top; B, bottom; C, centre; L, left; R, right)

Astronomical data taken from *A concise guide in colour: constellations*, by Antonín Rükl and Josef Klepešta, © 1969 The Hamlyn Publishing Group/ARIA.
51 T is based on data from The National Grid Company plc.
Data on page 116 was supplied by the Chemical Industries Association.

Ace Photo Agency/Arnand Razdan 59 TR, John David Begg 64, 94 TR, Vibert Stokes 94 BR
Allsport UK/Simon Bruty 169, Tony Duffy 202
Angloco 17 T
Animal Photography 80 C, 90
Ardea London/Wolfshead/Ben Osborne 26 TR, Tony Beamish 139 BL, J. E. Swedberg 154 TR
Aviation Picture Library 59 CL
Bart's Medical Picture Library 31 B, 107
BBC 103
Biophoto Associates 76 BR, 88 B, 94 TL
John Birdsall Photography 13 B, 21, 38 TC, 38 BR, 68 B, 71 TC, BC, BR
Pat Brindley 86 B
British Cement Association 61 C
British Diabetic Association 29
BT Pictures 104, 110
Adrian Cherry 191
Clynol 8
Cystic Fibrosis Research Trust 75 BR
Documentation Française/Heurtier 52 T
Alan Drummond/Federation of Astronomical Societies 160 T
Energy Technology Support Unit 52 C
English Electric Valve Company 108
Environmental Picture Library 17 BC, Irene R. Lengui 140 TR, P. Glendell 145 BR, Graham Burns 201 C

Vivien Fifield 80 T
Leslie Garland Picture Library 203
Genesis Space Photo Library 172, 185 BCL, 185 BCR
Geoscience Features Picture Library 2 TC, 13 T, 50 T, 61 BR, 77
Greenpeace Communications/Germain 140 BR, Morgan 154 C
Michael Holford 94 C, 177 B
Holt Studios International/Duncan Smith 88 T, Nigel Cattlin 129 B
Hulton Picture Company 66
Hutchison Library 85 T, 109
IBM UK 199 C
ICCE Photo Library/Mike Hoggett 51, Christer Agren 129 T
ICI Biopolymers 126 B
ICI Chemicals and Polymers 65
Image Bank/Color Day Productions 95 TR, Peter Miller 157
The Independent 149, 181
Andrew Lambert 2 TL, 4 C, 4 B, 9 C, 10, 14, 26 C, 27 T, 27 B, 28 T, 42, 44 TC, 45, 48 B, 54 BR, 71 TR, 76 TC, 124, 130, 199 CR
Frank Lane Agency/F. Polking 23 TL, S. McCutcheon 23 TR, Hosking 23 C, R. Bird 55, P. Perry 140 TL, B. Borrell 141, W. Wisniewski 145, 146 TL, H. D. Brandl 146 TL
Life Science Images/Ron Boardman 2 BR, 4 TR, 13 TC, 27 C, 34 T, 44 BL, 54 CR
London Transport 39 BL
Mansell Collection 160 B
Microscopix/Andrew Syred 23 CL, 98
Millbrook House Ltd/Hugh Ballontyne 189 B
Muscular Dystrophy Group 75 TL
National Grid 50 B
National Medical Slidebank 28 C
National Power 49
National Remote Sensing Centre/EOSAT 105 BR
Natural History Museum 87 T, 156
Olympia and York 38 T
Oxford University Press 113
Panos Pictures/Jeremy Hartley 145 BC, Tryeve Bolstad 152 B
Philips 199 B
Planet Earth Pictures/Norbert 23 BL, Warren Williams 153 L, R. Arnold 153 R, A. Mounter 164 TR, TC, Jonathan Scott 189 T, Wayne Harris 193 T, Ken King 193 B
Plant Genetic Systems, Gent 91
Polaroid 99
Bill Rafferty/English National Opera 95 BL
Ann Ronan at Image Select 48 T, 56, 85 T, 85 C
Royal Observatory, Edinburgh/J. D. Waldron 164 BR, 179 B
Science Photo Library/Dr. Jeremy Burgess 13 BC, Simon Fraser 17 TC, Petit Format/Nestlé 23 CR, Eric Grave 24, Chris Priest 31 CL, Novosti 34 B, Dr. J. Burgess 41, Peter Menzel 52 B, Françoise Sauze 53 CR, Adam Hart-Davis 61 TR, A. B. Dowsett 68, Carlos Goldin 69 C, David Taylor 69 B, A. Hart-Davis 76 TL, Peter Menzel 76 BC, Science Source 78 T, National Institute of Health 78 C, Dr. Gopal Murti 79 T, Eric Grave 79 B, Jean-Loup Charmet 87 B, Martin Dohrn 94 BL, David Parker 95 TR, Martin Dohrn 105 TR, Dr. Gene Feldman/NASA GSFC 106 C, ESA/PLI 106 B, Simon Fraser 116, Martin Bond 126 T, Martin Land 128 T, Bonnie Sue Rauch 144, NASA/GSFC 146 C, Sinclair Stammers 147, George East 161, Fred Espenak 162, George Post 164 L, NASA 174, John Sanford 176, NOAO 177 TR, Rev. Ronald Royer 178 T, Roger Ressmeyer/Starlight 178 B, Dept. Physics Imperial College 179 T, 179 C, NASA 184, 185 TL, TR, TC, BR, David A. Hardy 185 BL, Sinclair Stammers 192 B, Sheila Terry 201 T
Scotch Whisky Association 12
S. D. Pictures 2 TR, 5, 9 TL, 9 TR, 31 CR, 44 T, 44 BR, 59 CR
Shell UK 32
Still Pictures/Mark Edwards 139 TL
Telegraph Colour Library/Space Frontiers 183
Thames Water 18
Michael Thompson 139 TR
Tropix/J. Woollard 140 BL, D. Charlwood 145 TR, J. Schmid 145 TC, D. Charlwood 152 C
John Walmsley 38 BL, 53 BR
Tony Waltham 59 BL, 128 B
John S. Whiteley 38 BC

CONTENTS

PART 1   Topics for study

PART 2   Reference section

CHAPTER ONE

CHEMISTRY IN THE HOME

You have more chemicals at home than you think. The pictures show just some of these. We use them for cleaning, for cooking and for killing germs. We also use them for making nice smells and for treating some simple illnesses.

But the pictures only show the most obvious ones. As well as these there are also the chemicals we eat. After all, foods are really chemicals. There are also the fuels we use. And we mustn't forget all the chemical substances that the walls, floors, curtains and furniture are made from.

In fact, most of the everyday things we find at home are useful because of their *chemistry*. Some chemicals are *reactive*. We use them to change things — think of bleaches, disinfectants and other cleaners. Some chemical materials are very *unreactive* — so that they stay the same for a long time. We don't want saucepans and cutlery, or furniture and fittings to react with air, or with the chemicals that we use to clean them.

▲ Even very common household chemicals can be hazardous.

Some chemicals in your home are dangerous. They might be *corrosive* or *toxic*. Corrosive chemicals attack metals, cloth or even human tissue. 'Toxic' means poisonous. Your kitchen will have quite a lot of these dangerous chemicals. Dangerous chemicals must have a warning label on them. The label should also give you some first-aid advice. This tells you what to do if the chemical is swallowed, or gets into your eyes, for example. Are these

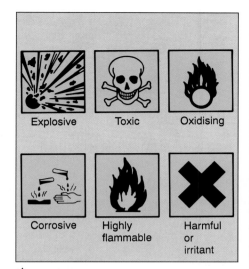

These symbols are all found on chemicals that you might have at home.

warnings good enough? Are the containers safe? — bearing in mind that homes often have young children in them! Activity 1 asks you to think about the safety of some household chemicals. Quite a lot of accidents happen because of home chemicals. This table shows the number of accidents that were serious enough to be reported in one year.

Some common household chemicals involved in home accidents with people of different ages (United Kingdom, 1987)

| Chemical | Number of accidents | | | | Total |
Age (years)	0–4	5–14	15–64	>64	
aspirin/painkillers	195	14	1	0	210
cough mixture	75	1	0	0	75
detergent	16	1	1	0	18
glues	21	1	1	0	23
hair treatments	17	1	0	2	20
liquid bleach	61	6	5	3	75
nail varnish remover	24	1	0	0	25
paint	13	0	0	0	13
paint stripper/thinner	8	0	0	0	8
perfume	32	0	0	0	32
shoe polish	3	0	0	0	3
toilet cleaner	39	0	1	1	41
turps/white spirit	71	2	1	1	75
vitamin pills	42	5	0	0	47
washing-up liquid	11	0	3	1	15
weedkiller	13	1	2	0	16
window cleaning fluid	12	1	0	0	13

Source: Department of Trade and Industry

Chemicals that you can find at home

Everyday name	Chemical name
baking powder	sodium hydrogencarbonate
salt	sodium chloride
bleach	strong solution of sodium hypochlorite
aspirin	acetylsalicylic acid
ammonia	ammonium hydroxide
'liver salts'	mixture of sucrose, citric acid, sodium hydrogencarbonate and magnesium sulphate
'gas'	methane
soap	mixture of sodium and potassium stearates and oleates, plus perfumes, etc.
'Tipp-Ex®'	1,1,1-trichloroethane
vinegar	ethanoic acid
washing soda	sodium carbonate
rubber	polyisoprene
peroxide	hydrogen peroxide
Perspex	polymethyl-methacrylate
Teflon	polytetrafluoroethene

Many home chemicals are the same as those you might find in the school laboratory. But their names may be different. Modern chemical names tell you exactly what the chemicals are made of. They are usually pure compounds. Household chemicals may have a trade name, or use the old-fashioned name. The table shows some everyday chemicals and their correct chemical names.

This chapter is about the use — and misuse — of chemicals in the home. It also tells you about how some of these chemicals are made. You should learn how to use chemicals safely and sensibly; and also learn some important chemical ideas.

▲
A collection of household acids.

Acids and alkalis: corrosive chemicals?

What do you first think about when you hear the word *acid*? A dangerous liquid? A liquid that burns? A sour taste? A lot of people have thoughts of a fuming liquid that burns through solid objects like table tops!

Concentrated sulphuric acid will dissolve away most of the human body! But we like the citric acid in oranges and lemons and put ethanoic acid on our fish and chips. Acetylsalicylic acid cures headaches – it is aspirin. But too much aspirin will kill us.

In the laboratory we must take proper precautions when we use acids. Even if they are weak we still need to protect our eyes and immediately wash any spills with plenty of water.

Look at the photograph (above, right). You will see a selection of familiar-looking liquids that are all acids. Why should one of these be dangerous but not the others?

The second picture shows substances that are all *alkalis*. Alkalis are the opposites of acids. They are just as useful, but they can be just as dangerous as acids.

▼
Household alkalis.

Some naturally occurring acids and where they are found.

Acid	Where found
Acetic or ethanoic	Vinegar
Citric	Oranges and lemons
Oxalic (ethanedioic acid)	Rhubarb leaves
Hydrochloric	In your stomach!

Some common acids used in the laboratory

Acid	Chemical formula
Sulphuric	H_2SO_4
Hydrochloric	HCl
Nitric	HNO_3

Some common alkalis used in the laboratory

Alkali	Chemical formula
Sodium hydroxide	$NaOH$
Potassium hydroxide	KOH
Ammonium hydroxide	NH_4OH
Calcium hydroxide (called lime water in solution)	$Ca(OH)_2$

Indicators and the pH scale

How can we tell the difference between an acid and an alkali? Some natural colours in plants change when placed in an acid or an alkali. Beetroot and blackcurrant juices will do this, but the one most commonly used is *litmus*. Litmus is a natural dye made from tiny plants called lichens. Litmus will be red in acids and blue in alkalis. Chemicals that change their colour depending on the acidity or alkalinity of the liquid they are testing are called *indicators*.

Other examples of indicators are universal indicator and methyl orange.

How can we tell how strong an acid or alkali is? Acids and alkalis contain certain ions. Ions are electrically charged particles dissolved in water. Acids are solutions that contain hydrogen ions (H^+) and alkalis

▲
Litmus in an acid solution (left) and an alkali.

contain hydroxide ions (OH^-). The strong acids and alkalis contain more of these ions and the weak ones contain fewer.

The strength of an acid or alkali is measured on the pH scale. The scale is a set of numbers running from 0 to 14. Solutions with pH less than 7 are acidic, those with pH more than 7 are alkaline. The middle number, pH 7, indicates a neutral substance, which is neither acid nor alkali.

Litmus is only useful in finding out whether a solution is an acid or an alkali. To find out how *strongly* acidic or alkaline a solution is, we need a universal indicator.

Universal indicator has a range of colours and each colour corresponds with a certain pH number.

▼
Some common household substances on the pH scale.

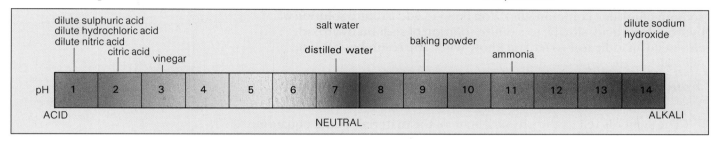

Look at the pH numbers of some common solutions found in the laboratory and around the home. The strong acids have the lowest pH numbers and the strong alkalis the highest pH numbers.

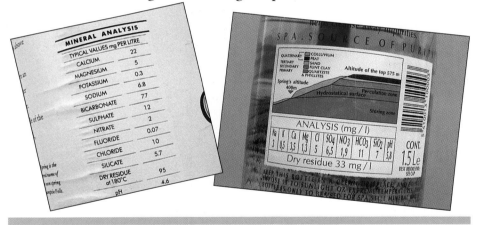

◄
Sparkling and still mineral waters have different pH values. Why do you think this is?

Acids vs alkalis – neutralisation

One effect of acids and alkalis being opposites is that they can *neutralise* each other. This means that they cancel each other out. This effect is useful in clearing up acid spills, or treating insect bites! An ant bite stings because the ant squirts formic acid into the wound. A mild alkali like baking soda will neutralise the formic acid. You can use the same treatment for bee stings. But wasp stings are alkaline, so they can be treated with a mild acid, like vinegar.

A neutral solution has a pH of 7 – like distilled water. In fact, when acids neutralise an alkali the reaction produces water. It is made from the positive (H^+) and negative (OH^-) ions that these chemicals contain:

$$H^+_{(aq)} + OH^-_{(aq)} \rightarrow H_2O_{(l)}.$$

Bases

The correct name for a substance that can neutralise an acid is a *base*. An alkali is simply a base that can dissolve in water.

Neutralisation reactions

When a base neutralises an acid, water is always formed. But the reaction also produces another substance, called a *salt*.

$$acid + base \rightarrow salt + water$$

An interesting example that you could try in the laboratory is to make sodium chloride (common salt). You need to add a dilute solution of hydrochloric acid, slowly, to a dilute solution of sodium hydroxide. You also need an indicator to let you know when the result has become neutral:

hydrochloric acid + sodium hydroxide → sodium chloride + water,
$$HCl_{(aq)} + NaOH_{(aq)} \rightarrow NaCl_{(aq)} + H_2O_{(1)}.$$

(The symbols tell us the physical state of the materials in the equation: (aq), aqueous solution; (1), liquid; sometimes you will see (g), for a gas.)
Other useful neutralisation reactions are:

nitric acid + potassium hydroxide → potassium nitrate + water,
$$HNO_3 + KOH \rightarrow KNO_3 + H_2O.$$

stearic acid + sodium hydroxide → sodium stearate + water.
(soap)

(Stearic acid is more correctly called *octadecanoic acid*.)
With carbonates the action of the acid is to produce a salt, water and carbon dioxide gas, which bubbles off:

hydrochloric + calcium → calcium + carbon + water,
acid   carbonate   chloride   dioxide
$$2HCl_{(aq)} + CaCO_{3(s)} \rightarrow CaCl_{2(aq)} + CO_{2(g)} + H_2O_{(1)}.$$

Agricultural fertilisers
A very useful fertiliser, ammonium phosphate, can be made by neutralising phosphoric acid with ammonium hydroxide:

$$H_3PO_{4(aq)} + 3NH_4OH_{(aq)} \rightarrow (NH_4)_3PO_{4(aq)} + 3H_2O_{(1)}.$$

Acid spills
These can be made harmless by adding just the right amount of alkali. But can you tell if you have added too much or too little? The neutralisation may be done more safely by using a substance like baking powder. Why?

Ammonia

Ammonia (ammonium hydroxide, NH_4OH) is another useful, but dangerous, household alkali. It has a very strong smell and is used as a cleaner because it dissolves grease. But its main use in is fertilisers. See Chapter 4, *Controlling chemical reactions* and Extension task 8.

Neutralising acid soils

Some soils may be too acidic to allow plants to grow properly. A pH of 5.5 or below will need to be neutralised to support the healthy growth of plants. Farmers and gardeners will add *lime* to the soil (an alkali called calcium hydroxide).

This reaction is getting hot!

Try adding equal volumes of a dilute acid to a dilute alkali. It gets warm. Where does this energy come from?

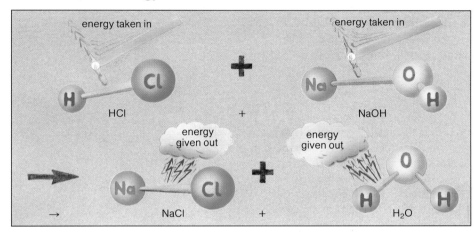

▲ Plants are sensitive to soil pH.

◄ Energy is absorbed when chemical bonds are broken, and released when bonds are formed. In this reaction, more energy is released than was needed to break the bonds. This is called an *exothermic* reaction.

In the diagram, the energy that is given out from the new bonds forming is greater than the energy being absorbed by the old bonds breaking. Energy is therefore given out during neutralisation reactions and the reaction mixture will become warm.

Energy is always involved when a chemical reaction takes place; it is either released (an *exothermic* reaction) or has to be supplied (*endothermic*). There is more about this in Chapter 4, *Controlling chemical reactions*.

Oxidation and reduction

You have already learned about some chemical and biological changes where oxygen has combined with a substance. For example:

- a simple chemical change: magnesium burning:
  $2Mg + O_2 \rightarrow 2MgO$ (plus energy release);
- a biological change, as in respiration: the slow 'burning' of a sugar:
  $C_6H_{12}O_6 + 6O_2 \rightarrow 6CO_2 + 6H_2O$ (plus energy release).

When a substance gains oxygen in this way it has been *oxidised*. If oxygen had been taken away it would have been *reduced*. See Chapter 4 for more about oxidation and reduction.

Chemicals that are good at adding oxygen to other chemicals are called *oxidising agents*. Chemicals that do the opposite are called *reducing agents*.

Bleaches and stains

Stains made by natural dyes can usually be removed by using an oxidising agent. This is called bleaching. Household bleach contains the very active oxidiser *chlorine*. Bleach is useful for taking ink stains away, or giving your blue jeans a nice faded look. But there is always the problem of washing away the excess bleach. If it is left on the fabric, the bleach will 'rot' away the material. And, of course, you shouldn't use it for coloured clothes – or for your hair.

Hydrogen peroxide is another useful oxidising agent. It has the formula H_2O_2, which is like water, with an extra oxygen atom. This extra atom is held loosely, and so quickly joins on to other chemicals. Hydrogen peroxide, in very dilute solutions, is used for bleaching hair. Oddly enough, oxygen can be a poison – too much is deadly to all life. This means that hydrogen peroxide can be used as an antiseptic because it kills germs.

The chemistry of the perm

Oxidising and reducing agents are also used at the hairdressers when you have a perm. Hair is composed of a very long-chained protein molecule called keratin. At regular intervals along the length of the keratin are molecules of cystine – an amino acid. Cystine contains sulphur atoms, which, when linked together form strong 'bridges'. These bridges keep each hair in its shape. A reducing agent breaks these bridges and allows the hair to be reshaped. The bridges are reformed when an oxidising agent is added.

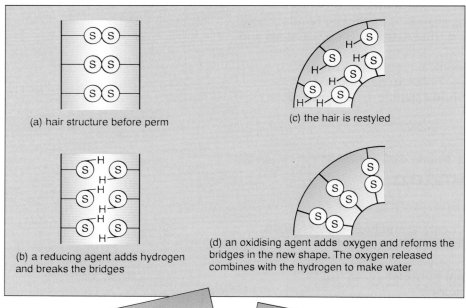

(a) hair structure before perm

(c) the hair is restyled

(b) a reducing agent adds hydrogen and breaks the bridges

(d) an oxidising agent adds oxygen and reforms the bridges in the new shape. The oxygen released combines with the hydrogen to make water

◄ Breaking and making chemical bonds in hair: how the chemicals in a perm work.

◄ Changing the chemistry of a hair fibre with perming solution gives your hair a totally different shape!

Why do cut apples go brown?

When air reaches food, oxygen can react with some of the chemicals in the food and cause a change in its colour and taste. The reaction is helped to go faster by *enzymes* in the apple.

Vitamin C is a reducing agent and can stop this oxidation from happening. Vitamin C (ascorbic acid) is a very common additive in food as an *anti-oxidant*, but of course it is also useful to have a little extra in our diet. It is also added to bread as a 'flour improver', where its reducing properties are needed. Look at some food labels to see how many foods contain an 'anti-oxidant'.

▲
Once the inside of an apple is exposed to oxygen in the air, oxidation occurs, which causes the brown colour. Enzymes (catalysts) in the apple speed up this process.

Enzymes — the biological catalysts

Enzymes are 'living catalysts'. They can speed up biological reactions without being used up themselves. We use the enzymes in yeast to break down sugars to make alcohol and carbon dioxide in a process known as fermentation. We also use enzymes in 'biological' washing powders. There is more about enzymes in Chapter 7, *Chemical economics*.

▲
Most enzymes do not work well when the pH is too far away from neutral. The browning process in the salad on the left has been stopped by adding lemon juice that contains citric acid, which has lowered the pH.

The kitchen laboratory

'Laboratory' means 'work room'. The kitchen is the work room of your home. A modern kitchen has a lot of expensive equipment for heating and cooling some very complicated chemicals.

When chemicals are heated two different things can happen. The chemicals could *melt* or *boil*. Or something more permanent could happen. Fat first melts. As it gets hotter it might boil. If it gets too hot it might break down into rather nasty fumes — or it could catch fire.

Melting and boiling are called *physical* changes. No new substances have been made; the fat has just changed into a liquid and then into a gas. Solid, liquid and gas are the three *states of matter*. The fat is said to have changed its state.

▼
Molecular changes when a substance changes state.

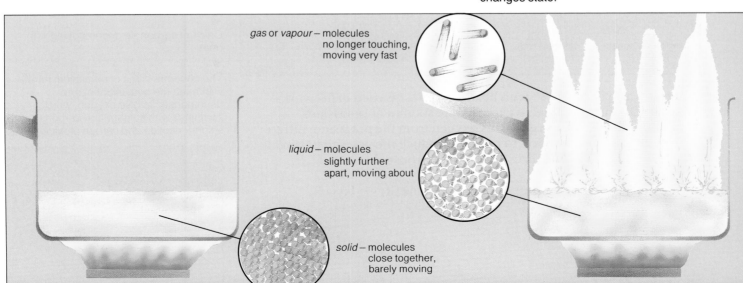

gas or *vapour* – molecules no longer touching, moving very fast

liquid – molecules slightly further apart, moving about

solid – molecules close together, barely moving

The most common chemical whose state we keep changing is water. A kitchen uses ice, water and steam every day.

States of matter – a summary

A solid has a certain shape and the molecules are held together tightly.

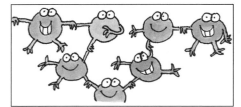

A liquid has no fixed shape; the molecules are still close but are held together less firmly.

A gas has no fixed shape and the molecules are a long way apart because they are not held together at all.

The missing liquids!

Some solid substances do not melt when heated, but change straight into a gas. When the gas is cooled it will change back into a solid again. For some reason these substances miss out the liquid stage. This is known as *sublimation*. Examples of substances that sublime are iodine and 'dry ice' (solid carbon dioxide).

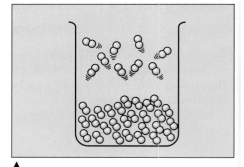

▲ Iodine evaporates easily from the solid.

▼ Iodine vapour leaving a beaker of solid iodine.

Heating and chemical changes

When some substances are heated they don't just melt or boil. The energy put in makes atoms break apart from each other and rearrange themselves to make new substances. A good example of this type of reaction is the *decomposition* reactions. When compounds decompose on heating they split up into simpler substances.

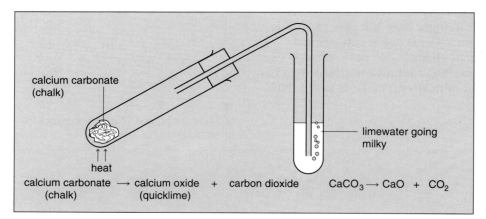

calcium carbonate (chalk)

limewater going milky

heat

calcium carbonate → calcium oxide + carbon dioxide $CaCO_3 \rightarrow CaO + CO_2$
(chalk)   (quicklime)

◄ Calcium carbonate decomposing with heat.

▼ The decomposition of potassium nitrate with heat: the potassium nitrate decomposes to give oxygen, which combines with sulphur and carbon to give sulphur dioxide and carbon dioxide gases.

Nitrates also decompose with heat. This effect is used in fireworks. Nitrates of the more reactive metals like sodium or potassium decompose to give off oxygen. This oxygen from the potassium nitrate helps the sulphur and carbon to burn to produce the gases that provide the explosive power (the thrust) in firework rockets.

potassium nitrate → potassium nitrite + oxygen,
$$2KNO_3 \rightarrow 2KNO_2 + O_2.$$

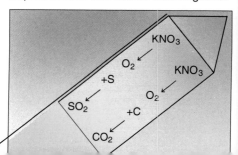

Chemistry and cookery

Most chemical reactions happen when particles of one substance knock into particles of another substance. The collisions that take place between particles need to have sufficient energy before a reaction will take place. By 'energy' we normally mean the speed of the particles. Slow collisions will mean particles just bounce off each other without any reaction taking place. The more energetic the collisions are, the faster the reaction will be. Other reactions involve groups of particles splitting apart. These are the decomposition reactions as described above.

Both of these reactions speed up if we heat the substances. The heating gives them more internal energy to break and remake chemical bonds.

Cooking food makes it easier to digest. Food is made of very complicated natural (organic) molecules. These are mostly made of carbon, hydrogen and oxygen. They are often very strong, especially in vegetables. Cooking breaks these molecules down into smaller ones that our digestive juices can cope with. Potatoes are completely indigestible until the tough cell walls are broken down so that our bodies can get at the starch inside the cells.

The higher the cooking temperature, the quicker the changes happen. This is why frying potatoes is quicker than boiling them. The oil for frying reaches 180°C – much higher than the boiling point of water.

But pressure cookers boil food at a higher temperature than normal, so pressure cooking is very much quicker than ordinary braising or stewing. For example, a beef and vegetable stew might take 2 hours to cook in an ordinary saucepan, but only 15 minutes in a pressure cooker.

If food is overcooked the molecules may break down even more. Flavour is lost, and vitamins are destroyed. If food is 'burnt' the molecules break down completely and we are left with black, indigestible lumps of carbon.

Enzymes are also useful in cooking. When an animal is killed the meat begins to 'digest' itself, using its own natural enzymes. This makes the meat easier for us to digest. (Grilled gammon is served with pineapple because *enzymes* from the pineapple act on the meat to make it more tender.) Enzymes are also very useful in making bread, wine and beer. These enzymes come from the yeasts used.

Chemistry also works more quickly if the substances involved come in small pieces. This gives them a greater overall surface area (see page 64). As a result chemicals can react or decompose more easily. This is why it is quicker to cook meat or vegetables when they are cut up into small pieces. Sugar dissolves more quickly as fine caster sugar than as lumps.

Chapter 4 deals with *rates* of reaction in chemistry, and there is a useful summary in the 'Reference section' (page 234).

Mixtures

Many household materials are *mixtures*. In a mixture the different substances can be separated. The substances are not chemically bonded together. (In a compound the substances *are* bonded together.) For example, we can separate a mixture of oil and water by waiting for the oil to float to the top and then pouring it off. We could separate a mixture of peas and beans by hand. If the beans are a lot bigger than the peas we could use a sieve. This will only work if the holes in the sieve are big enough to let the peas through, but too small for the beans to go through. This seems simple enough, but it is in fact the way that you digest your food. The human gut has small holes in it that let broken-down food materials through but keep out useless wastes. This process, on a very small scale, is called *osmosis*.

Osmosis and filtration are *physical* processes, because they depend on the physical properties of the materials, like size or density. Other physical processes for separation that you have come across are shown in the diagram.

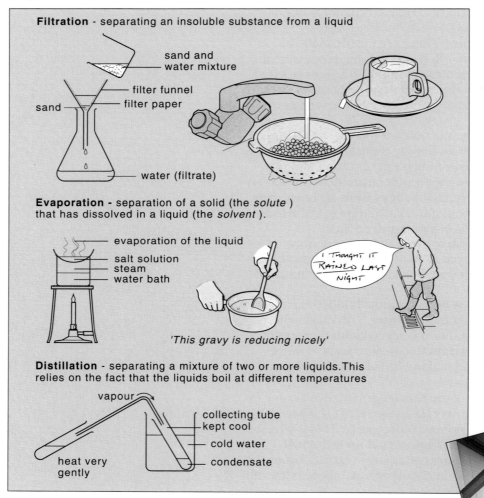

Filtration - separating an insoluble substance from a liquid

sand and water mixture

filter funnel
filter paper
sand
water (filtrate)

Evaporation - separation of a solid (the *solute*) that has dissolved in a liquid (the *solvent*).

evaporation of the liquid
salt solution
steam
water bath

'This gravy is reducing nicely'

I THOUGHT IT RAINED LAST NIGHT

Distillation - separating a mixture of two or more liquids. This relies on the fact that the liquids boil at different temperatures

vapour
collecting tube
kept cool
cold water
condensate
heat very gently

◀ Filtration, evaporation and distillation. Distillation is used a lot in industry.

▼ Industrial distillation – making whisky. The raw materials are heated in the pear-shaped flasks and the alcohol boils off through the tube at the top.

These processes are all useful in using or making everyday household materials. For example, find out how a cook can separate unwanted fat from the liquid in a stew or casserole. Remember, we don't want to lose any of the nice-tasting floating bits!

A fractionating column is a special way of using distillation to separate a mixture of different liquids. You won't find one of these in a kitchen, unless you are trying to make illegal whisky! But many of the fuels we use are made from crude oil by using this method. There is more about this in Chapter 7, *Chemical economics* (page 119).

Chromatography

Particles in a solution can be separated by using chromatography. A coloured sweet might have several different colour dyes in it. Make a solution from the sweet and 'dot' it on to one end of a filter paper strip. Then wait while the water rises slowly up the strip, past the dot made from the sweet. The water carries the dissolved dyes from the sweet with it. But some dyes move faster than others because they have different-sized molecules. The result is that we can separate the different types of dye.

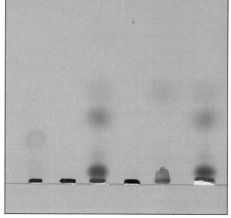
▲
Using chromatography to show which colours are used to make the inks in felt pens.

Treating water

The water we drink is not pure – and it never has been. All water contains dissolved chemicals. They are picked up from the ground that the water runs through or over. In some areas there is so much dissolved material that it affects cooking utensils and central heating systems. Water like this is called *hard water*. It produces a hard scale ('limescale') on the inside of kettles, boilers and even hot water pipes. What chemicals are in limescale? Do they do us any harm?

▲
Limescale on the inside of a kettle.

Making water softer

There are two types of hard water – *temporary* and *permanent*. Both types form a scum with soap. This is really what chemists call a *precipitate*. A precipitate is formed when a chemical reaction produces a new substance that doesn't dissolve in water.

The chemicals dissolved in hard water are salts of magnesium and calcium. The magnesium and calcium react with a chemical in soap to form a substance that doesn't dissolve in water. This makes the scum.

Temporary hard water

In temporary hard water the dissolved substance is calcium hydrogencarbonate:

calcium hydrogen-carbonate	+	sodium stearate (soap)	→	calcium stearate (scum)	+	sodium carbonate (dissolves).

The hardness is called temporary because it can be removed by boiling or even just heating the water. This turns the calcium hydrogencarbonate into calcium carbonate – which is insoluble (it is really limestone):

$$Ca(HCO_3)_{2(aq)} \rightarrow CaCO_{3(s)} + CO_{2(g)} + H_2O_{(1)}.$$
(limescale)

▲
The crystals of calcium sulphate are long and pointed; calcium carbonate crystals are shaped like small pebbles.

▼
Soap scum forms when soap is used with hard water.

One picture shows the 'limestone' scale in a kettle. The limescale clogs pipes and filters, and makes heating systems less efficient. Water that just circulates in heating systems ought to be *softened* before it is used.

You can buy special chemicals to descale kettles, coffee machines, steam irons, etc. These chemicals are strong acids, and are very poisonous. You must take care to follow the instructions exactly.

Permanent hard water

Some water has calcium sulphate and magnesium sulphate dissolved in it.
These chemicals are not affected by heating. This is good news for kettles,
but the chemicals still make a scum with soap.

If you want to save soap you can soften this kind of water by using
'washing soda'. This is sodium carbonate. It reacts with the metal ions
(calcium and magnesium) to form calcium and magnesium carbonates.
These are not soluble and so they precipitate out as small solid flakes.
'Bath salts' are made with sodium carbonate and do the same job. But they
have colour and scents added.

Water-softening machines

Many people now get rid of hard water by using special 'filters'. These are
put in the water-supply system before the tap. They actually take out the
unwanted metal ions by using an ion-exchange resin. The resin is coated
with sodium ions, and swaps the magnesium and calcium ions for harmless
sodium ones. Eventually all the sodium ions are used up. But they are easily
replaced by flushing the resin with a strong salt solution (sodium chloride).
The sodium ions from the salt then push away and replace the calcium and
magnesium ions.

Very pure water is needed to do chemistry accurately in laboratories. Ask
your teacher to show you how your school makes its pure 'distilled' water.

▲
A still for making distilled water.

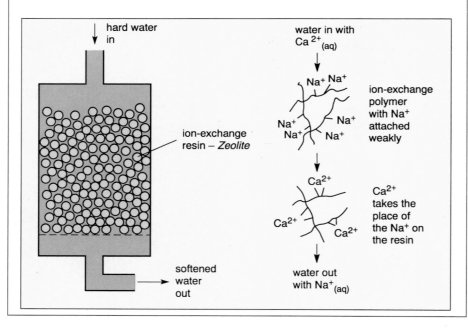

◀
Softening hard water by using an ion-exchange column.

Soaps and detergents

Soap is made by boiling up a fat with an alkali like sodium hydroxide. Fats
are compounds of *fatty acids* and a molecule called *glycerol*. The sodium
hydroxide added makes the sodium salt of the fatty acid. *Stearic acid*
($C_{17}H_{35}CO_2H$) is common in fats, and *sodium stearate* ($C_{17}H_{35}CO_2Na$) is
a soap.

The substances we call *detergents* are designed so that, although they still react with the 'hardness' in water to soften it, they don't form a scum. A modern washing powder or washing-up liquid is made of a carefully designed mixture of chemicals, all of which have different jobs to do. The main trick is to separate the jobs of 'cleaning power' and 'water softening'. In a soap the same chemical (sodium stearate) does both jobs. In a soapless detergent (like washing powder) these two jobs are done by different chemicals.

Getting rid of grease

Ordinary dirt clings to surfaces – fibres in cloth, skin, plates, cutlery and so on – because it is mixed with grease, fat or oil of some kind. Hot water will melt the grease, and some of the dirt comes with it. But there will always be a thin film left behind to smear the surface, so it will not be properly clean. (*Stains* are different and are explained below.) Both soaps and synthetic detergents clean away dirt in the same way, by using a special property of the molecules they contain – *surface action*.

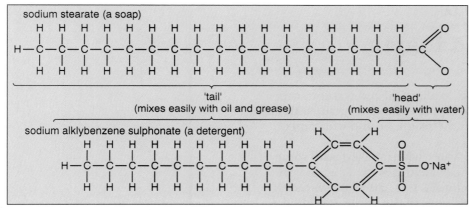

◄ Soap and detergent molecules.

▼ How detergent molecules lift away dirt.

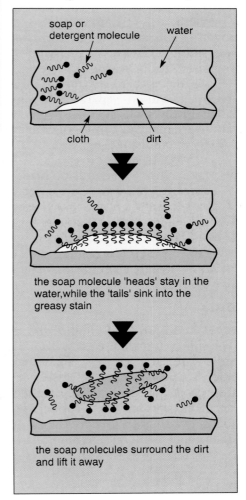

the soap molecule 'heads' stay in the water, while the 'tails' sink into the greasy stain

the soap molecules surround the dirt and lift it away

Soap and detergent molecules are long, and one end is chemically different from the rest of the molecule. This 'head' end mixes easily with water; the rest of the molecule mixes easily with grease, oil and fat. The result is a mix of grease and detergent that is dissolved by the water.

Softening the water

As explained above, the advantage of synthetic detergents is that none of the cleaning power is lost by the active molecules having to react with the hardness in the water (caused by ions of calcium and magnesium). The 'softener' does this instead – and the resulting chemical stays dissolved in the water, so that there is no scum to make the water look dirty, or to stay on the clothes or plates even after rinsing.

A liquid detergent – washing-up liquid

The chart on page 16 shows the main chemicals that are in a washing-up liquid, and the jobs that they do. The bubbles (lather) don't actually do anything, but people like them – they give the impression of cleanliness. The makers of detergents do in fact use them to give consumers an idea of when the real cleaning power is all gone. This is what the foam stabiliser does: it holds the lather until all the detergent is used up, and then the bubbles collapse.

Formulation of your detergent

Raw material	Amount	Function
base detergent	30 cm^3	basic detergent property
foam detergent	120 cm^3	aids the base detergent and gives good lather
foam stabiliser	5 cm^3	holds lather until all detergent used, then foam collapses
water	240–285 cm^3	adjusts viscosity – makes detergent thinner
ammonium chloride	trace (if needed)	adjusts viscosity – makes detergent thicker
alcohol	trace (if needed)	adjusts viscosity – thins detergent more easily than water
dye	trace ⎫	to give appeal but not revulsion! too little – product lacks 'strength'
perfume	trace ⎭	too much – produces stains or taints

Emulsions, gels and foams

One of the ways that detergents work is to allow oil and water to mix together. Oil and water are *immiscible* liquids. The detergent, with its 'tail' liking oil and its 'head' liking water, helps the oil and water mix together. It acts as an *emulsifier*.

This means that a mixture of oil and water when shaken with some detergent will *not* separate out. A mixture like this is made up of very small droplets which are dispersed in a liquid. It is called an *emulsion*. There are many examples of emulsions found in the home, based on a variety of emulsifiers.

- Mayonnaise – an emulsion made from mixing vegetable oil and vinegar using egg yolk as the emulsifier.
- Cold cream – a mixture of beeswax, paraffin, rosewater and borax. The emulsifier here is a soap-like substance formed when the borax reacts with the fatty acids in the beeswax.
- Many cosmetics including hand creams and cleansing creams.
- Milk – mainly an emulsion of fat in water.

Gels

A *gel* is composed of a liquid with many particles of a solid substance in it. The solid parts are linked to each other. It is as if the liquid is dissolved in a solid! The particles are so small that they cannot be seen even with a microscope. Gels may be elastic, or 'jelly-like' e.g. gelatin or fruit jelly. But they can be solid and rigid, e.g. the silica gel which is used to keep things dry. This takes in water vapour from the air. Packets of silica gel can be found in containers where the air needs to be kept dry – around electrical equipment, cameras and binoculars.

Foams

A *foam* is a collection of bubbles. Detergents are good at making a foam in water. They lower the *surface tension* of the water which would normally prevent a foam from forming. Actually, foams don't help the cleaning action of detergents at all, but people seem to link the presence of a foam with washing things clean. Foam stabilisers are added to detergents to prolong the life of the foam during washing.

Foam bubbles carry gas. In *foam fire extinguishers*, carbon dioxide gas is contained inside the bubbles. Foam and carbon dioxide help to smother the fire by keeping oxygen away from the flames.

▲
The foam stops oxygen reaching the flames.

▼
Detergents in a sewage outfall near Macclesfield.

Water pollution

Back in the 1960s, the sight of foam on the surface of rivers had become a familiar sight. Detergents used in the home passed straight through sewage works. The detergents ended up in the rivers and made 'soap suds'. Foam stops oxygen from dissolving in the water and cuts down the amount of light reaching aquatic plants.

Ordinary soaps can be broken down easily by bacteria because they have been made from vegetable oils or animal fats. These soaps are said to be *biodegradable*. It was found that synthetic detergents were not being broken down in a similar way. Nowadays, detergents are made with different chemicals that are biodegradable.

Also, many detergents used to contain phosphates. These helped to soften water by locking up the calcium and magnesium ions in a complex structure. Phosphates have a similar effect on water as nitrates do: they increase the rate of plant growth. As well as choking the river with a lot of weed, the major problem is that the decay of dead plant material uses oxygen. The level of dissolved oxygen is reduced. Animals such as fish will die, and so will the useful bacteria that help to break down waste. The river has become so polluted that it is unable to cope with waste as it enters the river water.

▲
Phosphates in sewage make algae grow so fast that rivers become clogged. Modern detergents do not contain phosphates.

Obtaining pure water — the water treatment works

▼
The main stages in purifying water.

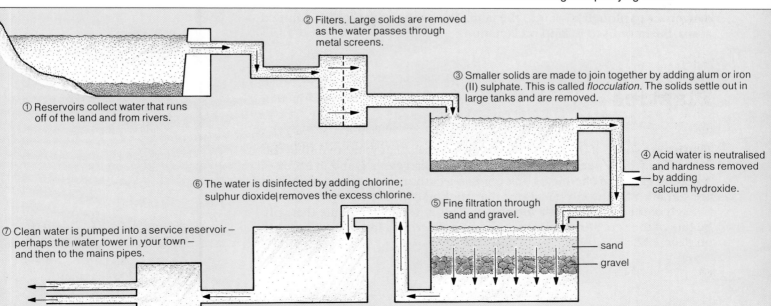

① Reservoirs collect water that runs off of the land and from rivers.

② Filters. Large solids are removed as the water passes through metal screens.

③ Smaller solids are made to join together by adding alum or iron (II) sulphate. This is called *flocculation*. The solids settle out in large tanks and are removed.

④ Acid water is neutralised and hardness removed by adding calcium hydroxide.

⑤ Fine filtration through sand and gravel.

⑥ The water is disinfected by adding chlorine; sulphur dioxide removes the excess chlorine.

⑦ Clean water is pumped into a service reservoir — perhaps the water tower in your town — and then to the mains pipes.

sand
gravel

1. Untreated sewage from the drains is filtered through large gratings to remove solid objects. 2. The sewage then stands in large tanks where the sludge settles out and is raked to one end. 3. The water then has air bubbled through it to encourage bacterial growth. The bacteria break down organic molecules. 4. The almost clean water is trickled through gravel beds where bacterial 'cleaning' continues. Finally, 5, clean water is discharged into rivers or the sea; in some treatment works, the sludge is loaded onto barges and then dumped at sea.

◄ A sewage treatment works in East London.

The sewage works

The sewage works has to deal with water that ends up in the sewers. This water will contain waste from homes and factories, and rainwater that has washed off the streets. In some areas the waste in sewers is piped directly into the sea. This has caused many beaches to fail to come up to minimum safety levels. European laws mean that these beaches have to be checked regularly.

Dirty water is passed through sieves and grit to remove floating rubbish. Smaller particles and solid organic waste (sludge) is then allowed to settle out from the liquid in large settling tanks. The liquid is then filtered through more gravel where, under suitable conditions, *bacteria* break down the pollutants. After yet more settling, another batch of sludge is produced which is composed of bacteria and the products that they have made by decomposing the sludge. The liquid left is now safe to discharge into the rivers. But it might still contain a high proportion of nitrates, which can pollute the river. Clean sludge from the sewage works is used as a fertiliser to give nitrogen compounds to the soil. Some sludge may also contain high levels of 'heavy metals' which make it too dangerous to plough back into the land. This sludge will then be dumped at sea, burnt or used in land reclamation.

Plastics

Plastics are some of the most common chemicals that you can find in the home. They have been made from the liquids and gases found in crude oil. A certain group of chemicals that contain a carbon-to-carbon double bond are suitable starting chemicals for one method of making plastics.

Each of the chemicals is a *monomer*. This is a small molecule that will be one of the repeating units in the plastic. There is a lot more about this on page 122.

▼ These simple molecules make good starting reagents for making plastics.

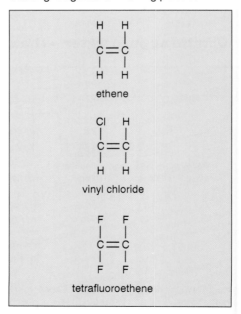

When many ethene molecules join together they form a very long chain molecule called a *polymer*. This long-chain molecule was formed by monomers 'adding' on to each other, so the process is called *addition polymerisation*. Adding ethene molecules together makes 'poly-ethene' or polythene.

You can find polyethene being used for hundreds of different jobs without even having to look too hard! This is because it has many important properties like lightness, flexibility, strength, and it is a good insulator of heat and electricity. But there are problems with making plastics. Crude oil is a non-renewable resource, and most plastics are not affected by bacteria or corrosion, so great care has to be taken when disposing of waste plastics.

There is a lot more about the petrochemical industry, and making plastics in Chapter 7, *Chemical economics* (pages 122–124).

Properties of materials

There are many different materials used in the home. What makes one material different from another is its properties. The difference in properties can be explained by looking at the atoms and molecules in the material – how they are arranged and the forces that hold them together. There is more about this in Chapter 10 of GCSE book 1, *Atoms, molecules and materials*. See also the 'Reference section', page 249, in this book, which tells you about the physical properties of materials.

Fibres
- Cotton and linen are vegetable fibres and are made of cellulose
- Wool and silk are animal fibres and are made of protein
- Nylon and Terylene are synthetic fibres. They are polymers of products from crude oil

By examining the labels on clothes you will see many different kinds of fibres. The clothing manufacturer has to decide which fibres have the qualities that will be best for the clothes. Cotton is a natural fibre and can be dyed very easily. It is able to absorb moisture, which makes it comfortable to wear against the skin.

Terylene (a *polyester*) is a synthetic fibre and is particularly hardwearing. It can be permanently creased and does not absorb moisture very easily. People don't find it as comfortable to wear as cotton. A combination of fibres like polyester and cotton is very popular as it makes use of the best qualities of each. Wool is comfortable to wear and has great water-absorbing qualities. But unfortunately wool shrinks when washed. Acrylic pullovers are very popular because they look and feel like wool and when washed they will dry very easily without shrinking.

Check the labels on your own clothes to see which fibres have been used.

Composite materials

A composite material is made up of a mixture of materials. The idea is that the mixture will have more useful properties than each material on its own. The ancient Egyptians were some of the first to use composite materials over 5000 years ago. They mixed straw in with clay to make their bricks. The addition of straw fibres produced a stronger and tougher material. Brittle materials are weak because little cracks are able to spread through the material very quickly. The fibres stop or deflect these cracks. This increases the *tensile* strength of the material. Reinforced concrete is a common example of a composite material. The steel rods give the concrete added tensile strength. More recently, glass fibre and nylon have been used in place of the steel. What benefits would these have over steel?

Ceramics – like glass, earthenware, stoneware and porcelain – are very hard materials indeed. Their great weakness is that they are brittle. To cut glass, the surface is just scored with a sharp edge made of hard steel or diamond. The glass will break easily along this scored line when light pressure is applied.

There is a lot more about this in GCSE book 1, Chapter 10, *Atoms, molecules and materials.*

Activities

1 In the work you are doing at school you probably looked at the safety of chemicals that are kept at home. What kind of container is best for holding a dangerous chemical? Where should these chemicals be stored? Make a list of good and bad materials and designs, and good and bad places to store them. Find some chemical containers in your home and check them against your lists. You should only look at the containers and never touch, smell or taste the contents! What conclusions can you make from the information that you have obtained?

2 At home you will probably have:
- a weak alkali – sodium hydrogencarbonate (baking powder – bicarbonate of soda);
- a weak acid – acetic acid (vinegar);
- an indicator – beetroot or blackcurrant juice.
Use these to find out what colour an indicator goes in acids and alkalis. See if you can obtain a neutral solution by carefully adding the baking powder to the acid. Your indicator will help you to get it right.

3 Universal indicator paper can be used to find the pH of substances. Ask your teacher if you can take some home to do an experiment. Test the pH of some substances at home and record your results in a suitable table you could design yourself. You might like to test these substances: vinegar, baking powder (bicarbonate of soda), detergent, soap, salt, diluted bleach (take care), lemonade, scouring powder, liquid cleaners and toothpaste. Remember:
- test only small samples;
- do not touch the chemicals;
- try to dissolve solid samples in water before testing;
- have a copy of the pH scale to refer to.
Remember that the samples you have been testing will be contaminated with the dye from the universal indicator paper so do not eat or drink them!

4 Anti-oxidants are used extensively by the food industry to prevent food spoiling through oxidation. Ascorbic acid has an 'E' number of 300 on food labels. How many different types of food can you find that has added vitamin C? How many other types of anti-oxidants can you find? (They have 'E' numbers in the 300s.)

5 Acid can prevent the oxidation (browning) of apples. There are many dilute acids that can be found in the kitchen: lemon juice, orange juice, vinegar, for example. Plan and try out an experiment to find out which is the most effective at slowing down the browning of cut apples.

6 In distillation, steam can be changed back into water (condensed) in the condenser. Around the home, water vapour or steam changing to liquid can be an irritating problem. Find out where it is happening, what is causing it and what could be done to prevent it from happening.

7 Limescale is formed wherever temporary hardwater is heated. Where are these areas in your house? Temporary hardwater is a weak solution of calcium hydrogencarbonate, $Ca(HCO_3)_2$.
(a) Find out how this gets into the water supply.
(b) Do you live in a hard water area? How can you tell?

8 A household can pollute the environment in various ways. Make a list for your household and then make a list of the ways your household could make improvements. Recycling is a good way to make scarce resources last longer. What substances do you think that it would be a good idea to save and recycle?

9 There are three types of fibre: natural fibres, artificial fibres and mixtures of fibres. Clothes labels list the fibres that have been used. What qualities do you think the manufacturer was looking for when those particular fibres were chosen? Make a table of your results.

Questions

1 Have a look at the bleach bottles in the photographs. Have the bottles been well designed? Some important features of bleach bottles are listed in the table below. Draw up a table like the one below and use it to say how good or bad you consider the designs to be.

Name of bleach		
Bottle easy to handle if wet?		
Cap well designed?		
Clear hazard signs given?		
Clear safety instructions?		

Can you suggest any improvements to these designs to make them safer? Try and design a new bottle. What advantages and disadvantages would advertising your bleach on television have on the ability to sell your product?

2 Bleach can remove the colour from ink. The stronger the bleach is, the more ink it will decolourise. A student did a simple experiment to find out which bleach was the 'best buy' by considering the price, volume and strength of the product. Here are the results:

Name of bleach	Price paid	Volume of container	Cost of $1\,cm^3$ of bleach	Volume of ink decolourised by $10\,cm^3$ of bleach
A	45p	$1000\,cm^3$		$2.0\,cm^3$
B	52p	$750\,cm^3$		$1.7\,cm^3$
C	35p	$750\,cm^3$		$2.2\,cm^3$
D	63p	$739\,cm^3$		$4.5\,cm^3$
E	55p	$825\,cm^3$		$1.9\,cm^3$

(a) Which bleach is the strongest? Which one is the weakest?
(b) What is the volume of each bleach that reacts with $10\,cm^3$ of ink?
(c) Copy out the table and complete the blank column. Then, using your answers from (b) find the cost of each of the volumes of bleach.
(d) Which bleach is the 'best buy'?

3 Write a few sentences to explain the meaning of the following:
(a) a solution is strongly acidic;
(b) a solution is only a weak alkali;
(c) acids can be neutralised by alkalis;
(d) the pH scale.

4 Look at the following pH numbers: pH1, pH5, pH7, pH8 and pH11. Now look at the solutions below and give each of them what you think is the most suitable pH number.
The solutions are: *limewater* (calcium hydroxide), *lemon juice, sulphuric acid, soap, salt water* (sodium chloride).

5 Many food items found in the home are preserved in vinegar. Plan an investigation to produce a 'league table' for the strengths of the acids. *Hint:* washing soda (sodium carbonate) neutralises acids, and as it does so bubbles of carbon dioxide are given off.

6 Here is a list of physical processes.
A – filtration
B – chromatography
C – distillation
D – evaporation
E – dissolving
F – condensing
Select the one that is most likely to be involved in the following:
(i) Finding out about the colouring used in drinks.
(ii) Getting a stain out of clothes.
(iii) Straining cooked peas.
(iv) The kitchen window steaming up.
(v) Washing on the line.

Checklist

These are the facts and ideas that you should have learned by studying this topic.

To reach Basic Level you should:

- be able to name three useful chemicals you use at home and say why they are useful
- understand that even useful chemicals can be dangerous (i.e. bleach, ammonia)
- know that acids turn universal indicator red and alkalis turn it blue/purple
- know how to separate mixtures by filtering and evaporating

To succeed at Foundation Level you should:

- know that chemical reactions can change raw materials into new, useful products
- know how to separate and purify the parts of a mixture
- know what the following types of mixture are and how they are used: gels, foams, solutions, emulsions
- be able to classify solutions as acidic, neutral or alkaline on the pH scale, using indicators
- know that an alkali can neutralise an acid
- be able to classify materials as solids, liquids or gases and relate this to their everyday use
- be able to describe the use – and dangers – of everyday household chemicals, and safe ways of storing them

To succeed at Merit Level you should:

- know what happens in polymerisation
- be able to explain the pH changes that occur during neutralisation
- understand the importance of reactions between acids and alkalis as producers of salts
- be able to make up simple word equations for chemical reactions
- be able to relate the properties of materials to their everyday uses (especially detergents, solvents, fertilisers, emulsions, gels and plastics)
- be able to describe and explain the chemical changes involved in some important manufacturing processes and everyday effects
- know that some chemical processes are reversible and how pressure, temperature and concentraiton affect the equilibrium state
- know about the reasons for the safety precautions used when handling and storing chemicals

To succeed at Special Level you should:

- be able to use scientific information from a range of sources to evaluate the social, health and safety, economic and environmental effects of a major manufacturing process
- be able to describe the differences between emulsions, foams, gels and solutions
- be able to predict the products of common neutralisation reactions
- be able to use symbolic equations to describe reactions
- know that alkalis in solution contain hydroxyl ions and acids in solution contain hydrogen ions, and be able to relate this to what happens in neutralisation
- be able to use data about materials to make sensible comments on their uses
- be able to explain the physical and chemical processes involved in making chemicals from crude oil
- understand the problems involved in disposing of both domestic and industrial wastes

CHAPTER TWO

A kingfisher with its prey.

Humpback whale.

Common garden snail.

A five-month old human foetus.

e jumping
ra spider has
ound vision
hunting.

HOW LIVING THINGS WORK

Spiders, snails and jellyfish; human beings and whales. Earth is home to a vast array of magnificent and often mysterious life-forms. They may look very different. They may behave in very different ways. But they all face the same problem — staying alive.

The bodies of all these different living organisms are complicated living machines. The bodies must fit the animals' life-styles, and the places where they live. Spiders and snails have different problems, and solve them in different ways.

But the basic life processes in living things are very similar, whether you are a jellyfish, a whale, or a human being.

Living bodies need food. They require a supply of oxygen from the air or water in which they live. They must be able to move, and they grow and reproduce. They must get rid of the harmful waste products that they produce. All of these processes must be monitored, maintained, and controlled with precision.

And what of other life-forms which may exist on planets other than Earth? Is life as we know it the only way in which living things can flourish? Biologists would dearly like to study the workings of a genuine extra-terrestrial to find out. No doubt it would enjoy taking a very close look at us!

A jellyfish.

Building bodies

The wall of a house is obviously a large and solid structure. But if you look closely at the wall you can see that it is made of much smaller sub-units joined together to make the whole – as if you didn't know – bricks!

Living things are constructed in the same way. The individual units of life are microscopic living cells.

Some living organisms consist of only one single cell, which can carry out all the necessary processes to maintain life.

The multicellular way of life

Larger creatures are made up of millions of cells, all working together. The cells are all carefully organised so that they can work together.

- Similar cells are grouped together to make *tissues*.
- Different tissues are grouped together to make *organs*.
- Different organs work or function together as living *systems*.

Think again of your house. How many of us could build a complete home, on our own, from scratch? We would need an architect to plan and design the building, a bricklayer to build the walls, a plumber and an electrician for water pipes and wiring, and several other people with specialist knowledge and skills. These specialist people must all work together to produce a properly functioning new house.

Living bodies are much more complicated than a house. The body is designed to carry out many more different jobs. But plants and animals build themselves – starting from a single cell – and this cell carries the complete plan of the adult organism. There is more about this in Chapter 8, *The living inheritance*.

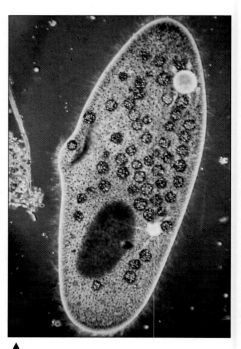

▲ A very simple form of life: a single-celled *Paramecium*. You can see the nucleus (the 'control centre') very clearly.

▼ Organisation: cell, tissue, organ, system.

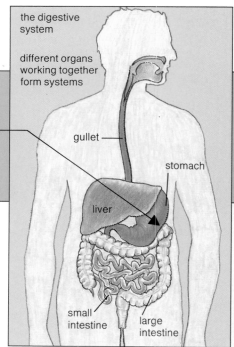

the digestive system

different organs working together form systems

gullet

stomach

liver

small intestine

large intestine

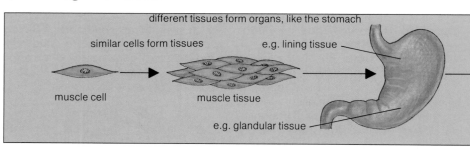

different tissues form organs, like the stomach

similar cells form tissues

e.g. lining tissue

muscle cell

muscle tissue

e.g. glandular tissue

Systems of the human body

The human body, like many other animal bodies, has six main systems.

- Circulatory system: the heart pumps blood through a system of blood vessels, transporting heat and important substances around the body and helping to fight against disease.
- Respiratory system: the lungs take oxygen into the body from the air we breathe and remove carbon dioxide (and water) from the body.

- Digestive system: digests the food we eat. The food can then be chemically 'burnt' using oxygen, to release energy.
- Excretory system: the kidneys filter the blood to remove harmful wastes, spare water and salts.
- Nervous system: the brain, nerves, and spinal cord help to control and co-ordinate the workings of all the other systems.
- Endocrine, or hormone system: produces chemicals that also help to control other body systems.

You have already learned about some of these systems. This chapter explains how the systems work together to keep you alive. There are more diagrams and details in the 'Reference section'.

The main life process: using energy

Without energy, no living organism can survive. All life processes require a constant supply of usable energy.

Animals obtain their energy from the animal and plant food they eat and digest. Plants also release energy from food, but plants don't have the problems of finding, eating and digesting food. They can manufacture their own supply of foodstuffs by *photosynthesis*. This uses the energy carried by sunlight.

The release of energy from food is called *respiration*. You can find out more about this process in the GCSE Introductory Book, but to remind you, the main facts about respiration are:

- respiration takes place inside living cells;
- the food is 'burnt' using oxgen to release chemical energy;
- some of this energy is transferred for use in other life processes but much of it is released to heat up the surroundings;
- two waste products (water and carbon dioxide) are also released.

This flow chart shows that a number of different body systems must work together to ensure that respiration can actually happen in living cells.

▼
Respiration.

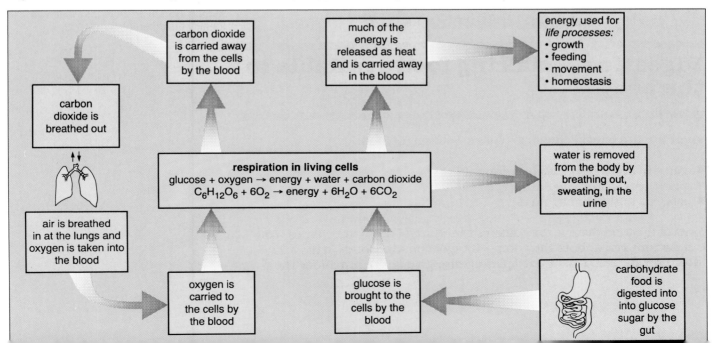

carbon dioxide is carried away from the cells by the blood	much of the energy is released as heat and is carried away in the blood	energy used for *life processes:* • growth • feeding • movement • homeostasis

carbon dioxide is breathed out

respiration in living cells
glucose + oxygen → energy + water + carbon dioxide
$C_6H_{12}O_6 + 6O_2 \rightarrow$ energy $+ 6H_2O + 6CO_2$

water is removed from the body by breathing out, sweating, in the urine

air is breathed in at the lungs and oxygen is taken into the blood

oxygen is carried to the cells by the blood

glucose is brought to the cells by the blood

carbohydrate food is digested into into glucose sugar by the gut

Taking in fuel — food and digestion

Respiration is a form of combustion. Energy is released in an internal combustion engine when fuel (petrol) reacts with oxygen. Humans, and other animals, take in the fuel they need for respiration by feeding.

Ideally, feeding happens regularly every day, and we tend not to think about what happens to the food we eat after it has disappeared into our bodies. But we all share the inconvenience of removing what is *left* of our food after it has passed through the digestive system. Waste emerges just as regularly at the other end.

The food changes a great deal during its passage through the body. To understand why, and how, this happens, we need to look at the *digestive system*.

The digestive system consists of a long tube running through the body, beginning at the mouth and ending at the anus. Different parts of the tube are specialised to carry out particular jobs or functions. You can find out exactly how the different parts work together in the 'Reference section' pages 225–6. The basic function is to digest and absorb the food molecules that we eat.

▲
The Giant Panda has to eat almost constantly just to get enough energy to survive. They eat lying on their backs because that uses up less energy. The panda lives close to 'starvation' all the time.

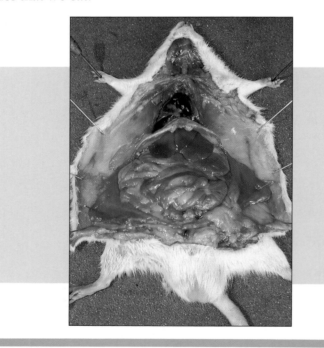

◄
The digestive system of the rat. Compare this with the simplified diagram of the human system on page 226. Can you identify the different parts?

Digestion — making food available to the body

There are three main chemical types, or classes, of food:

- carbohydrates, e.g. starch and sugars;
- proteins, e.g. meat and fish;
- fats, e.g. butter and egg yolk.

Most of the food that we eat contains a mixture of these three types. You can find out more about the composition of common foods in the 'Reference section'. Many food packets also give this information. The chemical molecules of the proteins, fats, and carbohydrates that we eat are very large. They are much too large to pass through the wall of the gut.

So the main job of the digestive system is to break down or digest these large and complicated food molecules. They are turned into simpler, much smaller molecules. These are small enough to pass through the walls of the intestine and dissolve in the bloodstream.

The main food chemicals in the blood are:

- glucose (from carbohydrates), for energy;
- amino acids (from protein), for growth and repair;
- glycerol and fatty acids (from fats and oils), for growth, repair and as a store of energy.

Taking these molecules into the blood is called *absorption*. Once absorbed into the blood these simple food substances can be carried to all the living cells of the body.

The digestion of large carbohydrate, protein and fat molecules is carried out by special chemicals called enzymes. These enzymes are released and mixed with our food as it passes through the gut. You can see what enzymes do to food in the diagram below. There is more about enzymes in the 'Reference Section', on pages 226–227.

Homeostasis

Homeostasis is a word that means 'staying the same'. What has this idea got to do with living bodies?

If the living cells of our tissues and organs are to work properly, they must have the conditions they need to stay alive. Most of our cells exist deep inside our bodies. So the environment inside the body, which surrounds the living cells, must be strictly controlled.

This is what biologists mean by the term homeostasis: making sure that conditions within the body are kept constant. The body cells must have everything they need to function correctly: water, chemicals and the right temperature.

▲
These foods are rich in carbohydrates.

▼
Foods that are rich in protein.

▲
Fatty foods.

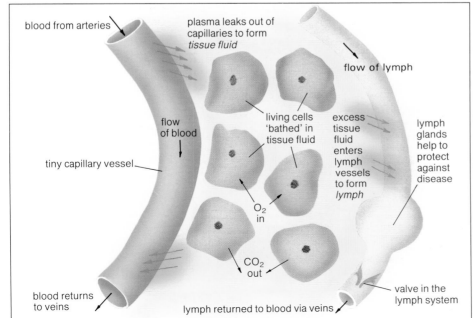

blood from arteries

plasma leaks out of capillaries to form *tissue fluid*

flow of lymph

flow of blood

living cells 'bathed' in tissue fluid

excess tissue fluid enters lymph vessels to form *lymph*

lymph glands help to protect against disease

tiny capillary vessel

O₂ in

CO₂ out

blood returns to veins

lymph returned to blood via veins

valve in the lymph system

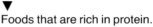
◄
Blood plasma moves from the blood to form lymph: tissue fluid.

Tissue fluid — the fluid of life

Living cells are surrounded by a liquid called *tissue fluid*. This fluid comes from the blood. It is the liquid part of blood, called the *blood plasma*. Some of the plasma is forced out of the tiny blood vessels or capillaries which carry blood through living tissues.

After bathing the cells this fluid is drawn back into the capillary blood vessels. Any extra liquid is drained away in a different system of tubes called the *lymph vessels*. Eventually, this liquid returns to the blood system. In humans it is fed back through a vein in the neck.

Many of the major body systems contribute to keeping this environment of tissue fluid constant, making sure that cells are supplied with raw materials and that harmful waste products are removed.

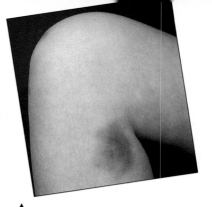

▲ When tissues are damaged, tissue fluid floods into the damaged area. This causes the swelling around an injury.

▼ The disease *elephantiasis* is caused by a parasite that stops tissue fluid moving away from the lower part of the body.

Insulin and blood sugar — an example of homeostasis

When we eat a meal containing starch, the starch is broken down into simple glucose sugar units by the digestive system. These small glucose molecules are absorbed across the wall of the small intestine into the bloodstream.

So after a large carbohydrate meal, the level of glucose in the blood will go up. This could cause serious problems, because if the blood sugar level – the amount of glucose in the blood – gets too high, the brain will be affected and the person will go into a coma. If untreated this condition can cause death.

But if the blood sugar level falls too low the effects are just as dangerous. We faint and, in serious cases, might die from the lack of glucose sugar in the blood. This can happen if we do not eat any carbohydrate food for a long time, and do hard exercise.

Normally, if we skip the occasional meal or eat a plateful of starchy food, we do not expect to suddenly faint! This is because our bodies have an automatic system to control the level of glucose in our blood at all times.

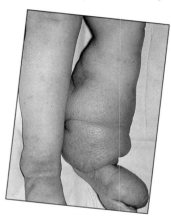

▼ An example of homeostasis: controlling blood sugar level. The liver is the largest organ in the body. One of its jobs is to convert glucose to glycogen for storage. Glycogen is changed back to glucose when it is needed.

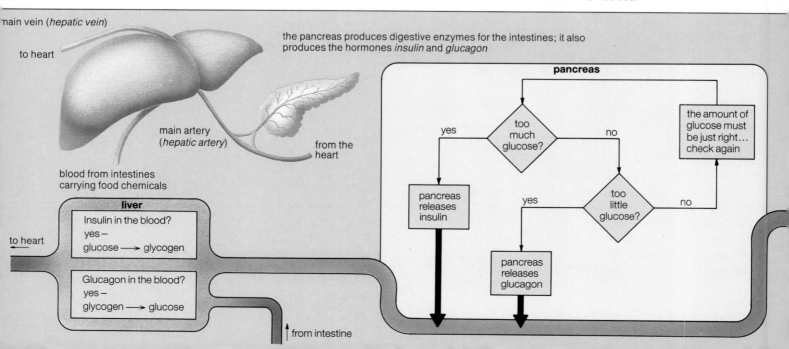

main vein (*hepatic vein*)

to heart

the pancreas produces digestive enzymes for the intestines; it also produces the hormones *insulin* and *glucagon*

pancreas

main artery (*hepatic artery*)

from the heart

blood from intestines carrying food chemicals

too much glucose?

yes

no

the amount of glucose must be just right... check again

pancreas releases insulin

too little glucose?

yes

no

liver

Insulin in the blood?
yes –
glucose ⟶ glycogen

to heart

Glucagon in the blood?
yes –
glycogen ⟶ glucose

pancreas releases glucagon

from intestine

Sorting out the sugar

After a meal, the glucose from starch digestion is carried to the liver by a large blood vessel called the *hepatic portal vein*. The liver can store the glucose by converting it into another type of carbohydrate called *glycogen*. The liver is a very important organ. It does many other jobs as well (see the 'Reference section').

If the blood sugar level gets too high, a chemical called *insulin* is released from special cells in the *pancreas*. Insulin is a *hormone*, a kind of chemical messenger.

Insulin travels to the liver in the blood and makes the liver convert more glucose to glycogen, which is then stored. The higher the blood sugar level rises, the more insulin is produced and the more glucose is taken out of the bloodstream and stored. This causes blood sugar level to fall back to normal levels.

If the blood sugar level falls below normal levels, the amount of insulin released from the pancreas is reduced. Another hormone called *glucagon* is released instead. Glucagon stimulates the liver to convert glycogen back into glucose and to pass glucose into the bloodstream. The blood sugar level will then rise back towards normal levels.

The graph on page 35 shows the slight daily changes in blood sugar level as a result of this control mechanism operating in the body. This example of the way that the internal environment of the body is controlled and regulated is a typical example of a homeostatic mechanism.

Homeostasis works by the principle of *negative feedback*:

- a high sugar level tiggers off a mechanism that makes it lower;
- a low sugar level triggers off a mechanism that makes it higher.

So a change produces its opposite.

A system like this is self-regulating. It operates automatically to keep the amount of glucose in the blood to an almost constant, normal level. Many other homeostatic mechanisms work in the same way. You should know about the changes that happen to your body when you are too hot or cold. How does this fit in with what you know about homeostatic controls?

Not enough insulin – things go wrong

In some people, the pancreas gland cannot produce enough insulin to regulate their blood sugar level. This disease is called *diabetes mellitus* or sugar diabetes. The symptoms are:

- almost constant thirst;
- general weakness;
- loss of weight;
- too much sugar in the blood, and so glucose is present in the urine;
- possible coma followed by death.

In the old days, doctors used to test for this disease by tasting the patient's urine! If it tasted 'sweet', sugar must be present and the doctor would know that the person was suffering from diabetes. No one would recommend testing urine that way these days!

People with diabetes are now able to live relatively normal lives. They must regulate their diet very carefully, and may also require daily injections of insulin hormone. The balance between sugar taken in as food and the amount of insulin needed to control it must be exactly right. This balance is something that the rest of us take for granted.

▲ Test strips are used to check for glucose in urine.

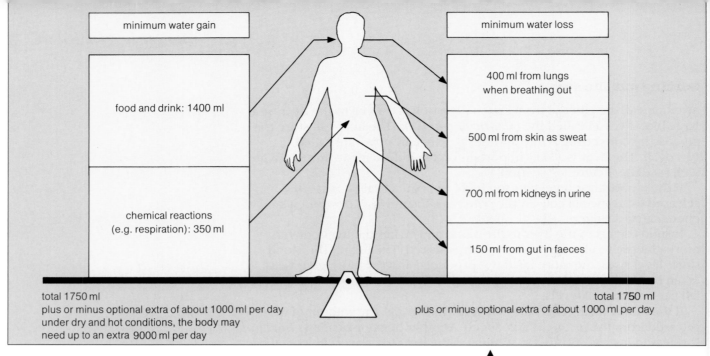

food and drink: 1400 ml

chemical reactions
(e.g. respiration): 350 ml

minimum water loss

400 ml from lungs
when breathing out

500 ml from skin as sweat

700 ml from kidneys in urine

150 ml from gut in faeces

total 1750 ml
plus or minus optional extra of about 1000 ml per day
under dry and hot conditions, the body may
need up to an extra 9000 ml per day

total 1750 ml
plus or minus optional extra of about 1000 ml per day

▲
The water balance for an average person.

Water control

The human body is two-thirds water. The average person, under normal conditions, loses about 3 litres of water a day in various ways:

- in liquids waste (urine) from the kidneys;
- in solid waste (faeces) from the gut;
- by breathing out water vapour from the lungs;
- by sweating from the skin.

You can see some actual figures for water loss and gain in the drawing.

Some water is gained for the body by certain chemical reactions – such as respiration – where water is one of the main waste products. We get water from the food we eat as well as the liquids that we drink.

If we lost just about a tenth of our body water, we would die from dehydration. If you didn't take in any water at all, this would happen in about ten days – but a lot faster in hot and dry conditions. Long before that time you would be very uncomfortable. The sensation of thirst would become unbearable.

Keeping the amount of water constant in the blood, and therefore in the whole body, is another important example of homeostasis.

The kidneys – important organs of homeostasis

The kidneys carry out two main functions:

- removing waste products such as urea from the blood by forming urine;
- regulating the salt and water content of the body.

Urea is a nitrogen compound formed by the breakdown of proteins in the body. We have two kidneys which are quite small, each weighing about 150 grams. Each is about the size of a clenched fist. Yet a quarter of the blood in the body is passing through them at any instant, at the rate of over a litre a minute! The kidneys are so efficient at filtering blood that if they stopped working suddenly, death would result in only a few minutes.

Kidney structure

If a kidney is sliced in half horizontally, three distinct regions can be seen. These are called the *outer cortex*, the *middle medulla* and the *inner pelvic region*. The kidney looks like this because of the arrangement of the kidney tubules it contains. You can see these three parts of the kidney in the diagram.

Dissecting kidney tissue under a microscope reveals that it is made up of blood vessels and tiny kidney tubules called *nephrons*. There are over a million of these nephrons in each kidney. These tiny tubes are the parts that actually do the work of filtering the blood. You can study one of these kidney tubules and find out exactly how it works in the 'Reference section'.

Kidney failure – homeostasis in crisis

We can survive with only one working kidney. But if both kidneys become diseased or injured the effects will be fatal, unless you receive some very special medical treatment.

There are two forms of treatment for people whose kidneys don't work very well.

Dialysis

An artificial kidney machine is used to filter the waste urea from the patient's blood and to draw off excess fluid and salts which the patient's body has accumulated. Each treatment lasts many hours and must be repeated three times every week. Kidney machines are expensive and there are not enough of them to treat everybody with kidney failure. Sometimes doctors have to make very difficult decisions in choosing which people will be given time on a machine.

Transplant

A healthy donor kidney from a person who has died very recently can be transplanted into a patient with kidney disease. The new kidney is inserted into the groin and attached to an artery and vein in this region of the body. The end of the ureter is sewn into place in the bladder. A successful transplant can bring a relatively normal life for a kidney patient. But a shortage of donor kidneys means that there are long waiting lists for this operation.

Controlling body temperature

Steve Cone is a college lecturer. Once a month he takes his class to the end of a dock in Lowestoft Harbour and throws them into the sea. At least he does if they won't jump in of their own accord. They don't like it,

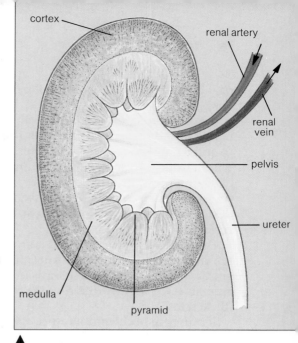

▲ The internal structure of the kidney.

▼ This large machine is needed to do the job of the kidneys. It filters water and waste products out of the blood.

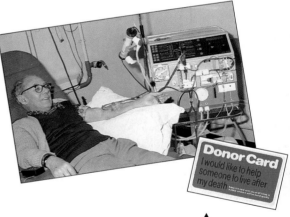

▲ Many people carry donor cards so that their organs can be used to help others.

▼ A transplanted kidney is placed into a person's groin.

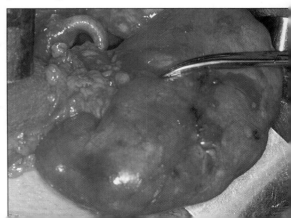

particularly in winter, but it's all part of a course on how to survive in a very cold environment.

Steve's 'pupils' are workers from North Sea oil rigs. They run the risk of falling into the sea from an oil platform or ditching into the sea as they fly to and from the rigs in a helicopter. Survival time in the North Sea in winter, for a normally clothed human body, is only a few minutes. So the class don't just wear bathing suits – otherwise the lecturer would soon run out of pupils – they are dressed in special 'immersion suits'. These are designed to conserve body heat so the wearer survives long enough to be rescued.

Humans are warm-blooded animals. We must keep our core body temperature at a constant level (about 37 °C) at all times. Doing this is another example of homeostasis in action. Different warm-blooded animals have slightly different body temperatures as you can see in the illustration.

If our core body temperature rises above 40 °C we are very close to death. If it gets below about 35 °C, we die of hypothermia. The temperature range over which all of our bodily functions work properly is very narrow, and so the control of body temperature must be efficient and precise.

▲ Offshore workers in survival clothing getting ready to be winched aboard a rescue helicopter.

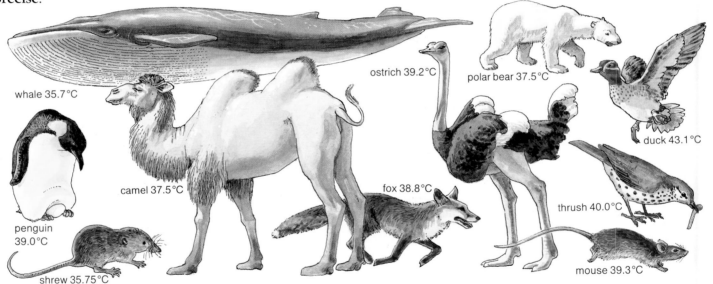

whale 35.7 °C

ostrich 39.2 °C

polar bear 37.5 °C

duck 43.1 °C

penguin 39.0 °C

camel 37.5 °C

fox 38.8 °C

thrush 40.0 °C

shrew 35.75 °C

mouse 39.3 °C

▲ Normal body temperatures of some warm-blooded animals.

Personal central heating

We keep warm by using the 'waste' energy from chemical reactions – like respiration – in the cells of the body. You can find out more about how we gain and lose heat from our bodies in GCSE book 1, Chapter 1, *Staying alive*.

Our muscles release energy when they contract. This heats them up, which is why you feel hot when you take vigorous exercise. In cold conditions we 'shiver'. This is because our muscles contract spontaneously to produce extra heat to keep us warm.

The liver is the heaviest organ of the body. It is the main 'chemical factory' of the body, continually changing chemicals from one kind to another. Most of these reactions also produce heat, which warms blood flowing through the liver and so it is carried to other parts of the body. You can find out more about this important organ in the 'Reference section'.

Responding to change

Not only must all of our body systems and life processes be regulated and controlled, they must also be able to cope with the altered needs of our body when conditions change.

One good example of this is when we take vigorous exercise. Suddenly we require a lot more energy than usual because our muscles are having to work so much harder.

Many systems in our bodies are affected by this change and they must all work together to meet the new demands being placed upon them. This is called an *integrated response*.

What are the main effects of taking exercise?

This integrated response to exercise, involving several different systems of the body, is brought about and controlled by the nervous system and by the release of *adrenaline* hormone. This hormone comes from the endocrine system, which is a set of glands.

Adrenaline is made in glands near the kidneys, called the adrenal glands.

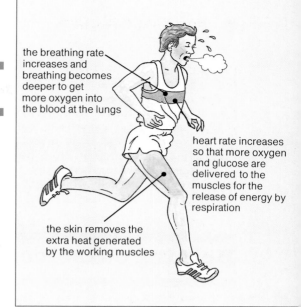

▲
The main effects of taking exercise.

▼
The positions of the main endocrine glands in the body.

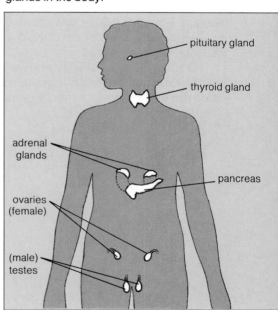

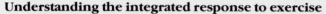

Understanding the integrated response to exercise
The part of the brain responsible for control and co-ordination of important automatic reflex functions such as heart rate and breathing is called the *medulla oblongata*.

Inside the medulla of the brain are groups of neurons (nerve cells) which make up the control centres for rhythmic breathing and heart rate. These centres are in turn governed to a certain extent by 'higher' *voluntary* centres in the brain. (Voluntary means that you can control something. For example you can over-ride normal breathing by holding your breath, although most of us do not have any conscious control over the rate at which the heart is beating.)

As soon as we begin exercise the rate of respiration in our muscles increases and more carbon dioxide is released into the blood. This increase of carbon dioxide concentration is detected by peripheral *chemoreceptors* in two areas of the body. These are the carotid and aortic bodies – small structures located in the carotid artery and the aorta respectively. Central chemoreceptors in the medulla itself are also stimulated by the increased carbon dioxide concentration in the blood.

These receptors send impulses to the medullary centres which bring about the appropriate response. The nerves to the diaphragm muscle across the base of the thorax (chest) (*phrenic nerves*) and the intercostal nerves to the intercostal muscles between the ribs are stimulated. This brings about faster and deeper inspiration (breathing in).

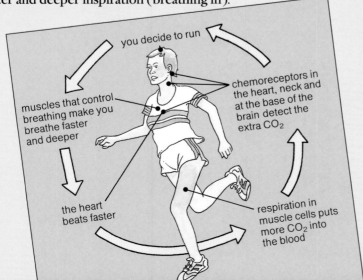

◄
This is what happens when you start to run. What happens to this control system when you stop running?

33

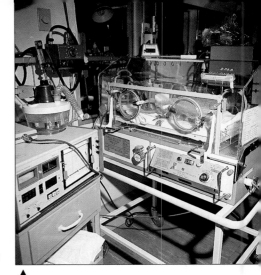

The sympathetic nerve to the heart 'pacemaker' (the *sino-atrial node*) is also stimulated, causing the heart to beat faster.

It is possible to hold your breath for a very long time. You might hold it long enough to fall unconscious, but as soon as you lose consciousness the automatic centres in the medulla become operational and make you breathe again. Depressant drugs 'damp down' these essential medullary brain centres, making them unable to ensure that your breathing and heart rate continue normally. This is why these drugs are often fatal.

▲
Many babies born prematurely cannot survive without equipment to control all sorts of body functions, like temperature, breathing and to give food for energy.

▼
A space suit gives the human body the conditions needed to survive outside the Earth's atmosphere. This suit kept Helen Sharman, the first Briton to go into space, alive for nearly 8 days.

Helping ourselves to survive

Humans don't have to rely totally on natural body systems to keep cool or to stay warm. We have used technology (clothes, fire and shelter, for example) to such good effect that human beings can live in all parts of the world, and even beyond, for short periods of time. Modern medical techniques enable us to intervene in the workings of our living machines when things go wrong. We can aid our natural defences in fighting disease by vaccination and taking drugs. We can help our bodies repair themselves after injury and accident by first aid and surgery. We can even build machines to replace important organs of our body in carrying out the vital functions of life.

It is interesting to think about what might be happening many years into the future. How much greater might be our ability to understand and alter the human body – our personal living machine?

Activities

1 How much energy did you 'take in' yesterday?
(a) Make a complete list of all the food and drink you have consumed recently in one full day.
(b) Work out as accurately as possible your personal food and energy intake for that period. Use the data of food energy values in the 'Reference section' (page 228) or the data on the food packaging. Was your intake more or less than the average values suggested?
(c) Look at the data again to find out how much of your daily food was carbohydrate, how much was fat, and how much was protein. Draw a bar or pie chart to show these amounts.
(d) Make a list of all the vitamins and minerals you also consumed in the food you ate during that day.

2 Choose three different animals: one that lives in the tropics, one that lives in Britain (temperate climate) and one that lives in the Arctic (or Antarctic). Find out how these animals keep their body temperatures at a safe level. You will have to look in other books for this. Make a full report of your findings.

3 Imagine that you are a single glucose sugar molecule joined to lots of other glucose sugars in a molecule of starch.
Describe exactly what happens to the starch molecule (and to you!) from the moment the starch is eaten by a person as part of a mouthful of potato until you enter a living cell and are chemically 'burned' to release your energy in respiration.

Questions

1 The two lists below give the main organs of the human body and their functions or 'jobs'. But the two lists have been muddled up. Write out the two lists and then join with lines or arrows the correct organ with its correct function.

Organ	Function
Heart	take in oxygen by breathing.
Kidneys	helps to control our body temperature by sweating.
Gut	carries out a lot of chemical reactions which release heat.
Lungs	controls how the body works and how we behave.
Skin	get rid of waste water, urea, and salts by filtering the blood.
Liver	pumps blood around the body.
Brain	digests our food.

2 Study the part of the 'Reference section' dealing with how the kidney works (page 225), and then copy out and fill in the chart below. Place a tick in each box if the substance is present in each of the places given in the chart headings and a cross if the substance is not present.

3 The graphs show how the blood sugar (glucose) levels changed in two people, Paula and Santos. Both had eaten the same kind of food at 1.00 p.m.
(a) One of them has a disease which means that he or she is unable to control his/her blood sugar level. Which person?
(b) What is this disease called?
(c) The disease is caused by the failure of a certain gland to produce a certain hormone. What is the gland called? Where in the body is it located? What is the name of the hormone it should produce?
(d) What would have happened to the blood sugar level of the diseased person if this hormone had been injected at 3.00 p.m.?

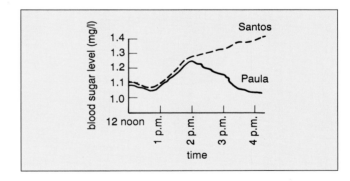

Substance	Parts of the kidney				
	Renal artery	Glomerulus blood vessel	Glomerular filtrate	Collecting duct	Renal vein
Water					
Salts					
Glucose					
Urea					

4 You come out of a warm open-air swimming pool and stand in a strong wind for a few minutes. You begin to feel very cold. What happens to your skin? Why?

5 Give three ways in which warm-blooded animals keep themselves warm in winter.

6 'Cold-blooded animals can't control their body temperatures by chemical means – they do so by means of their *behaviour*.'
Explain what this sentence means, and give an example of a cold-blooded animal keeping itself *cool* by its behaviour.

7 Put the following life activities or features into two lists, headed 'controlled by hormones' and 'not controlled by hormones':
seeing   breathing   ovulation
hearing   puberty   sweating
growing   heart beat   blood sugar level

8 The diagram shows the kidney and the three tubes that lead into and out of it.
(a) The tubes that carry blood are labelled A and B. What fluid is carried by tube C?
(b) The blood in tube A contains living cells, but also the substances listed below:
protein; salt; sugar; urea and *water*.
Is tube A carrying blood *into* the kidney or away from it?
(c) Which of the substances listed in (b) is taken from blood by the kidney?
(d) In a simple (but old-fashioned) medical test a doctor tasted the urine of a patient and found that it tasted sweet. What illness would this be a sign of?
(e) If the urine contained *protein*, what would this be a sign of?

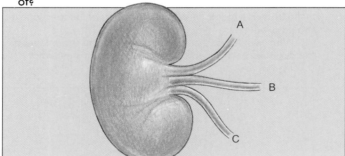

9 An Australian scientist, Dr C. Dundee, investigated the body temperature of a very large reptile (*Crocodilius spurium*). He did this by fixing a remote-sensing radio thermometer inside the animal's body, and reading the temperature every hour. He also measured the air temperature every hour.
The results for a 16 hour period are shown in the table.
(a) Draw two graphs, in the same time axis, showing how the air temperature and the crocodile's temperature changed.
(b) From midnight to 2.00 p.m. the temperatures of the air and of the crocodile both rise, more or less together. Explain briefly why this is.
(c) Between midnight and 7.00 a.m. the crocodile is slightly warmer than the air. Suggest a reason for this.
(d) In the early afternoon the air gets very hot (after 2.00 p.m.), but the crocodile's body temperature goes down. Suggest how the animal might have cooled off – and give the reason *why* it probably needed to do so.
(e) What time of the day is the animal most likely to go hunting for food? Give a reason for your answer.
(f) What would be the best time for Dr Dundee to put his radio thermometer inside a crocodile?

Time	Air temp. (°C)	Crocodile temp. (°C)
midnight	8	9
1.00 a.m.	7	8
2.00 a.m.	6	7
3.00 a.m.	5	6
4.00 a.m.	5	6
5.00 a.m.	5	6
6.00 a.m.	6	7
7.00 a.m.	9	10
8.00 a.m.	11	10
9.00 a.m.	13	10
10.00 a.m.	16	12
11.00 a.m.	19	17
noon	23	22
1.00 p.m.	27	28
2.00 p.m.	31	31
3.00 p.m.	33	26
4.00 p.m.	35	24

Checklist

These are the facts and ideas that you should have learned by studying this topic.

To reach Basic Level you should:

- be able to name and locate the major organs of the human body
- know what the following organs do: stomach; small intestine; heart; lungs; bladder
- know four basic differences between living and non-living things

To succeed at Foundation Level you should:

- be able to name the main organs of the body, know what they do and know where they are in the body
- know what living things do and need to keep alive
- know that we get water from food and drink and lose it by breathing and in urine
- know that our bodies work at a temperature of 37 °C
- know about sugar levels in the blood
- know what happens in the body when we exercise hard
- know what happens in respiration

To succeed at Merit Level you should:

- understand what happens in the major life processes – movement, respiration, circulation, excretion and nutrition
- know, in outline, how the body uses some important organs (the kidneys, skin, lungs, pancreas) to keep its internal state steady (homeostasis)
- understand what happens when green plants respire

To succeed at Special Level you should:

- be able to describe how an animal keeps its internal environment constant
- understand how homeostatic and metabolic processes contribute to maintaining the internal environment of organisms, i.e. understand the role of negative feedback in water balance, temperature regulation, glucose regulation and carbon dioxide levels

CHAPTER THREE

USING ELECTRICITY

Beams of light produced by electricity.

▼

Electricity heats the air in this hair dryer.

Electricity drives the motor in this train.

Electricity for communication and computation!

◄

Electricity turns the drill rotor.

For most of us, it is hard to think about living without electricity. The pictures on this page show just some of the everyday things that we take for granted. All use electricity to make them work. We could fill the pages ten-times over if we showed all of the things that are made by *using* electricity.

Electricity is useful because it is a very good way of carrying energy from one place to another. It can be used to energise things in four main ways.

1 Making things hot — as in heaters and filament lamps.

2 Making magnetism to get things moving — as in electric motors and loudspeakers.

3 Producing an electric force — as in electrolysis, to separate chemicals, or in a television set to move a stream of electrons.

4 Making light — by rearranging atoms as in LEDs (light-emitting diodes), television screens and 'neon' lamps.

Electricity can carry large amounts of energy. Electric trains are very powerful. Factories make great use of electricity. Many homes and work places use electricity for heating. About 15% of the energy supplied in Britain today is carried through wires by electricity. How this is done is explained later (page 49).

Electricity has been known about for over 2000 years. The word comes from the Ancient Greek name for amber — 'elektron'. Amber is a fossilised tree resin used to make necklaces and other jewellery. The Greeks discovered that it could become 'charged' with a mysterious force that attracted dust. This was due to what we now call 'static electricity'.

'Moving electricity' or electric *currents* were first discovered about 200 years ago (1799). The currents were produced by chemicals arranged in cells or 'batteries' of cells. At first the currents were very weak, and weren't much use for supplying a lot of energy. The first practical use of electricity was for *sending messages*. This is still one of the most important uses of electricity.

The first electric telegraph was set up in 1833. By 1854 a telegraph system was carrying messages between Paris and London, and four years later an undersea telegraph was set up between London and New York. You couldn't talk along a telegraph wire — you had to use a dot–dash code. But the first 'talking telegraph' — the *telephone* — was in use two years before the first electric lights. The first electric lighting system was working in London in 1880.

Electric power couldn't be made in large quantities until someone had invented a practical *generator*. This was being done in the 1870s, and soon there were not only electric lights but also electric street 'buses' — trams.

This chapter deals with the way we use electricity to do *work* for us, and how it can be controlled. Chapter 6, *Communications* deals with the way we use electricity (and other things) to send messages.

Controlling electric currents

Most electrical devices work by making use of a flow of electricity. (But some use static electricity, of course). A flow of electricity is called an electric *current*, and is measured in amperes (A). For a flow to happen you need a complete circuit and a source of energy. But what is actually flowing?

Electric charge

Matter is made up of atoms. In turn, atoms consist of a small, massive nucleus surrounded by a cloud of very light particles called electrons. Atoms are in fact held together by electricity. The nucleus has a positive charge, and attracts the electrons, which have negative charges.

In a good conductor some of the electrons are free to move. When they do, we have our electric current. It might surprise you to think that the electricity is in the circuit all the time, even when it is switched off, but it is. All that the switch does is to let the electricity flow.

Of course, the electrons won't move along the wire on their own. They need a source of energy. This is what the battery or generator is.

The energy available from a supply is indicated by its *voltage*. The higher the voltage of a supply the more energy it can supply per second for each ampere of current that flows. There is more about this quite difficult idea below (page 42).

When the circuit is working, the charges are just circulating through it. The battery doesn't 'make electricity', it just provides the energy to move the electric charges that are already there. It's like the trains on the Circle Line of the London Underground – they don't have to make new trains all the time, just supply energy to the ones already there!

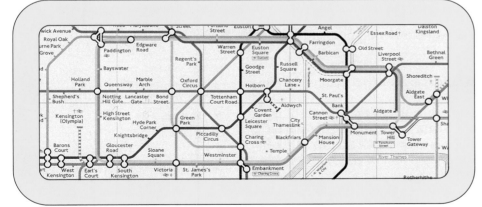

LRT Registered user number 92/E/557.

Circuits

The drawings show some simple circuits. You have probably already studied these in the laboratory. A list of the symbols used to show the different components used to make circuits is given in the 'Reference section'.

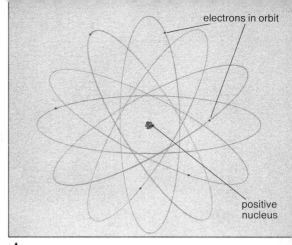

▲
An atom is electrically neutral: the positive charge on the nucleus is equal to the negative charges carried by the electrons.

▼
An electric current in a metal is a slow drifting of 'free' electrons bouncing from atom to atom in the metal crystals.

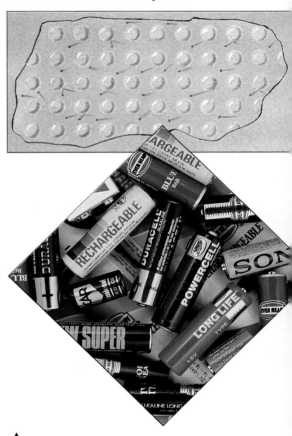

▲
The voltage on the label tells you how much energy you can get out of a battery: 1.5 V means 1.5 joules of energy per second for every ampere of current that flows through the battery into a circuit.

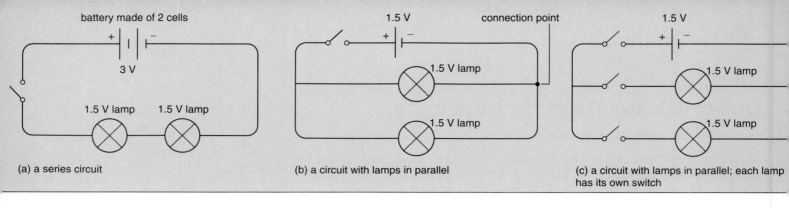

battery made of 2 cells

3 V

1.5 V lamp   1.5 V lamp

(a) a series circuit

1.5 V   connection point

1.5 V lamp

1.5 V lamp

(b) a circuit with lamps in parallel

1.5 V

1.5 V lamp

1.5 V lamp

(c) a circuit with lamps in parallel; each lamp has its own switch

Series circuits

Circuit (a) in the diagram (above) is a series circuit. In a series circuit the components follow on from one another. There is only one path for the charge to flow through. This means that the current is the same in all parts of the circuit. What goes in at one end must come out at the other, or charge would keep building up more and more. Of course a circuit can 'leak' charge to somewhere else, the ground for example. But this means that the circuit is faulty — it is no longer a simple series circuit.

Parallel circuits

Circuit (b) in the diagram is a parallel circuit. In parallel circuits there is more than one path for the charge to flow through. These circuits can be very complicated — the diagrams show just two simple ones. In one case the switch controls both lamps, in the other each lamp has its own switch.

Household electric circuits are parallel circuits. This allows each component to be controlled by its own switch, as in circuit (c). You wouldn't want every electrical appliance in the house to come on at the flick of a single switch!

Parallel circuits are useful for other reasons, as well:

- each component is connected directly to the power supply, so gets its proper voltage;
- each component can have its own fuse, with a suitable rating (see below, page 43);
- if the component goes wrong, it doesn't stop other components working.

Compare these advantages with what would happen if one lamp 'blew' in the series circuit in diagram (a).

Even so, series circuits are very useful. You will find them in flashing lights (on a Christmas tree, for example). These can be made to flash on and off together. One of the series of lamps is special. It contains a thermal switch which stops the current when the lamp filament gets hot. When it cools down it remakes the connection, so the lights go back on again.

Resistance and resistors

Whenever charge flows in a conductor it has to move between the atoms. As the electrons bounce from atom to atom they tend to lose some energy. This energy makes the conductor get hot.

In a good conductor the electrons lose hardly any energy this way. But other materials are harder for the electrons to get through. We say that

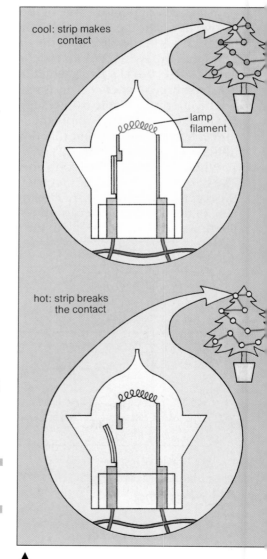

cool: strip makes contact

lamp filament

hot: strip breaks the contact

▲
The bending contact is a bimetallic strip. The 'dark' metal expands more than the other when heated, so the strip bends.

these materials have a high ability to resist the flow. We use such materials to make *resistors*.

When charges flow through a resistor the energy they lose makes the resistor hot. This effect is used to make electric heaters and filament lamps (see page 41). Special alloys are used to make resistors, such as *nichrome*, which you will find in the coils of an electric fire element. These alloys can get hot without burning or melting. Electric lamp filaments get white hot, reaching a temperature of over 2000°C. They have to be made from a metal with a very high melting point – tungsten – and have to be kept from the air. There is more about lamps on page 44.

The *resistance* of a conductor tells us how many volts we have to put across it to drive a current of 1 ampere through it:

$$\text{resistance} = \frac{\text{voltage across the component,}}{\text{current through it}}$$

$$R = \frac{V}{I}$$

Resistance is measured in ohms (Ω).

Insulators

In an insulator there aren't any charged particles that are free to move. Good insulators include: plastics, oil, porcelain, air, paper, rubber, etc. It would be hard to control electricity without the use of insulators. We couldn't have switches, for example.

Semiconductors

Some materials are in between insulators and the good conductors like metals. These are called *semiconductors*. Examples are: carbon, silicon, germanium, and some compounds of these elements. Germanium is about 30 million times *worse* as a conductor than a metal like copper.

But semiconductors do contain some electrons that are free to move. There just aren't as many of them as there are in a piece of metal of the same size. Semiconductors are useful because the number of free electrons can be easily altered. This allows them to be used as *temperature sensors*, and as *transistors* in the integrated circuits that are at the heart of computers.

▼
A microchip is made of layers of semiconductors that form many very small, complex circuits. This is just a tiny part of one circuit.

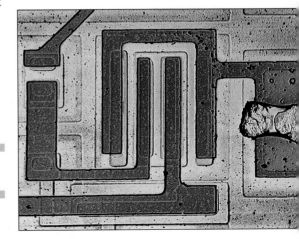

Heating and lighting

An electric heater contains a length of resistance wire. As current flows in it, the wire is heated. The heater can be used to warm a room in two main ways:

- by using radiant energy;
- by warming air that then flows around the room.

Radiant heaters usually make the wire of the heating element red hot. This then emits *infrared radiation*, as well as some red light. Some radiant heaters are kept cooler, so that they don't glow with visible light. Infrared rays carry energy in the form of electromagnetic waves. The rays are absorbed by most materials, which are heated as a result. There is more about these waves in Chapter 9, *Space*.

If 'space heating' is required, i.e. you want to warm all of a room, it is better to use some form of *convector heater*. In these heaters the hot wire is used to heat air. Hot air expands and rises, being replaced by cooler air. Eventually all the air in a room is heated by passing through or over the heater. This process is called *convection*.

Calculating the energy delivered

The energy delivered depends on the voltage, the current and the time for which the current flows:

$$\text{energy delivered} = \text{voltage} \times \text{current} \times \text{time},$$
$$[\text{joules}] = [\text{volts}] \times [\text{amperes}] \times [\text{seconds}]$$

or, $E = VIt$.

The quantity 'voltage × current' is important. It tells us how much energy is delivered each second. This is called the *power* of the appliance. Power is measured in *watts*. All electrical appliances should have their *power rating*, in watts, marked on them.

So a hair dryer rated at 600 watts will deliver energy – in the form of moving, heated air – at the rate of 600 joules per second. If you use it for 5 minutes you will have transferred:

600 watts × 300 seconds = 180 000 joules of energy.

A joule isn't very much energy! We would normally write this as 180 kilojoules (kJ).

▲
Voltage, wattage and current marked on an electric drill.

Choosing the heater resistance

A mains-operated appliance is designed to work off the 240 V mains supply. This is also marked on the label. For a simple device like a heater, this allows the designer to specify what resistance the heating coil must have. The calculation goes like this:

power rating desired: 600 W;

supply voltage to be used: 240 V.

Use power = voltage × current to calculate I, the current needed (the symbol for current value is I):

600 watts = 240 volts × I.

This gives $I = \dfrac{600}{240} = 2.5\text{A}$.

Remember that resistance is the ratio voltage/current, so:

$$R = \frac{V}{I} = \frac{240}{2.5} = 96 \text{ ohms.}$$

The designer will have to choose a length of wire with a resistance of 96 ohms.

Alternative formulae

The power formula and the resistance formula are often used together. It is often easier to combine them before we start making calculations:
power $P = VI$, and resistance $R = V/I$.
Begin by rearranging the resistance formula as:
$V = IR$, or $I = V/R$.
Instead of V in the power formula we can put IR:

so, $P = IR \times I = I^2R$.

Again, instead of I we can put V/R:

so, $P = V \times V/R = V^2/R$.

There are some calculations involving power and energy in the questions at the end of the chapter.

Domestic electricity supplies

In a typical house lighting circuit, each lamp is connected directly to the full 240 V mains supply. This is a typical example of a parallel circuit. Most lamps have their own switches; in some cases there are two lamps run off the same switch.

Each lamp is connected to the mains with just two wires: the *live* wire and the *neutral* wire. The switch must be connected in the live wire. This is for safety reasons so that when the switch is off, no part of the lamp is 'live'.

Domestic electricity is supplied as *alternating current* (a.c.). The 'live wire' in the lamp circuit is connected to a terminal whose voltage changes from $+340$ volts to -340 volts 50 times a second. When a lamp is switched on, charge flows *backwards and forwards* in its filament to make it hot. We still need a complete circuit, of course, and the return wire is connected to the neutral terminal of the house supply. This is usually kept at 0 volts.

Houses will also have a *ring-main* circuit with much thicker wire. This is the circuit to which the wall sockets are connected. It is designed to supply devices which either need to take more current, or need to be *earthed*. Earth wires are usually connected to a water pipe.

The earth wire is a safety feature. Many electrical devices have metal parts to make them strong. They are not meant to be part of the circuit. If a fault develops the metal could become live, and dangerous. But if these metal parts are connected to the earth they will always be at earth voltage (0 volts). Usually when a fault develops the earth connection makes a low resistance path between the live wire and the earth. The current will be large and will blow a fuse.

Sometimes the metal parts will be very well insulated: they have *double insulation*. These will not need an earth connection.

Fuses

There are two main kinds of fuse: *thermal* and *magnetic*.
Thermal fuses consist of a ceramic or glass tube with a thin wire inside.

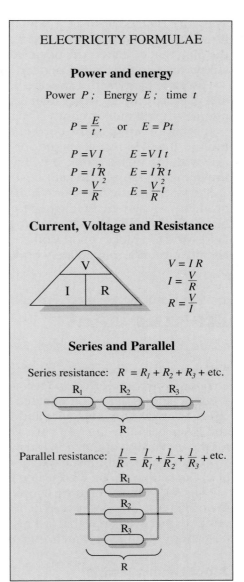

ELECTRICITY FORMULAE

Power and energy

Power P; Energy E; time t

$$P = \frac{E}{t}, \quad \text{or} \quad E = Pt$$

$$P = VI \qquad E = VIt$$
$$P = I^2R \qquad E = I^2Rt$$
$$P = \frac{V^2}{R} \qquad E = \frac{V^2}{R}t$$

Current, Voltage and Resistance

$$V = IR$$
$$I = \frac{V}{R}$$
$$R = \frac{V}{I}$$

Series and Parallel

Series resistance: $R = R_1 + R_2 + R_3 +$ etc.

Parallel resistance: $\frac{1}{R} = \frac{1}{R_1} + \frac{1}{R_2} + \frac{1}{R_3} +$ etc.

▼
Electrical sockets are on a ring main.

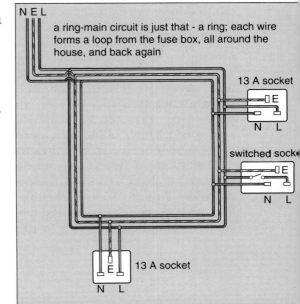

a ring-main circuit is just that - a ring; each wire forms a loop from the fuse box, all around the house, and back again

13 A socket

switched socket

13 A socket

This wire is made of an alloy which melts if it gets too hot. The fuse is fitted into the live side of any circuit. It could be in the device itself or in the plug that connects the device to the supply socket. Also, there are always fuses in the mains connection box.

Fuses are made with a specific *rating*, in amperes. Thus a *5 amp fuse* will melt if a current larger than 5 amperes flows in it for more than a few minutes. It will melt instantly if a large current, say 10 A, flows.

It is important to fit the correct fuse into a circuit. If the fuse rating is too low it will blow even if the appliance is working properly. If you fit a fuse with too high a rating, it will not protect you from shock or possibly a fire in the device when a fault develops.

Simple magnetic fuses, or *circuit breakers*, contain a coil which produces a magnetic field when a current flows through the coil. The bigger the current, the stronger the field. If the current gets too large the field attracts a piece of soft iron connected to a switch. The switch opens and the circuit is immediately broken.

▲ A correctly wired 13 A plug.

▼ The fuse box in a house. You can see the wire fuse inside the ceramic holder.

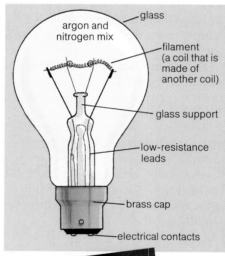

Making light

A filament lamp contains a coiled tungsten wire. The lamp is a sealed glass envelope, surrounded by an inert gas (a mixture of argon and nitrogen). A modern lamp is quite complicated. The very thin wire coil is itself coiled again, to give a very long wire and so more light from a small space. The coil is supported by metal struts. The glass has to be capable of allowing for the expansion of the metal strips that carry current to the coil. These strips get warm, but must have a low resistance to stop them getting too hot. The lamp must be well sealed to stop air getting in.

Even so, ordinary electric lamps don't last very long – about 1000 hours in normal use. The design can be improved, and you can buy special, rather expensive lamps that last more than sixteen-times as long. They cost about six-times as much as an ordinary lamp.

Fluorescent lamps

In a filament lamp the energy supplied is used to make the filament hot. Very little of this energy is emitted as light: about 3% in practice. The rest is used to warm the surroundings, by conduction and convection, or is emitted from the filament as infrared radiation. You can feel these 'heat rays' by putting your hand near the lamp.

So-called *fluorescent* 'daylight' lamps work on a completely different principle. The lamps are usually tube-shaped, and contain a mercury vapour at a low pressure. When the lamp is working, a high voltage is set up between two terminals, one at each end of the tube. The vapour is slightly 'energised' to make ions and some free electrons. These charged particles are attracted to one or other of the terminals and start to move at high speed. They collide with mercury atoms in the tube and disturb the arrangement of electrons in the atoms.

The electrons are in fact given some extra energy. When the disturbed electrons go back to normal the energy is released, mostly as ultraviolet radiation. This radiation is invisible. It is dangerous to eyes and skin. But the inside of the tube is painted with a fluorescent chemical (similar to the chemicals on the screen of a TV tube). The ultraviolet radiation is safely

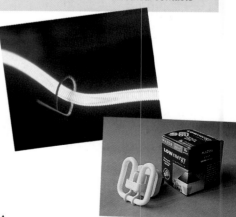

The filament in a lamp is a very long *coil* of wire. Filaments in lamps get very hot and eventually burn out. This filament (bottom) works at a lower temperature and so lasts longer.

Glass diagram labels: glass; argon and nitrogen mix; filament (a coil that is made of another coil); glass support; low-resistance leads; brass cap; electrical contacts

absorbed by this paint, which in its turn emits a whole range of *visible* radiation. White light is a mixture of 'all the colours of the rainbow', so we simply see this mixture of radiation as white light.

Electromagnetism: electricity making things move

The pictures show the magnetic fields near a wire and a coil of wire when they carry an electric current. The small iron filings line up with the *lines of force* of the magnetic field.

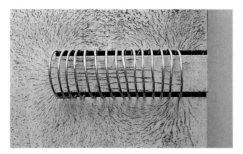

▲ The magnetic field around a wire coil.

▲ The magnetic field around a single wire.

The magnetic effect of a coil can be made stronger by:

- using larger currents;
- having more turns of wire in the coil;
- wrapping the coil around a core made of 'soft iron'.

'Soft iron' is iron that can be hammered without breaking (compared with the brittle 'cast iron'). It also has the ability to be magnetised very strongly and demagnetised very easily.

This means that a coil can be turned into an *electromagnet* with a field much stronger than that of the coil on its own, even though the current is the same. Electromagnets can be made to be much stronger than ordinary magnets, which also have to be made of special, expensive alloys to be really useful. Another advantage of electromagnets is that they can be switched on and off. Ordinary metal magnets can't be; they are *permanent* magnets.

Magnets can attract and repel other magnets. Things become very interesting and useful when we use electromagnets to interact with each other and with permanent magnets. The result is a set of useful devices: relays, electric motors, dynamos, microphones, loudspeakers and transformers.

Electric fields have a direction

Exactly what happens when magnetic fields interact depends on the direction of the fields. In turn, this is decided by the direction of the electric current that makes the field. We show the direction of a magnetic field by a small arrow on the lines of force. The arrow points in the

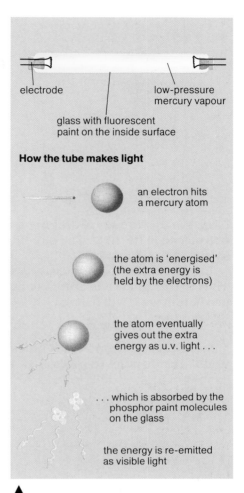

electrode   low-pressure
                   mercury vapour

glass with fluorescent
paint on the inside surface

How the tube makes light

an electron hits a mercury atom

the atom is 'energised' (the extra energy is held by the electrons)

the atom eventually gives out the extra energy as u.v. light . . .

. . . which is absorbed by the phosphor paint molecules on the glass

the energy is re-emitted as visible light

▲ How a fluorescent tube makes light.

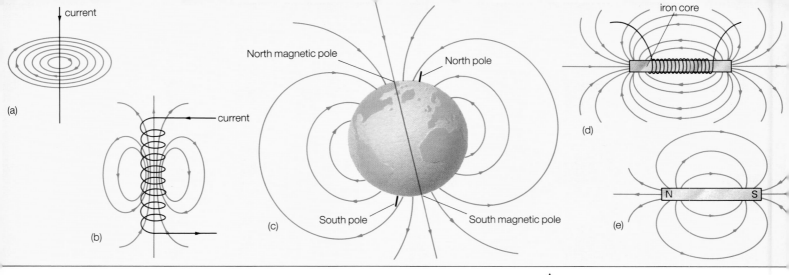

direction that the *north-seeking pole* of a small compass would point if it was placed in the field. The directions of a number of everyday fields are shown in the diagrams.

Interacting fields produce forces on the objects producing the fields. Thus two magnets will attract or repel each other. There is a rule for predicting what will happen:

like poles repel; unlike poles attract.

So, north-seeking poles (N-poles) repel other N-poles but will attract south-seeking poles (S-poles).

▲
(a) The magnetic field of the Earth; (b) the field produced by a current in a wire; (c) the field of a current in a coil (this is the same as for a bar magnet); (d) the field of an electromagnet; (e) the field of a bar magnet. In all of these drawings, the arrows show the direction that a compass needle would point if placed in the field (north).

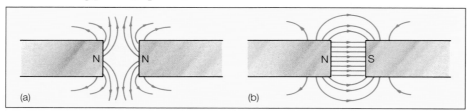

◄
The fields between the poles of magnets.

But electric currents don't have poles. The rules for predicting what happens uses the directions of the field and the currents. The rules are better shown in diagrams than in words.

◄
Two ways for working out the direction of the magnetic field produced by a current.

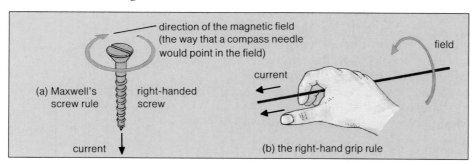

These rules assume that an electric current goes from the positive towards the negative terminal of a supply. Note that the forces, fields and currents are all at right angles to each other. These rules describe what happens in devices like electric motors and loudspeakers.

▼
Fleming's left-hand rule for showing the relationship between the field, current and the direction the wire moves.

The motor effect

A single wire carrying an electric current through a magnetic field will have a force exerted on it. The diagram (right) shows the direction of the force; check it by applying the 'left-hand rule'.

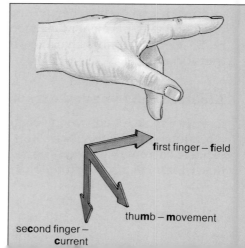

first finger – field

thumb – movement

second finger – current

To make a practical motor based on this effect we have to overcome a few problems, which boil down to:

- making a larger force;
- getting the force to produce a rotation (e.g. to get wheels to turn); and,
- getting an electric current in and out of a rotating coil.

The diagram (below) shows how this is done in a small motor used, say, in an electric drill. The fixed (non-moving) field is made stronger by using many turns of wire wrapped around a soft-iron core. The rotating coil also has many turns of wire, with each turn having a force exerted on it to help the spindle turn. A device called a *commutator* simultaneously acts as a rotating switch and contact. It changes the direction of the current through the coil as it spins, so making sure that the force on the current in the wires keeps pushing the coil in the same direction of turn. The contacts slide over each other, but still make good connections. The moving contact is usually copper, the fixed one is made of good-quality graphite.

A simplified diagram of the commutator action is shown in the diagram.

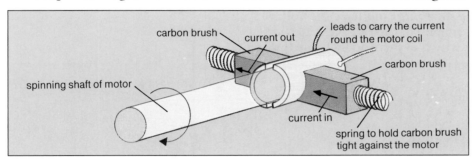

carbon brush · current out · leads to carry the current round the motor coil · carbon brush · spinning shaft of motor · current in · spring to hold carbon brush tight against the motor

◀ Direct-current motors use a *split-ring commutator*.

Electromagnetic induction: movement makes electricity

One of the most useful and surprising things in electromagnetism is that it can work forwards and backwards. Moving some electric charge, as a current, through a magnetic field will produce a force. This can act on the current and so move the conductor. Moving a conductor in a magnetic field can make charges move, and so produce a current. This effect is called *electromagnetic induction*.

▼ Electromagnetic induction: movement producing electricity.

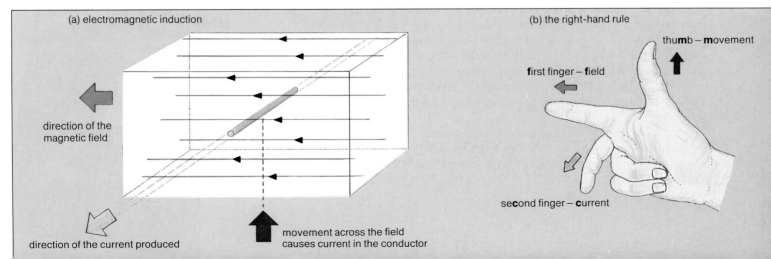

(a) electromagnetic induction

direction of the magnetic field

direction of the current produced

movement across the field causes current in the conductor

(b) the right-hand rule

thumb – **m**ovement

first finger – **f**ield

second finger – **c**urrent

Electromagnetic induction is the basis of the electricity industry. It was discovered in 1831 by Michael Faraday, in England. But it was little more than an interesting laboratory demonstration for many years. Faraday realised its importance. When a politician asked him what use it was, he is said to have replied, 'I don't know yet – but one day you will be taxing it!'.

▲ Michael Faraday made it to *The Illustrated London News* in 1846 with his lecture on electricity and magnetism.

Generating and distributing electricity on a large scale

An electric generator is very like a motor, but works in reverse. It needs a supply of energy to turn the *rotor*. This is a set of large coils wound on a soft iron core (the *armature*). The coils carry an electric current and produce the strong magnetic field.

The spinning fields of these coils induce a voltage in the outer coils. The outer coils are fixed. (By comparison, in a simple generator like a bicycle dynamo, the magnets stay fixed and the *spinning* coils have the voltage produced in them. It is the *relative* movement of field and conductor that produces the voltage. It doesn't matter which of them actually moves!)

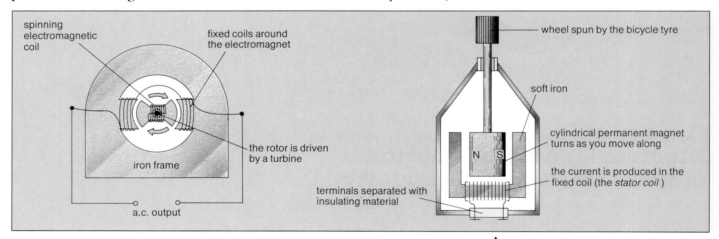

spinning electromagnetic coil

fixed coils around the electromagnet

iron frame

the rotor is driven by a turbine

a.c. output

wheel spun by the bicycle tyre

soft iron

cylindrical permanent magnet turns as you move along

the current is produced in the fixed coil (the *stator coil*)

terminals separated with insulating material

▲ A simple a.c. generator and (right) a bicycle dynamo.

▼ Simple dynamo on a bicycle.

The energy supply

The bicycle dynamo needs the cyclist to put in a bit of extra energy as the bike is moving. Power stations get their energy from coal, gas, oil, moving water or nuclear fission. In each case the energy is first used to boil water. The steam is produced at a high temperature and pressure, and is used to spin turbines. The turbines are connected to the same shaft as the generator rotor. The speed of rotation has to be kept very accurately constant. It is arranged so that each coil – there are many on each rotor – takes exactly a fiftieth of a second to make one turn.

As the spinning fields cut through the fixed coils a current is produced. This results in an *alternating current*: its direction changes 50 times a second.

A typical generator produces this current at 25 000 volts. This is far too high for making ordinary devices work. But it is too small for efficient *distribution* of electricity over large distances! The reason for this is explained below.

In the U.K. most electricity is generated in a few very large power stations with an output of at least 1 million kilowatts (1 gigawatt, 1GW). A single modern turbine generator can produce two-thirds of a gigawatt on its own.

A 1GW power station like this would provide enough power for the needs of nearly 300 000 houses. The total power generated in the U.K. is about 48 GW (48 million kilowatts), most of which is used in industry. This output is about a fifth of the country's total energy needs. Not all the power stations may be fully in use at any one time, and allowance has to be made for extra demands, and for breakdowns. This means that if all the stations were working at the same time they could produce over 60 GW. We also buy electricity from France, delivered by undersea cables.

▲
Power stations are surrounded by huge cooling towers where the steam is released after passing through the turbines. Large power stations like this one supply electricity to a large area. In Germany, there are many more smaller generators producing electricity for the local area. This allows combined heat and power schemes.

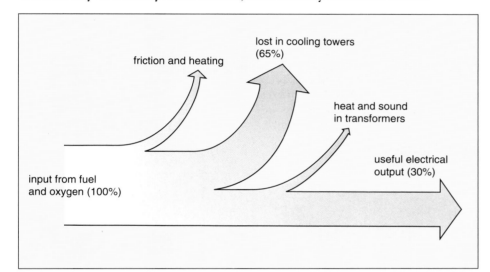

◀
The energy flow in a power station: a Sankey diagram.

Distributing electricity

Electricity goes through many stages before it gets to your home. It is carried at different voltages at different stages. Less energy is wasted in heating the cables if high voltages are used (see page 50). But high voltages are very dangerous, so much lower voltages are used in homes and factories. Voltages can be changed from one value to another by using a *transformer*.

▼
Voltage changes a great deal across the National Grid.

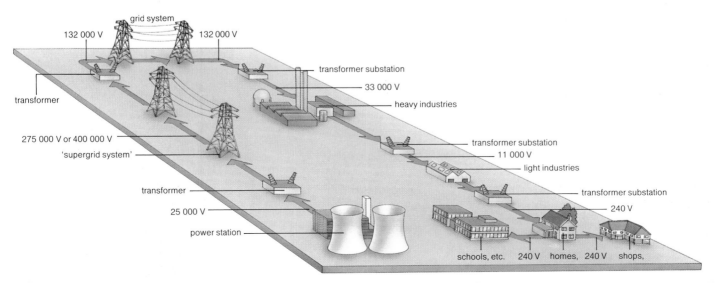

Transformers

The principle of the transformer was also discovered by Michael Faraday, over 150 years ago. Transformers can change the size of an alternating voltage. They consist of two coils wound around the same soft iron core. When an alternating current flows in one coil it induces a voltage in the second coil.

All currents produce a magnetic field. This is made much stronger when the current flows in a coil of many turns, and when the coil is wound around soft iron, as already explained. In a transformer the input current is alternating, and therefore so is the magnetic field it produces. The input current is in what is called the *primary coil*.

The other coil – the *secondary* – is thus in a changing magnetic field. Just as in a generator, the changing field induces a voltage in this secondary coil. *But the induced voltage can be any value you like.* All the designer has to do is to decide on the number of turns in the coils.

If the number of turns in the secondary coil is double the number of turns in the primary, then the output voltage is double the input voltage. You can halve the voltage by giving the secondary coil half as many turns as the primary.

The *transformer rule* is:

$$\frac{\text{output voltage}}{\text{input voltage}} = \frac{\text{secondary turns}}{\text{primary turns}}.$$

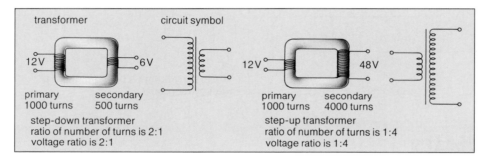

transformer   circuit symbol

12V   6V

primary   secondary
1000 turns   500 turns

step-down transformer
ratio of number of turns is 2:1
voltage ratio is 2:1

12V   48V

primary   secondary
1000 turns   4000 turns

step-up transformer
ratio of number of turns is 1:4
voltage ratio is 1:4

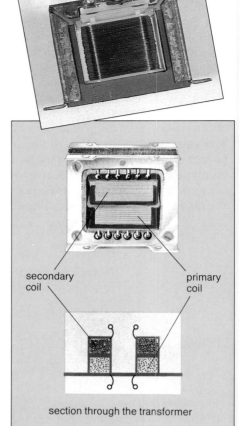

secondary coil   primary coil

section through the transformer

▲
Section through a very simple transformer.

◄
In transformers, the ratio of the voltages depends on the ratio of the number of turns on the coils.

Why use high voltages to transmit electricity?

The power loss in a resistor – as explained above (page 43) – is given by the formula:

power (in watts) $= I^2R$,

(where I is the current in amperes, R the resistance in ohms).

The lost energy heats up the resistor. A transmission cable is designed to have as low a resistance as possible. It is made of thick copper or aluminium as shown. A typical cable has a resistance of only 0.06 ohms per kilometre.

But even so, the cables have to be very long and so the resistance builds up. A way of reducing energy losses is to cut down the current. For example, if the length of cable has a resistance of 1 ohm, the power loss in it for various current values is:

Current (amps)	Power loss (watts)
1	1
10	100
100	10 000

▼
Cables from the National Grid: the thinner one is an overhead cable and the other one is used underground.

But we can't have power loss in the cable at the expense of power delivered to the user. The power delivered is calculated in terms of the supply voltage and the current taken from it. A small block of flats will have its power delivered at 240 V, and may take 200 A to run its lights, cookers and other machines. This represents a delivered power, given by $P = VI$, of 48 000 watts (48 kW).

If this was delivered from a power station at the same current, the power loss in a 1-ohm cable would be (from I^2R):
$200 \times 200 \times 1 = 40\,000$ watts! Thus most of the energy supplied would be lost *before* the user could get it.

By using transformers, the transmission voltage is increased to, say, 132 000 V. The same power requirement of 48 kW could now be supplied with a current calculated by:

$$\text{power} = VI, \text{ so } I = \frac{\text{power}}{V} = \frac{48\,000}{132\,000} = 0.37\,\text{A}.$$

The power loss in the cable is now:

$$I^2R = 0.37 \times 0.37 \times 1 = 0.13\,\text{W}.$$

A good economy!

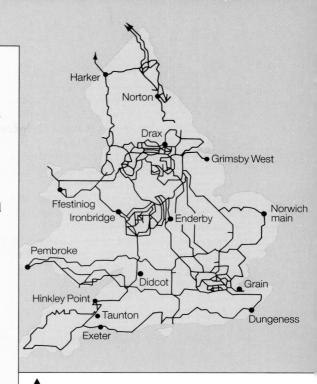

▲
The main power lines of the National Grid in England and Wales.

The problems with fossil fuels

So far, you have only read the good news about electricity! But most of our electricity is generated by burning fossil fuels. When fossil fuels burn, they produce pollutant gases. Power stations are responsible for most of the sulphur dioxide, half of the nitrogen oxides and a third of the 'extra' carbon dioxide in the atmosphere.

Another problem with fossil fuels is that we are using them up faster than they can possibly be replaced. In just over 200 years we have already used up coal, oil and gas deposits that took 60 million years to produce.

For all of these reasons, alternative sources of energy will have to be found eventually.

Alternatives to using fossil fuels

Hydroelectric power stations use the energy of moving water to turn the turbines that spin the generators. This source of energy is mostly used in countries with high mountains and plenty of rain. Norway produces all of its electric power in this way, compared with just 0.2% in the U.K. Some countries with large rivers can build huge dams, as Egypt has done with the Aswan Dam across the Nile. But artificial dams across rivers have a problem. Silt carried by the river can eventually fill the lake behind the dam. This is happening to the Aswan Dam, and to many dams built 50 or 60 years ago in the U.S.A.

Another way of using water power is to make use of the rise and fall of the *tides*. As the tide rises, water flows upstream in an estuary. Later, it flows back again. This happens twice a day. A dam with built-in turbines can use the water movement to make electricity. This is being done in the Rance

▼
The Aswan High Dam, Egypt. You can see the huge amount of water held back by the dam.

Estuary in northern France. There are plans to build a similar power station using the tidal flow in the Severn Estuary.

Sea *waves* contain a lot of energy. This can be harnessed to make electricity. The problem is that the energy is spread out over the length of the wave. Energy is more useful when it is concentrated. But some parts of Britain have large waves for most of the year, and especially in winter when electrical energy is most needed.

The *wind* carries a lot of energy. As in waves, the energy tends to be spread out. Also, like waves, the energy flow isn't very steady, and the wind may not blow when you need it! But wind energy was the main source of energy to power machines in many countries a few hundred years ago; the countryside in Eastern England and Holland was covered with windmills for grinding corn.

A single 'wind generator' of electricity can't produce a lot of power – it would have to be very big. This would make it very expensive – and unsightly. To get round this, lots of small ones are built together in wind farms.

The energy to move wind and water comes from the Sun. This will keep on happening for several billion years more and so as far as we are concerned the energy is *renewable*.

Energy for electricity in Britain

Energy source	Power produced in 1990 (MW)
Power stations using fossil fuels (mostly coal and oil)	38000
Nuclear power stations	10600
Imported from France (nuclear)	1500
Hydroelectricity	107
Wind power	25
Tidal power	0*
Rubbish-burning power stations (no more than 200 MW likely)	1?

*The Severn Barrage could provide 7200 MW

Many countries are now researching into making more use of these renewable sources of energy, but it will be many years before they can replace fossil fuels. One source that is readily available, and doesn't have the polluting effects of fossil fuels, is nuclear energy. But this source has problems of its own (see Chapter 12 in GCSE book 1).

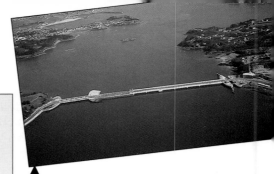

▲ La Rance tidal barrage. What is a disadvantage of this way of generating electricity?

▼ A scheme to use energy from waves to produce electricity on the Island of Islay in Scotland. Waves force air from the main chamber through a turbine, which turns a dynamo.

▼ A wind farm in California.

Electrons in space: current without conductors!

After he had invented his electric lamp, Thomas Edison noted a strange effect. In one of his experiments a current was able to flow, through empty space, between the hot filament and a piece of wire he had built into the side of a lamp. Edison was keen to make money from anything he

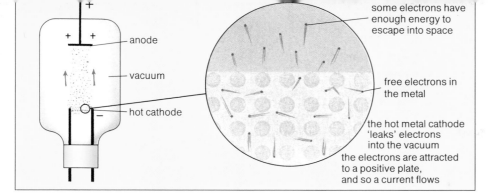

some electrons have enough energy to escape into space

anode

vacuum

hot cathode

free electrons in the metal

the hot metal cathode 'leaks' electrons into the vacuum
the electrons are attracted to a positive plate, and so a current flows

◄
This is what happens in thermionic emission.

discovered, so he registered the effect in case it would come in useful later. Then he forgot about it!

A few years later the effect became very important in a new invention that all sorts of people had been working on, a long-distance telegraph that could work without wires – the *wireless telegraph*. We now call it *radio*. Later still, it became even more important as the basis of the *television tube*.

Thermionic emission

Edison's effect is now called thermionic emission. What happens is that the electrons that carry the current through a metal – or carbon – are 'boiled' out of the conductor when it is made very hot (red hot). The electrons are then free in a vacuum and can be attracted by a positively charged metal plate.

Nowadays the emitter doesn't have to be red hot. A thin wire filament is used to heat a small cylinder coated with an oxide of certain metals (such as strontium). Electrons can leave this kind of material more easily at lower temperatures.

In a TV tube the electrons are attracted by a positive voltage and made to travel at a high speed. The beam of electrons can be focused by magnetic coils and made to sweep the screen of the tube. The screen is coated with fluorescent chemicals which glow when electrons hit them. Different chemicals produce different colours. The chemicals are arranged in small areas – the picture cells or 'pixels'. These glowing pixels build up the picture that you see on the screen.

In a radio the job that used to be done by small electron tubes or 'valves' is now done by transistors or integrated circuits made of semiconductor material. These not only work more quickly but they are less easy to break, much smaller and use less energy. Very small TV sets can even use semiconductor screens instead of the traditional 'cathode ray tubes'. There is more about television in Chapter 6, *Communications*.

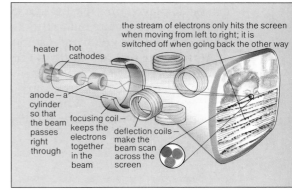

the stream of electrons only hits the screen when moving from left to right; it is switched off when going back the other way

heater   hot cathodes

anode – a cylinder so that the beam passes right through

focusing coil – keeps the electrons together in the beam

deflection coils – make the beam scan across the screen

▲
The electron beam in a TV tube 'scans' across the screen, moving down one line with every pass. There are 625 lines from top to bottom.

▼
Look at this picture from a distance. Then look at it very closely; the whole image is made from red, green and blue dots – even the white areas.

▼
Two wave forms on a cathode ray oscilloscope.

The cathode ray oscilloscope

One of the first uses of electron streams was the cathode ray oscilloscope.

The first effects of 'free electrons' in space were noticed before scientists knew what was really happening: they could make gases glow. The electron – and even the structure of the atom – hadn't then been discovered.

As in electrolysis (page 61) the negative terminal of a device is called the *cathode*, the positive is the *anode*. The new effects were known to be caused by 'something' coming from the cathode and so they were named *cathode rays*. We now know that these are electrons.

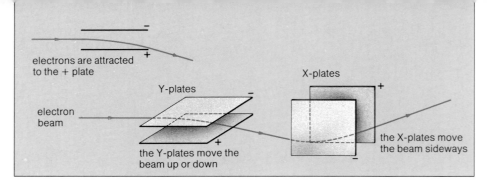

electrons are attracted to the + plate

Y-plates

electron beam

the Y-plates move the beam up or down

X-plates

the X-plates move the beam sideways

◀
How the electron beam is controlled in a cathode ray oscilloscope.

The cathode ray oscilloscope (CRO) is an instrument which uses a stream of electrons to show the pattern of rapidly changing voltages. Thus you can play a musical instrument into a microphone and produce a voltage that changes according to the changing waves in the sound. This can be displayed on the CRO screen.

The input is usually fed to the *Y-plates*, via an amplifier. Voltages on the Y-plates make the electron beam in the tube move up or down.

At the same time a steadily increasing voltage is applied to the *X-plates*. This moves the beam across the screen, at a steady rate. This has the effect of drawing out the trace as a copy of the voltage changes that have been applied to the Y-plates. When the beam reaches the right side of the screen the sideways voltage is changed very quickly so the beam gets back to where it started.

Electrostatics

'Static' means 'not-moving'. As explained above, all materials contain huge amounts of electricity. The electrons and protons in atoms are electrically charged. When you rub a plastic pen with a piece of cloth electrons are rubbed off one material and stick to the other. The material that gets the extra electrons becomes negatively charged. The material that loses electrons becomes positively charged.

Positive charges attract negative charges. The force of attraction is very large compared with other forces, such as gravity. For example, the force of gravity between a kilogram of matter and another kilogram, one metre away, is about a tenth of a billionth of a newton. This size force is just about measurable in a good laboratory! If we separated the electrons from the protons in a kilogram of matter, the force between them at the same distance would be 1 000 000 000 000 000 000 000 000 000 000 000 newtons.

Storing charge

It is hard to store large amounts of electric charge because it can have such a devastating effect (as we'll see later). Small quantities can be stored in devices called *capacitors*.

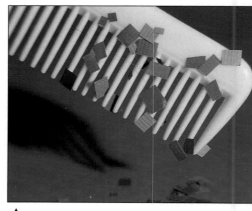

▲
A plastic comb can be given a charge by being rubbed with a piece of material. The plastic then attracts small pieces of paper.

▼
A selection of capacitors. The stripes are colour coding for the amount of electric charge that each can store.

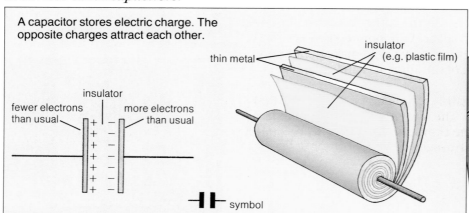

A capacitor stores electric charge. The opposite charges attract each other.

insulator (e.g. plastic film)

thin metal

insulator

fewer electrons than usual

more electrons than usual

symbol

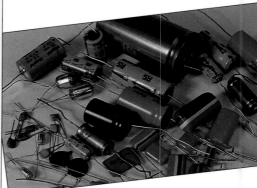

These are very useful in electronic circuits. Such circuits deal with quite small quantities of charge. If you can store charge for a few fractions of a second, you can control what the circuit does. For example, it takes time for charge to flow into a capacitor and away again, and so capacitors are very useful in *timing circuits*.

Coulombs

Electric charge is measured in *coulombs*. A coulomb of charge is moved when a current of 1 ampere flows for 1 second. So we can write:

$$\text{charge} \quad = \quad \text{current} \quad \times \quad \text{time,}$$
$$\text{(coulombs, C)} \qquad \text{(amperes, A)} \qquad \text{(seconds, s).}$$

Electrons do not have much of a charge. It takes six and a quarter million, million, million electrons to make a coulomb.

Earlier, we mentioned the devastating effect of a large electric charge. Lightning is caused when water drops in clouds are electrically charged by the friction of moving air. This happens easily in the fast-moving currents of rising air we get in thunderstorms. The charges build up, with positive and negative charges separated as shown. The Earth also gets charged. The negative charges in the base of the cloud repel electrons in the ground, leaving unbalanced positive charges behind. Lightning is a short burst of current between these charges – a giant spark. It can flow from ground to cloud, and back again. It can also move within the cloud itself, between one layer of charge and another.

Static electricity can build up on any good insulator, and even on conductors if they are well insulated. When you walk across a nylon carpet the friction of your shoes can produce a separation of charge. When you touch a metal object connected to the ground – say a doorknob – the charge on your body can flow away. You feel it go through you as an *electric shock*.

Often, the charge flows just before you touch the doorknob. Just as with lightning, you create a spark. You can even hear the crackle. This is a quiet form of thunder! A spark is simply a flow of charged particles. They are mostly *ions*: charged air molecules. They heat the air, and make it glow.

Lightning can split trees and set fire to buildings. Much smaller sparks from small amounts of static electricity can cause fires when the conditions are right. After all, it is sparks that cause the petrol to explode in the cylinders of car engines. Static sparks can be very dangerous in places where there are flammable substances in the air.

Flour manufacturers have this problem too. Fine grains of flour can burn very easily when they form a dust in the air. In fact, the burning is so rapid that it makes an explosion. In such places, everything has to be well earthed so that charges can't build up.

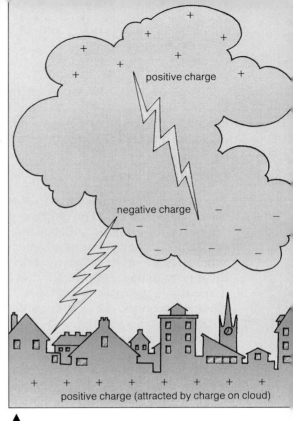

▲
In a thundercloud, air movements produce a separation of charges. Very high voltages are produced. Lightning occurs when charge flows back again.

▼
An oak tree shattered by lightning.

Electrochemistry: electrolysis and batteries

Ions and electrons are useful in *electrochemistry*. Chapter 7 deals with how charged particles can move and be separated to make new chemicals

55

using *electrolysis*. Also, many chemical reactions are driven by the electric forces between ions. The *reactivity series* of metals is due to the electrical differences between metal ions. A major use of these effects is to use them as a source of electricity in electric cells.

Cells and batteries

The first useful electric current was produced by chemical means just about 200 years ago. The discovery was made by accident: an Italian doctor called Luigi Galvani was preparing some frogs' legs for his wife to *eat*. At the same time he was experimenting with static electricity. Whenever there was a spark made by his equipment attached to the legs, the legs twitched. He thought that he'd invented a new kind of electricity detector – a *galvanometer*. Later, he discovered that frogs' legs twitched when he prodded them with a steel knife. He changed his mind; he now thought that the legs themselves were making the electricity. After all, if you can have electric eels, why not electric frogs?

But he was still wrong. In fact, the electricity was coming from a combination of salt water that the frogs' legs had been kept in, and two metals: steel (the knife) and the zinc dish containing the legs. Together, these made a simple cell (or 'battery'): the frogs' legs were just working as a detector of current. This was first understood by another Italian scientist, Alessandro Volta. He went on to make the first electric battery. It worked with any number of metals: copper and tin; silver and zinc and almost any salt solution.

Chemical cells like this have a low voltage, no more than about 2 volts. But they can be connected in series (in batteries of cells) to give higher voltages. Twenty years ago cells were mostly used in torches, and were heavy and didn't last very long. But the development of transistor technology has led to an improvement in chemical cells. Transistor circuits work with low voltages (usually 9 volts are enough). So small, portable devices are easy to operate, and can be of very good quality. Radios, cassette players, calculators, even computers and TVs can now be made that run off small batteries.

A good battery can be stored for a long time without losing its energy or leaking nasty chemicals. It should have a high *energy density*, which means being able to store a lot of energy in a small, light cell. The energy of an electric cell is usually measured in watt-hours (1 watt-hour is 1 joule being delivered every second for an hour. This is 3600 joules).

▲
Luigi Galvani (1737–1798) discovered that electricity made muscles twitch, while experimenting with frogs' legs.

The electrochemical series

Element	Voltage (V)
Calcium	−2.76
Sodium	−2.71
Magnesium	−2.37
Zinc	−0.78
Cadmium	−0.40
Hydrogen	0
Copper	+0.34
Mercury	+0.79

Energy densities of some cells

Chemical cell	Energy density (Wh per kg)
Zinc–carbon (as used in torches)	60
Zinc–manganese (alkaline), e.g. Duracell	140
Lithium–sulphur dioxide (special uses)	280

Activities

1 Take a good look at your bedroom, or your kitchen. How many electrical devices can you find? Make a list of them and then write a short account of what you could use instead of these if we 'ran out of electricity'.

2 Some people claim that you can get electricity out of fruit: oranges, lemons, even bananas! Plan an investigation to find out if this is so.

3 Find out where *electromagnets* are used. For each use, explain why they are better than, say, permanent magnets.

4 Use a library to find out more about the life and work of any one of the following people who made discoveries in electricity.
(a) Michael Faraday; (b) Thomas Alva Edison; (c) Luigi Galvani.

Write an essay, draw a strip-cartoon or a poster illustrating their main discoveries and any interesting features of their lives.

5 Find out how many different kinds of electric battery there are. What are the differences between them? Why are there so many different kinds? What are they used for?

Questions

1 What are the differences between series and parallel circuits? Why are parallel circuits used for most purposes in the home?

2 List the following electrical devices in order of which uses most power (put the largest user first):
• pocket calculator;
• electric kettle;
• microcomputer;
• electric cooker;
• a room ceiling lamp.

3 Here are three ways of writing the same formula relating current, voltage and resistance:

$$R = \frac{V}{I}, \qquad V = IR, \qquad I = \frac{V}{R}.$$

Choose one of them and use it to calculate:
(a) the resistance of a juice extractor that takes a current of 1 A from a 240 V supply;
(b) the current that would flow through a hair dryer of 60 ohms resistance when connected to the 240 V mains;
(c) the voltage of a battery that produces a current of 1.3 A in a motor of resistance 4.6 ohms;
(d) the current in a car headlamp of resistance 2.6 ohms connected to a 12 V car battery.

4 Three pupils were talking about electricity and how it flows and provides energy.
   Anwar said: 'Electricity flows around a circuit just like water flows in a river. The current can flow through a motor and make it turn without being used up, just like water can flow through a water mill to make that turn.'
   'That can't be right!' said Gary. 'Electricity has to flow in a circuit. A river isn't a circuit — the water just flows down from mountains to the sea.'
   'Well . . .', said Karen, thinking hard, 'I don't know — but does the water *stay* in the sea? And how does it get to the mountains, anyway?'
   Write a continuation of this discussion, or write down what you would say to help clear up the ideas involved. *Is* electricity used up in a circuit when something is made to work? Is water in a river part of 'circuit' or cycle? Where do water and electricity get energy from?

5 Work out what current would be shown on the ammeters in the following circuits:

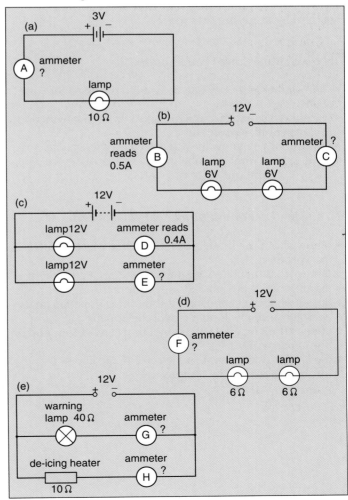

6 Explain what the following words or phrases mean:
(a) renewable source of energy;
(b) fuse rating;
(c) short circuit;
(d) hydroelectricity.

7 Explain what happens in *thermionic emission*. Give two uses of this effect.

8 Draw circuits to show the following.
(a) How three lamps would be connected in parallel to a power supply.
(b) How eight decorative lamps would be connected in series to a power supply (in an advertising display, for example).
(c) How you would connect a voltmeter to measure the voltage drop across a lamp.

9 Electrical power is calculated by using the formulae:
$P = VI$, or $P = I^2R$, or $P = V^2/R$.
Use these formulae, where needed, to answer the following.
(a) Complete the following table. Note that fuses are available in the following sizes only: 1A, 3A, 5A, 13A, 30A.

Device	Supply voltage (V)	Current taken (A)	Power rating (W)	Fuse rating (A)
CD player (portable)	9	0.2		
kettle	240		2000	
heater	240	12.5		
hair dryer		4.2	1000	
refrigerator	240		120	

(b) Calculate the effective resistance of (i) the kettle; (ii) the hair dryer; (iii) the refrigerator.

Checklist

These are the facts and ideas that you should have learned by studying this topic.

To reach Basic Level you should:

- know that electricity can be used to produce heat and light
- be able to set up circuits to make something work and solve everyday problems
- show that you know how to use electricity safely
- understand what the label on an electrical device can tell you (i.e. about volts and watts)

To succeed at Foundation Level you should:

- know about the three main effects that electric currents can produce
- know what the following units measure in electricity: amps, volts, watts and kilowatt-hours
- know what the cost of using something depends on its wattage and how long it is switched on for
- know about fuses, earth connections and colour coding for mains wires
- be able to make simple series circuits to solve problems or to make things work

To succeed at Merit Level you should:

- understand the magnetic effect of an electric current and how the effect is used in everyday applications
- know about the everyday and industrial applications of the heating and chemical effects of currents
- know how currents are affected by changes in voltage and resistance
- know the meaning of current, potential difference, power and resistance, and the units they are measured in
- know the safety systems and rules for using electricity, how they work and the reasons for them
- know the practical differences between series and parallel connections
- be able to draw and understand simple diagrams for both series and parallel circuits

To succeed at Special Level you should:

- understand the principles of electromagnetic induction
- understand the important applications of the magnetic, chemical and heating effects in everyday and industrial use
- understand about charge flow and energy transfer in a circuit
- be able to make calculations in electricity
- know the difference between a.c. and d.c. supplies
- understand the basic safety precautions in the use and supply of electricity
- be able to draw and interpret more complex circuit diagrams (i.e. including ammeters and voltmeters)

CHAPTER FOUR

MAKING CHEMISTRY HAPPEN

▼ The gas burns with oxygen in an exothermic reaction (heat is given out).

▲ Tomatoes produce tiny amounts of acetylene gas, as part of a reaction that turns them from green to red.

You have probably done the chemical test for hydrogen gas. The test is to place a lighted splint inside a test tube containing a mixture of hydrogen and air. There is loud pop and water is produced. Other reactions, like the rusting of steel and the ripening of fruit take place over longer periods of time. It may be weeks or months before we see any effect.

▲ Once the metal on this car was exposed to the air, it started to oxidise slowly.

The fuel in the burner releases large amounts of energy very quickly to heat the air in the balloon. Stalagmites and stalactites take thousands of years to form because the chemical reactions producing these beautiful pillars occur very slowly.

Sometimes chemical reactions happen very quickly; sometimes very slowly. The chemicals inside a firework react very rapidly; explosions are very fast reactions.

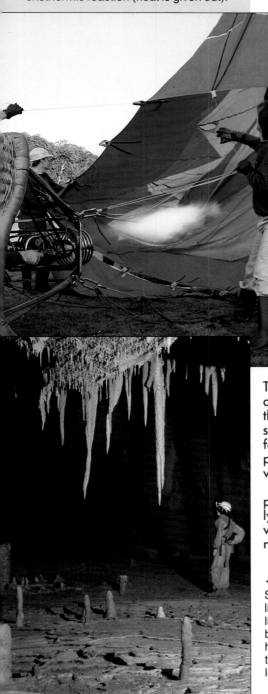

◄ Stalactites and stalagmites are common in limestone caves. Water dissolves limestone as it passes through the rock, becoming saturated with calcium hydrogencarbonate. As water drips through the roof of a cave, it evaporates, leaving deposits of calcium carbonate.

These changes are called chemical reactions. New products are formed.

A chemical reaction always results in the formation of a new product.

Making chemical changes happen

Chemistry is happening all the time — the world is full of chemical changes. The pictures on this page show chemical changes. But chemicals can't affect each other unless they meet. That sounds simple enough until you realise just how difficult this is.

This chapter is about how chemicals are brought together and made to react.

Gases are mostly empty space!

Look at the drawing. Test tube 1 contains the gas hydrogen and test tube 2 the gas oxygen. Each face represents an atom. Two or more atoms joined together is a molecule. Atoms and molecules are very small and inside each test tube there are about 600 000 000 000 000 000 000 molecules. Don't try to count this number! You would be a very old person before you finished! Chemistry can happen because there are so many molecules around. They are bound to bump into each other quite often.

▼
When a mixture of hydrogen and oxygen is lit, the molecules combine to make water.

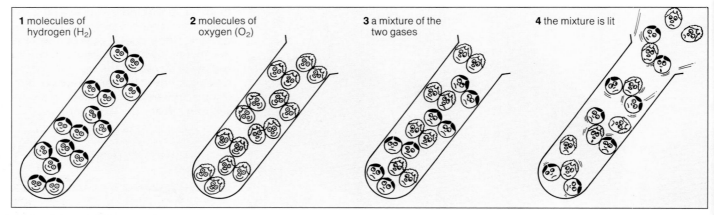

1 molecules of hydrogen (H_2) 2 molecules of oxygen (O_2) 3 a mixture of the two gases 4 the mixture is lit

There are some things that you must know before you read the rest of this chapter. You should have learned about them before.

- The smallest part of an element is called an atom.
- Atoms of the same element are exactly alike and different from atoms of other elements.
- Molecules contain two or more atoms joined together by bonds.
- In a chemical reaction, chemical bonds are broken and reformed.

If we simply mix test tubes 1 and 2 nothing happens. But when we light the mixture with a flame, we get an explosion. The reaction produces water, and a lot of heat.

If a reaction between hydrogen and oxygen is to take place the particles must come into contact. But even if they do, collisions between particles will not lead to a chemical reaction unless they have enough *energy*. The flame provides the energy. As well as having more energy, the molecules move around *faster*, and hit each other harder when they collide.

Bonds

If you look at the diagrams of test tubes above, you will notice that we have drawn the hydrogen and oxygen gas molecules as pairs of atoms. What holds these atoms together is a *chemical bond*. When the reaction occurs, some of these bonds are broken. The atoms can then recombine with different atoms to form a new kind of molecule (in this case, water).

Electrochemistry

These photographs show chemicals reacting together. But there is another way to make chemistry happen: by using electricity.

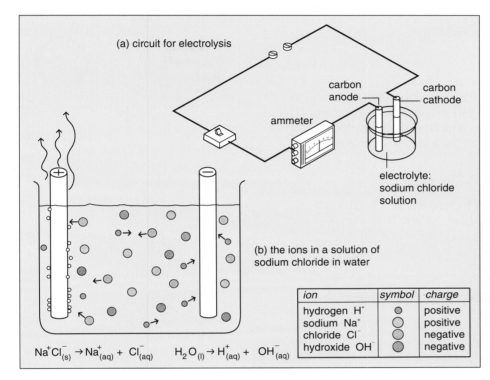

(a) circuit for electrolysis

carbon anode
carbon cathode
ammeter
electrolyte: sodium chloride solution

(b) the ions in a solution of sodium chloride in water

ion	symbol	charge
hydrogen H^+	○	positive
sodium Na^+	○	positive
chloride Cl^-	○	negative
hydroxide OH^-	○	negative

$$Na^+Cl^-_{(s)} \rightarrow Na^+_{(aq)} + Cl^-_{(aq)} \qquad H_2O_{(l)} \rightarrow H^+_{(aq)} + OH^-_{(aq)}$$

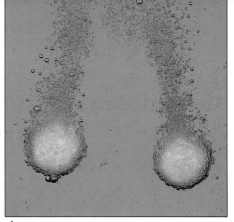

▲ Tablets reacting quickly with water.

▼ Chemicals in cement control the rate of the setting reaction.

▲ The art of chemistry used in art!

In the diagram, electric current is being passed through a solution of common salt (sodium chloride). Bubbles of gas can be seen at the positive electrode. The gas is chlorine. The solution becomes alkaline.

The decomposition of a compound by electricity is called *electrolysis*.

Ions

When some substances dissolve in water they break up into smaller bits. These bits are electrically charged. They are called *ions*. In the sodium chloride solution above, sodium ions and chloride ions have been released from the solid salt crystals. The solution also contains ions from the water: hydrogen (H^+) and hydroxide (OH^-) ions. The bubbles of gas seen at the negative electrode are hydrogen from the water.

Solutions that have ions that are free to move about can conduct electricity. The negative ions move through the solution just like the electrons in an electric circuit.

What is happening during electrolysis is quite complicated. But in effect the electricity is energising a reaction like this:

sodium chloride + water → sodium hydroxide + chlorine + hydrogen,

$$2NaCl + 2H_2O \rightarrow 2NaOH + Cl_2 + H_2.$$

This reaction wouldn't happen at all without the help of the electricity.

Describing chemical change

We are familiar with symbols in everyday life.

Symbols and equations

Chemists use a special 'language' to describe chemical reactions. This language uses symbols to represent the names of elements, and equations to represent chemical changes. We use symbols a lot in everyday life and we soon get used to recognising them.

An atom of hydrogen is represented by the symbol H, and oxygen by O. Hydrogen explodes when lit, to form water. Hydrogen and oxygen exist as molecules of two atoms each. We write these molecules as H_2 and O_2. Water is a compound of hydrogen and oxygen and has the formula H_2O: i.e. only hydrogen and oxygen. So, when the hydrogen exploded, it must have reacted with the oxygen present in the air. The equation for the reaction is shown below.

$$2H_2 + O_2 \rightarrow 2H_2O$$

As an extra help we often use letters to remind us whether the chemicals are gas (g), liquid (l) or solid (s). So you will often see the reaction written like this:

$$2H_{2(g)} \quad + \quad O_{2(g)} \quad \rightarrow \quad 2H_2O_{(l)},$$
hydrogen (gas) + oxygen (gas) → water (liquid).

Water is a *compound*. You can look up what this means in the 'Reference section'.

Making reactions go faster

What decides how quickly a chemical reaction happens? Can we speed it up? Or slow it down?

How quickly a chemical change happens is called its *rate*. How can we measure this? Think of chalk (calcium carbonate) reacting with an acid (hydrochloric acid).

Calcium + hydrochloric → carbon + calcium + water,
carbonate   acid   dioxide   chloride
$$CaCO_{3(s)} + 2HCl_{(aq)} \rightarrow CO_{2(g)} + CaCl_{2(aq)} + H_2O_{(l)}.$$

This reaction happens 'on its own'. It doesn't need any extra energy to start it off or to keep it going.

We could measure the rate of reaction by

- how quickly the chalk is used up, or,
- how quickly the acid is used up, or,
- how quickly carbon dioxide gas is produced.

These changes can be measured as changes of the *mass* of material, in grams per second, or *volume* for the gas. In practice, chemists will use the material whose mass change is easiest to measure. The apparatus in the

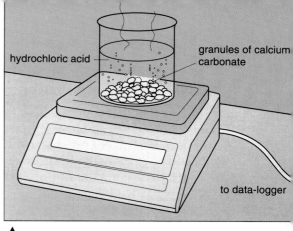

One way of following a reaction: the *change in mass* of the reactants over time.

drawing can be used to study this reaction. The balance reading gets less because carbon dioxide has bubbled away. If the balance is linked to a microcomputer the drop in mass will be recorded automatically.

Graph (a) is a plot of the results obtained in one experiment. After 90 seconds the reaction has come to a stop. No more gas is being produced.

A second way to do the experiment would be to measure the volume of carbon dioxide gas given off every ten seconds. Graph (b) is a plot of these results. Again, you can see that after 90 seconds no more carbon dioxide gas is given off.

The reaction has finished because either the chalk or the acid has been used up. Notice how steep both graphs are at the beginning of the experiment. The rate of the reaction is fastest at the start. This is because there are more chemicals there to react with each other.

The key factors

Chemists (and cooks!) have found that there are five key factors that decide the rate at which a chemical change happens:

- concentration (of a solution);
- temperature;
- pressure (in a gas);
- surface area exposed (in solids and liquids);
- using a catalyst.

Change the concentration

Chemists often talk about *concentrated* and *dilute* solutions. What do they mean? Some people like one spoonful of sugar in their cup of tea. If you have a very sweet tooth you might like 4 spoonfuls. The sugar still dissolves. The second cup has more sugar in it. The solution is more concentrated. The concentration of sugar in the first cup is one spoonful per cup. In the second sample it is four spoonfuls per cup. This is how cooks might measure concentration – as 'spoonfuls per cup'. Chemists would measure the *mass* of sugar dissolved in a standard volume. They would state the concentration of sugar dissolved in grams per litre.

In a concentrated solution there are more particles, so they are closer together. In a dilute solution the particles are further apart. So the particles in a concentrated solution are more likely to meet each other or bombard a solid. If you want to make a reaction go faster, you can increase the concentration.

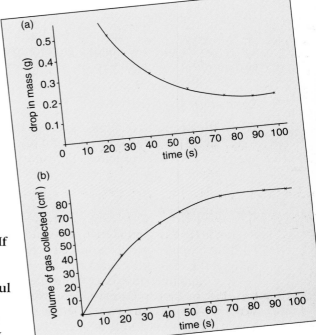

▲
If you plot the results from an experiment like the one above, you might get a graph like (a). If you measure the amount of gas given off instead, you might see something like (b).

◄
It is easy to see why concentration affects the rate of a reaction. (Imagine that each person is an acid molecule and that the floor is made of chalk.)

Change the temperature

In a solution of hydrochloric acid the particles are continually moving about. They do not all move about with the same speed. Some particles have more kinetic energy than others. These faster particles bombard the chalk and have enough energy to react and produce carbon dioxide gas. With an increase in temperature many *more* particles have enough energy to react with the chalk.

Increasing the temperature doesn't just mean that the particles move about faster, and perhaps collide more often, but also that when they do collide they have enough energy to *react*.

Change the surface area of the substance

Sprinkled iron filings burn brightly in a Bunsen flame. Powdered chalk reacts more quickly than marble chips. When a solid is broken up into small pieces, there is a bigger *surface area* to be attacked by any surrounding chemicals. So the reaction will take place more quickly.

Increase the pressure

When the pressure of a gas is greater, the particles will move closer together. (This is the same as reducing the volume of the gas, forcing the gas particles closer together.) The particles are more likely to collide and react together.

Use a catalyst

A *catalyst* is a chemical that helps a chemical reaction to go faster, without actually being chemically changed. The catalyst is exactly the same at the end of the reaction as it was at the beginning.

Hydrogen peroxide is a colourless solution. It is used, as a dilute solution, by hairdressers to bleach hair. On standing it decomposes very slowly to oxygen and water. The process happens faster in the light; this is why hydrogen peroxide is stored in brown glass bottles.

$$\text{hydrogen peroxide} \rightarrow \text{oxygen} + \text{water},$$
$$2H_2O_2 \rightarrow O_2 + 2H_2O.$$

A small amount of the black powder, manganese (IV) oxide added to a test tube of hydrogen peroxide causes rapid production of oxygen. At the end of the reaction the black powder remains unchanged. The manganese (IV) oxide *catalyses* the decomposition of hydrogen peroxide.

Catalysts are used very widely in the chemical industry. Biological catalysts are called *enzymes*. You should know about the enzymes that catalyse the break down of food in the gut (see page 227). Two very important chemical processes use catalysts. The first is the *Haber process* for making ammonia. Ammonia is a basic chemical for making fertilisers in the agrochemical industry, and is the basis for many explosives. The second example is the brewing industry for making beer.

▼ The iron filings on a sparkler burning in air.

even more
extra
surfaces

old surface: ——————

extra surfaces: ——————

▲ Cutting things into smaller pieces increases the area able to react. Solids can only react at their outside surfaces. Cutting them up increases the area that can be got at so the reactions happen more quickly.

Reaction rates and the chemical industry

The Haber process

All life on Earth depends on plants. Plants feed on water and carbon dioxide. But they also need minerals, to keep them healthy and to make proteins. The vital minerals they need for this are compounds of nitrogen called nitrates. How plants get these minerals naturally is explained in GCSE book 1 (also see the nitrogen cycle in the 'Reference section' of this book).

For millions of years, the nitrogen cycle was in balance. Dead plants and animals supplied matter containing nitrogen to the soil for new plants to use. Farming relied on this natural recycling. But in the past 100 years this balance has been upset. Human population growth has outstripped natural food production, and so artificial 'fertilisers' containing nitrogen have been used more and more to increase plant growth.

Haber and Bosch

The richest source of nitrates is the air. It contains the gas nitrogen, N_2. It is plentiful. The air contains about 78% nitrogen. But most plants can't use atmospheric nitrogen. It has to be converted into a nitrate, or another nitrogen compound called ammonia (NH_3). Most artificial fertilisers are made from ammonia.

Fritz Haber, a German chemist, worked out that the chances of nitrogen and hydrogen combining to make ammonia would be greatest at 200-times normal (atmospheric) pressure, and at a temperature of 400°C.

His theory worked on a small scale in a laboratory. But could it be made to work on the vast scale needed by industry? Haber needed the help of a good engineer. He was lucky enough to find the brilliant young engineer, Carl Bosch. Bosch designed and built the first factory that could produce ammonia. This plant was opened in 1913 at Oppau in Germany. The First World War began the year after. The same nitrates that would be used to produce more food were also used to produce nitric acid for explosives like TNT – tri-*nitro*-toluene. This became the main reason for developing the Haber process.

The equation to produce ammonia looks very simple:

$$nitrogen + hydrogen \rightarrow ammonia.$$

But think of the particles involved. There are four of them, which have to combine to make two molecules of ammonia:

$$N_2 + 3H_2 \rightarrow 2NH_3,$$

(nitrogen and hydrogen exist as molecules which consist of pairs of atoms).

Haber reasoned that if the gases were at high pressure it would help the reaction work because the molecules would be squashed closer together and collide more often. And if the gases are heated as well, the molecules will have more energy and be more likely to break up when they collide with each other. But this wasn't enough. The chances of the four particles

▲
An ammonia production plant. You can see the large pressure vessel where the nitrogen and hydrogen gases are forced together.

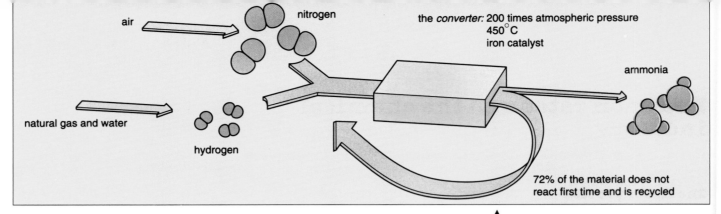

air → nitrogen

the *converter:* 200 times atmospheric pressure
450°C
iron catalyst

ammonia

natural gas and water →

hydrogen

72% of the material does not
react first time and is recycled

▲
The Bosch–Haber process to make
ammonia. The reactants have to be
recycled to get enough ammonia.

being in the same place at the same time is so small that the process is still too slow. The answer was to use a catalyst.

For the ammonia process, Haber and Bosch used finely powdered iron to 'hold' the reacting materials together even more closely.

The final problem is that the nitrogen–hydrogen reaction is reversible. This means that the ammonia could well split up and go back to hydrogen and nitrogen again. Bosch solved this by recycling the unreacted gases.

How do catalysts work?

The Haber–Bosch process *only* works with a catalyst. One theory about how a catalyst works is that its surface somehow traps the reacting molecules for a fraction of a second. It keeps them still long enough for the reactions to occur. After a time the catalyst stops 'working' and has to be replaced with fresh. This is usually because its surfaces get 'dirty'.

The brewing industry

Brewing turns a seed (barley) into an alcoholic drink through the process of fermentation. This involves the conversion of barley starch by enzymes to sugar, which is then fermented to ethanol by yeast. Alcohol, of course, is a kind of drug. In large doses it is a fatal poison. Some people do not approve of alcoholic drinks, but for others it is an acceptable 'social drug'. Brewing is one of the oldest industrial processes known. Brewing makes beer.

Raw materials

The raw materials used to brew beer are malt, hops, sugar, water and yeast.

Malt

Malt is made from barley, and is produced by soaking the barley for about two days, after which time the barley is ready to germinate. The barley is then allowed to grow under controlled conditions for about a week. Finally, germination is stopped by drying the grain in a kiln. The growth process makes the starch in the barley soluble. It also produces large quantities of *enzymes* which break starch down to sugar. The enzymes are *natural catalysts* for this reaction.

Hops

Hops give the finished beer its taste and aroma. They also have a natural *preservative* effect on the beer, but nowadays special additives are used.

▼
Gathering hops has always been a labour-intensive business. This scene is from 1930: thousands of workers travelled to the Kent hop fields from all over Britain every summer.

Most foods use additives like these. The hops are perennial herbs, which grow in Kent and Worcestershire.

Sugar
Extra sugar is added for colouring and flavouring purposes.

Water
A good supply of water is essential. Most breweries were built with their own wells. The salts dissolved in the water influence the final flavour of the beer. One of the most common salts dissolved in water is calcium hydrogencarbonate from limestone and chalk. The calcium ions help enzyme action during the 'mashing' process. The ions also help yeast separation during fermentation.

Yeast
Yeast is not strictly a raw material as it does not remain in the finalised product. It is a living organism, a fungus. It can't use photosynthesis and gets its food from the sugars made by green plants. As it feeds it produces two waste products: alcohol and carbon dioxide.

Alcohol is an organic compound. It contains the elements carbon, hydrogen and oxygen. It has the formula C_2H_5OH and is more correctly called ethanol. On standing, beer will go sour because some of the alcohol in it has been changed to vinegar. This happens because oxygen in the air reacts with the alcohol to form vinegar. The chemical name for vinegar is ethanoic acid:

$$C_2H_5OH \xrightarrow{[O_2]} CH_3COOH,$$
$$\text{ethanol} \qquad \text{ethanoic acid.}$$

The process
The complete process is shown below and involves three steps.
1 Germinating barley and using it to make malt: *the malting process*
2 Conversion of barley starch to sugar;
3 Yeast fermentation *in the fermenting vessel*

1 The germination of barley and malt production
Malt is a mixture of starch, sugars and enzymes. Some breweries produce their own malt, others buy it. It is the raw material for the next stage.

2 Conversion of barley starch to sugar
The malted barley is mostly starch. This has to be changed into sugar that the yeast can digest. Brewers call this process *mashing*!

Behind this rather strange term, there is a lot of work that affects the *rate* of the brewing reactions.

First, the malt is ground up. This makes smaller particles with a larger surface area, which helps to speed up the next reactions.

The ground malt is mixed with water to produce a solution that the yeast can feed on. The temperature, concentration and pH of this are controlled closely; so is the time that the reaction is allowed to go on for.

Enzymes that are naturally present in the malt convert starch to a mixture of sugars. The enzymes are called α- and β-amylase. (Salivary amylase in your mouth does the same sort of job.) These enzymes are very different, despite their similar names: the α-amylase produces lots of different sugars that are difficult for the yeast to digest and convert into alcohol. β-amylase, however, produces sugars like glucose. This is very easily converted into alcohol (ethanol) by the yeast. The glucose is said to be very *fermentable*. So, the brewer wants to make sure that the reaction produces as much of the glucose sugars as possible.

This is done by controlling the conditions that the enzymes are working under.

α-amylase works best at 65°C. β-amylase works best at 55°C. One characteristic of enzymes is that they are only effective at a particular temperature. By keeping the reaction temperature too low for the α-amylase to work properly, the brewer makes sure that as much glucose as possible is made.

The table shows the effect of the reaction temperature on the 'fermentability' of the products and the *yield* of glucose.

Mashing temperature (°C)	Fermentability (%)	Glucose yield* (%)
68	72	98.2
65.5	76	96.7
63	79	94.6

*Note: the *yield* is the amount of useful product that we get; see Chapter 7, *Chemical economics.*

This shows the balancing act that you often have to do with chemical reactions. As you lower the reaction temperature, the fermentability (the amount of glucose) goes up, but the yield goes down. A balance is needed between the sort of product that you want and the amount that you want to make. There is a lot more about this chemical balancing act in Chapter 7, *Chemical economics.*

What are the enzymes doing?

Starches are carbohydrates. Carbohydrates contain the elements carbon, hydrogen and oxygen. Starch is a *polymer* of glucose molecules. You will have come across polymers before, but put simply, the glucose molecules are linked together in long chains to make the large starch molecules. The mashing reaction breaks up the large starch molecules into smaller sugar molecules, like glucose, $C_6H_{12}O_6$.

3 Fermentation

This is the final stage. Yeast is added and the temperature controlled very carefully again, this time at about 18°C. Enzyme catalysts in the yeast cell work best at this temperature. The yeast enzymes can break down several sugars, but they work best on the smaller ones like glucose.

During the fermentation, the reaction temperature rises to 23°C, without being heated from outside! Fermentation is called an *exothermic* reaction. This means that energy is given out.

The temperature rise allows the brewer to keep a check on the reaction. If the temperature does not go up, they know that something is not working properly.

It should come as no surprise to you to learn that the temperature is used to *control* the fermentation as well. When enough ethanol has been produced, the brewer lowers the temperature and the yeast enzymes stop working.

The yeast is separated away and the beer is put into bottles and barrels.

▼
You can just about see yeast cells under a light microscope. This electron micrograph has been stained to show the inside of the cell: red is the *nucleus*, the green shapes are *mitochondria* and the blue areas with white speckles are fat deposits. Compare this with the cell drawing on page 77.

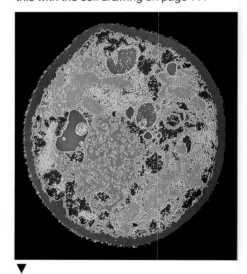

▼
Yeast used in breadmaking produces carbon dioxide. Bubbles of the gas make the 'holes' in bread.

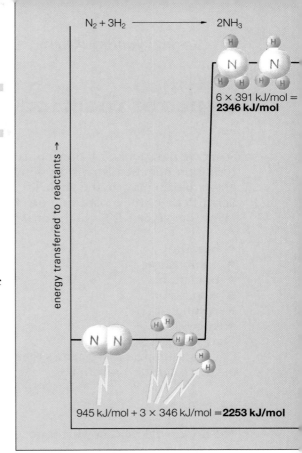

$N_2 + 3H_2 \longrightarrow 2NH_3$

6 × 391 kJ/mol =
2346 kJ/mol

energy transferred to reactants →

945 kJ/mol + 3 × 346 kJ/mol = **2253 kJ/mol**

▲
Making ammonia is an *endothermic* reaction: it takes more energy to form the bonds in the product than it does to break up the reactants.

How chemicals release energy

All chemical changes release energy. The yeast in the fermentation gave out energy as heat. Reactions that give out energy to the surroundings are called *exothermic* reactions. 'Exo' means 'out', as in 'exit'.

Other reactions take energy in from the surroundings. These are called *endothermic* reactions.

No chemical reaction can happen without some energy to start it off. Wood will burn (combine with oxygen) but only if it is lit. This raises the wood to a temperature at which the exothermic process of burning can carry on by itself. In an endothermic process, the energy would have to be supplied all the time.

Endothermic reactions

As we have said, these are reactions in which energy has to be put into a system continuously to make chemicals change. Many substances that we use in everyday life are manufactured from raw materials by endothermic processes. The Haber process on page 65 is an example.

This needs a great deal of energy. *The energy costs account for most of the cost of a bag of fertiliser.* The raw materials are quite cheap, just nitrogen from the air, hydrogen and natural gas. But a lot of energy is needed because nitrogen is not a very reactive chemical. It will only react at the high temperatures and pressures, where the energy of collision of the reacting particles is high.

Building up complicated molecules from simple ones needs energy.

Exothermic reactions

These are the reactions that produce energy as a by-product. The most obvious ones are burning oil or coal in air. We all know that the energy from these reactions is released in quite large amounts, but what is hard to explain is that the reactions do not 'just happen' on their own. Oil and coal can lie around for a very long time without bursting into flames.

Useful exothermic reactions need a small amount of energy to be put in to start them off. Think about what happens when you strike a match. The first reaction that counts is between chemicals mixed together in the head of the match. 'Striking it' means rubbing it on a rough surface. Here, the small amount of heat energy made by friction is enough to trigger off the much more energetic reaction between the chemicals in the match head. The energy from this is then enough to start off the reaction between wood and air.

Breaking and making bonds

What does this starting energy do? All substances are held together by chemical bonds. In a reaction, we have to break the chemical bonds of the reactants and then make new ones for the products. Breaking bonds needs energy to be put in, and making bonds gives out energy.

Now you can see why exothermic reactions need energy to start them off – the *activation energy* – the bonds of the reactants have got to be broken before the reaction can proceed. The stronger the bonds at the start, the higher the activation energy.

See Chapter 10, *The world system* for more about energy changes in chemical reactions.

▼
Two reactions with oxygen – carbon and magnesium. Which reaction is the easiest to start? Are bonds between carbon atoms stronger than those between magnesium atoms?

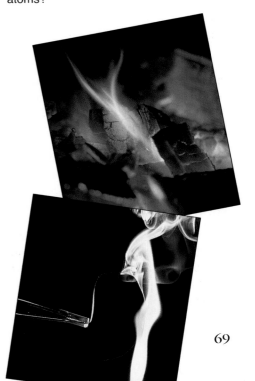

Types of reaction

So far we have looked at how human beings have controlled chemical reactions. But chemistry is happening all the time without our help: inside plants and animals, in the air, in the soil, under the sea and under the Earth. Perhaps the most common chemical reaction of all is the one involving oxygen. Depending on where it happens, it may be called:

- burning,
- combustion,
- oxidation,
- respiration,
- rusting, or
- corrosion.

Chemists lump all these names together and call the reactions with oxygen *oxidation reactions*.

Fires

The fire triangle shows what is needed for burning. Once a fire starts, it can only be stopped by

- removing the fuel, or
- removing the air, or
- reducing the temperature.

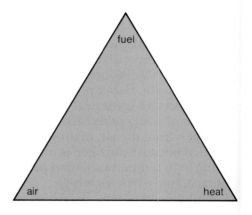

▲
The fire triangle.

During burning, the fuel (usually a hydrocarbon) reacts with oxygen to form carbon dioxide and water:

$$\text{fuel} + \text{oxygen} \rightarrow \text{carbon dioxide} + \text{water}.$$

'Natural' gas is mostly methane, which is the simplest hydrocarbon. The equation for burning methane is:

$$\text{methane} + \text{oxygen} \rightarrow \text{carbon dioxide} + \text{water},$$
$$CH_4 + 2O_2 \rightarrow CO_2 + 2H_2O.$$

This is a good exothermic reaction. It releases a lot of energy, which is why methane is such a useful fuel. Chemists always use equations to represent chemical changes. Equations have to be balanced. Count up the number of oxygen atoms on the left of the equation. There should be the same number on the right. There are four on each side. *Balancing* an equation means making sure that the number of atoms on the left of a chemical equation is the same as on the right. Try some of the questions at the end of this chapter for practice.

Rusting

Rusting is a common reaction that happens to iron. Other types of corrosion are dealt with in the study of metals. When iron rusts, it combines with oxygen and water:

$$\text{iron} + \text{oxygen} + \text{water} \rightarrow \text{hydrated iron oxide (rust)}.$$

This is the *balanced* equation:

$$4Fe + 3O_2 + 6H_2O \rightarrow 4Fe(OH)_3.$$

From the equation, you can see that rusting happens more easily when the air is damp.

A 'dry' rusting reaction is used in survival packs for mountaineers. Oxygen combines with powdered iron to produce black iron oxide with a release of energy that makes the pack hot:

$$iron + oxygen \rightarrow iron\ oxide.$$

So, oxidation reactions are reactions where something gains oxygen.

Reduction reactions

If one substance combines with oxygen, another substance must *lose* oxygen. Substances that lose oxygen in chemical changes are said to be *reduced*, and the process is called *reduction*.

Electricity is used to extract aluminium from bauxite (aluminium oxide). The aluminium oxide loses oxygen. The process is an example of reduction. Electricity made the change happen:

$$2Al_2O_3 \xrightarrow{\text{electrical energy}} 4Al + 3O_2.$$

Chemistry with light

Reactions that happen in the presence of light are called *photochemical* reactions. A common example of a photochemical reaction occurs every time you take a photograph. The light energy causes a change in the chemicals that are coated onto the film. The most important photochemical reaction of all is photosynthesis. Green plants use light to convert water and carbon dioxide into starch and sugars. There is more about this in book 1. Another photochemical reaction produces the *ozone layer* in the upper atmosphere. You can see the reactions on page 216. The chemistry is difficult, but it is worth trying to understand because we hear so much about the ozone layer these days. This layer is vital to life on Earth as it protects us from the most harmful ultraviolet rays from the Sun.

▲
A hot-pack.

▶
Light hits the photographic film and starts a slow chemical reaction to produce the picture. This sequence took about 2 minutes.

71

Activities

1 Put a sugar lump into a glass of cold water. Stir gently and time how long it takes to dissolve completely. Crush a second cube into very small pieces. Time how long the 'powdered' sugar takes to dissolve. Try to explain with the aid of diagrams why 'powdered' sugar dissolves more quickly.

2 (a) Why are some washing powders called 'biological'?
(b) Design an experiment to see if biological washing powders are more effective at cleaning clothes than non-biological ones. You may be able to do this experiment at home. Don't upset the family! (You don't need to use a washing machine.)
(c) Some washing powders work at lower temperatures than others, but how good are they? If you can prove that these work as well you might be able to save some money.
   Remember to make sure that your tests are 'fair'. You will need to think about a *control* in your experiments.

3 Investigating a biological enzyme.
A living cell contains about 500 different enzymes which help it to carry out its complicated chemistry. An easy enzyme to study is amylase which is contained in saliva.
(a) Wash your mouth out with fresh water. Put a 3 cm^2 square of sliced bread in your mouth and chew it well, without swallowing it, for a minute or two. Note any changes in taste.
(b) Bread is mostly starch which is not very soluble and not at all digestible. Salivary amylase converts it to a soluble food (with smaller molecules). What do you think this is?
(c) Amylase is used in industry. Here are some examples:
● Brewing: converts starch into soluble sugars.
● Textile-making: removal of 'sizes' added during manufacture.
● Bread making: added to flour, the amylase helps yeast produce more carbon dioxide.

● Paper making: starch is needed to 'size' the paper.
   Find out more about one or more of these industrial processes and explain what the enzyme actually does to help.

4 It is compulsory for many North American and European cars to have 'catalytic converters' fitted into their exhaust systems. These cars must use unleaded fuel. Read or ask questions to answer the following questions.
(a) Why were lead compounds added to petrol in the first place?
(b) What is a 'catalytic converter'? What does it do?
(c) Why can the cars with a converter only run on unleaded petrol?

5 There is a lot about the brewing industry in this chapter. There has been a recent growth in the sales of low-alcohol and alcohol-free beers.
(a) Conduct a market survey of bottled beers and draw up a table that clearly shows the differences in strengths of various beers from data on the labels.
(b) What is the recommended maximum limit for the daily consumption of alcohol for adults?
(c) The breath-analyser measures the amount of alcohol in the bloodstream. What does it mean to be 'over the limit'?
(d) Write a short dialogue between two people. One is a driver and the other is a concerned friend.
   The friend is trying to convince the driver to cut down on her drinking. She often has a few glasses of wine with her lunch before she goes back to work.

6 Manganese (IV) oxide, a black powder, catalyses the decomposition of hydrogen peroxide to oxygen and water. Design an experiment to show that the black powder is not used up in the reaction.

Questions

1 Make a list of:
(a) three chemical reactions that happen slowly; and
(b) three chemical reactions that happen very quickly.

2 How would you protect the following items from rusting?
(a) a pram, (b) a car, (c) an iron bridge and (d) cutlery.
Explain as fully as you can how one of the methods chosen for protection works.

3 Two students did an experiment to investigate how quickly hydrogen could be produced from hydrochloric acid when magnesium reacted with it. The reaction is:

magnesium + hydrochloric acid → magnesium chloride + hydrogen,

$$Mg + 2HCl \rightarrow MgCl_2 + H_2.$$

In the first experiment the students used a strip of magnesium metal and dilute acid. These are their results.

(a) Draw a diagram to show how the students might have collected and measured the gas given off.
(b) Suggest two possible reasons why the reaction stopped producing hydrogen after 70 seconds.
(c) Draw a graph showing the total amount of hydrogen produced (vertical axis) against time (horizontal axis).
(d) At what time was the hydrogen being produced most rapidly?
(e) Suggest (using the idea of particles) why it seems to get harder for the gas to be produced as time goes on.
(f) On your graph, sketch two more graphs which might be produced if:
(i) the same amount of magnesium had been used, but this time as a powder;
(ii) the experiment was done with magnesium strip but with ice-cold acid.
   Label your graphs clearly.

Time after mixing (s)	10	20	30	40	50	60	70	80	90	100	110	120
Volume of hydrogen produced (cm^3)	15	24	36	42	46	49	51	51	51	51	51	51

4 Write *balanced* equations for the following reactions.

(a) magnesium + hydrochloric acid → hydrogen + magnesium, chloride
   (Mg)   (HCl)   (H$_2$)   (MgCl$_2$);

(b) hydrogen + oxygen → water,
   (H$_2$)   (O$_2$)   (H$_2$O);

(c) magnesium + oxygen → magnesium oxide,
   (Mg)   (O$_2$)   (MgO);

(d) calcium + hydrochloric → calcium + carbon + water
    carbonate   acid   chloride   dioxide
    (CaCO$_3$)   (HCl)   (CaCl$_2$) (CO$_2$)   (H$_2$O);

(e) sodium hydroxide + sulphuric acid → sodium + water,
                                        sulphate
    (NaOH)   (H$_2$SO$_4$)   (Na$_2$SO$_4$) (H$_2$O).

5 An electric current was passed through several substances. Draw and complete the table. (Aqueous means a solution in water.)

Substance electrolysed	Product at positive electrode	Product at negative electrode
Molten sodium chloride Hydrochloric acid (conc.) Aqueous copper chloride Molten aluminium oxide		

6 Which of the following will affect the rate that charcoal will burn on a barbecue:
- the amount of charcoal;
- whether the charcoal is lumpwood or brickettes;
- the type of barbecue;
- the air pressure;
- the temperature of the air;
- the temperature of the charcoal at the start?

(a) Why doesn't charcoal burn with a flame?
(b) How would you stop the charcoal burning?
(c) Write an equation to represent the burning of charcoal.

7 Read pages 66–68 about the chemistry of brewing. Answer the following questions.
(a) Name the four basic raw materials used in the brewing process. State one contribution each makes to the process. Say how the reactions are controlled.
(b) Hops were not originally used just for their flavouring value. What do you think their original function was?
(c) What evidence is there that fermentation is an exothermic process?

8 The chemistry of breadmaking is similar to brewing. Draw a table to show the differences and similarities between the chemistry used in these processes.

Checklist

These are the facts and ideas that you should have learned by studying this topic.

To reach Basic Level you should:

- know that heating chemicals can make them change into something different and be able to give two examples
- know how we can get energy by changing chemicals (e.g. by combustion)
- know that a chemical reaction produces new substances (e.g. rusting)
- know that some reactions are fast, and others slow (i.e. burning compared with rusting)
- know two ways of speeding up a chemical reaction

To succeed at Foundation Level you should:

- know that chemical reactions can change raw materials into new, useful products
- know about reactions with oxygen, e.g. rusting and burning
- know that fuels react with oxygen to release energy and waste gases
- know that all chemical reactions either take in or release energy
- know what decides how fast a chemical reaction happens and that it stops when one of the starting chemicals is used up
- know about atoms, ions and molecules
- know what happens during fermentation

To succeed at Merit Level you should:

- understand that when we manufacture new products there are social, economic, health, safety and environmental consequences
- understand what happens in oxidation processes
- know what exothermic and endothermic reactions are, and how to measure the energy changes involved
- understand the factors that decide the rate of a chemical reaction (temperature, pressure, particle size, catalysis)
- know what happens in electrolysis
- know about enzymes, and the biochemical processes that occur in the fermentation of yeast

To succeed at Special Level you should:

- be able to use scientific information from a range of sources to evaluate the social, health and safety, economic and environmental effects of a major manufacturing process
- be able to apply your understanding of oxidation and reduction reactions to everyday effects
- understand chemical reactions in terms of the energy involved in making and breaking bonds, and be able to calculate the energy changes
- be able to explain how the factors that influence the rate of chemical reactions actually do so
- be able to predict the products of simple electrolytic reactions, write ionic equations and calculate quantities

CHAPTER FIVE

Sickle Cell Disease
A guide for teachers and others caring for children

Living from day to day doesn't mean he's got nothing to live for.

This is Jamie Lavan. He's ten. And he suffers from Duchenne muscular dystrophy, a fatal muscle-wasting disease that attacks young boys.

To Jamie and the other boys fighting this painless condition day after day, having something to look forward to – to live for –

A place where you can plant a seed one year and watch it flower the next. It's also an appropriate symbol for the work of the MDG, which relies on generous donations from the public in order to improve the quality of life for Jamie and all the other boys like him.

A contribution from you today will help ... research programme and ... the one thing ... anything else ... the difference

who cures?

There is no cure for cystic fibrosis. If you care, help us find one.

cf CYSTIC FIBROSIS TRUST

RESEARCH
SUPPORT
EDUCATION

MAKING GREAT STRIDES

1992

CYSTIC FIBROSIS RESEARCH TRUST 5 BLYTH ROAD, BROMLEY, KENT BR1 3RS. PHONE 081 464 7211. REG. CHARITY NO. 281287

The Living Inheritance

You have probably heard of the diseases on these posters. They are *inherited* diseases. People don't 'catch' these diseases like they catch measles or chicken pox; they are born with them. Nowadays, doctors know a lot more about how to look after children born with these diseases, and, as you can see, there are lots of charities to support sufferers and relatives, and to fund scientific research.

Colour blindness is inherited through both parents. Red-green colour blindness affects about one in thirty people.

Other effects can be inherited. If you are a boy, you have roughly a one in six chance of being born colour blind. You might not even know about it. Colour blindness doesn't do you any harm, but it would stop you from becoming an airline pilot.

You and your genome

You began your life as a single cell. The cell holds all of the information needed to make the millions of new cells that become you. This set of information is called your *genome*. You inherit this from your parents: half from your mother and half from your father. As your body grew, every new cell was given a copy of this information. It is the blueprint for what makes you, you! It gives you arms and legs, eyes and ears; it decides whether you are going to be a boy or a girl.

Genes

The word genome comes from another word, *gene*, which is the Greek word for 'giving birth'. Inside your body there are thought to be between 50 000 and 100 000 genes. Nobody knows the exact number — yet. The genes work on their own or in groups to decide exactly what you are going to look like. Your genome is the name for your complete set of genes.

The genes are kept in the *nucleus* of the cell. They are carried on long string-like objects called *chromosomes*. Chromosomes were seen under the microscope long before anyone knew what they were for. Human cells have 23 pairs of chromosomes.

▼
Do you have the gene that allows you to roll your tongue?

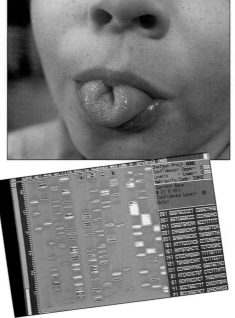

Mapping the genome

Scientists are now beginning to find out what each of the human genes actually does. For some genes, they can tell which chromosome the gene is on. They can even tell where it is on the chromosome. For example, they now know where to find the gene that decides your hair colour, and the one that controls your growth hormone.

There is a huge international project, called *The Human Genome Project*, which aims to map what every gene does and where it is on the chromosomes.

This chapter will explain what this could tell us.

◀
There are 3 billion base pairs in the human genome. The Human Genome Project aims to reveal the position of every gene on the 23 pairs of human chromosomes.

▼
The complete set of human chromosomes in a male: you can see the X and Y (bottom right). A female has two X chromosomes.

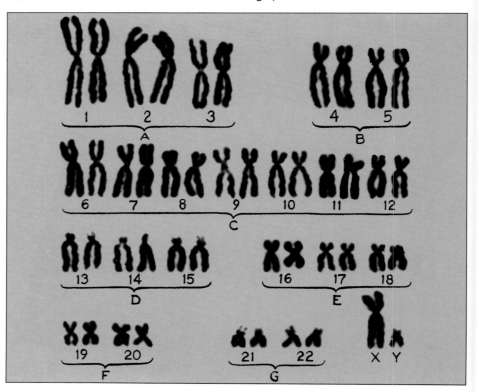

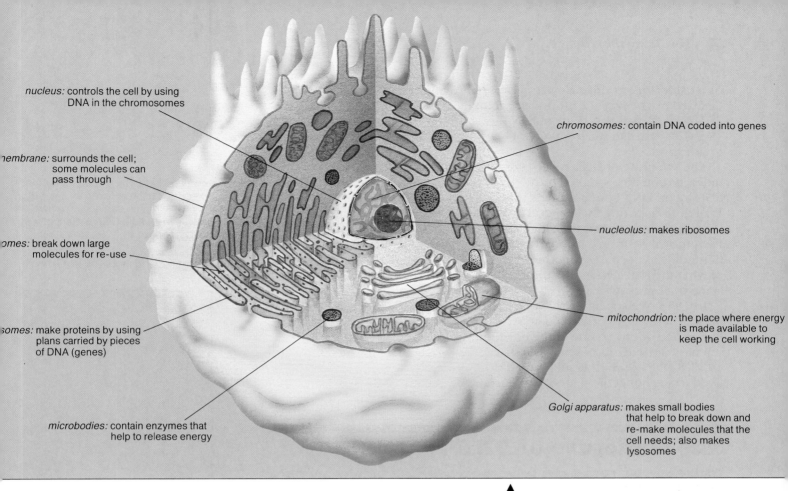

nucleus: controls the cell by using DNA in the chromosomes

chromosomes: contain DNA coded into genes

membrane: surrounds the cell; some molecules can pass through

nucleolus: makes ribosomes

...omes: break down large molecules for re-use

...somes: make proteins by using plans carried by pieces of DNA (genes)

mitochondrion: the place where energy is made available to keep the cell working

microbodies: contain enzymes that help to release energy

Golgi apparatus: makes small bodies that help to break down and re-make molecules that the cell needs; also makes lysosomes

▲
Cells are very complicated. This drawing shows the main parts of an animal cell.

What genes do

Genes do two main things: they make proteins, and they ensure that the offspring of plants and animals are like their parents. Proteins are some of the complicated chemicals that make up our bodies and make them work. Muscle is made of protein. So are the enzymes that digest food, or control the chemical reactions inside cells. The hormones that control growth, affect the brain and the central nervous system are all proteins.

Genes are found in the nucleus of the cell. They are very small parts of the chromosomes mentioned in the introduction. A living cell is very complicated, despite its small size.

Most of the time, the chromosomes in the nucleus are spread out and are almost impossible to see, even with a powerful microscope. But we can see them just as the cell is about to divide. Cell division has to happen for organisms to grow and reproduce.

Looking more closely

We know that sugar is made of glucose molecules; air is molecules of lots of different gases all mixed together, but what are genes made of? Chromosomes and genes are made of a huge molecule called *deoxyribonucleic acid*. Of course microscopes aren't powerful enough to look at these molecules, but we can use a special technique: *X-ray crystallography*. DNA can be taken from cells and crystallised. When X-rays are fired into the crystal from different angles, they come out of the

▼
The giant chromosomes in the fruit fly, *Drosophila*. The stripes are the locations of different genes.

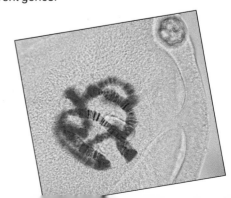

other side and produce a pattern on a photographic plate. This pattern is decided by the way the atoms are arranged in the crystal.

This work was first done on DNA by Rosalind Franklin in the early 1950s. As you can see from one of her pictures, the results were not easy to interpret.

The structure of DNA is very complicated. It is made up of four different chemicals, called *bases*. Each base is made from about 12 atoms. A strand of DNA contains many millions of these bases. While Rosalind Franklin was taking these pictures at King's College in London, another team was working at Cambridge University, trying to build a model of the DNA molecule from cardboard! James Watson and Francis Crick tried to fit models of the bases together. They based their models on a knowledge of what the real DNA molecule could do in cells, a lot of chemistry, and some pure guesswork.

In 1953, Watson and Crick combined their model with Franklin's X-ray images of the DNA crystals. The structure of the molecule was revealed. It has turned out to be one of the most important discoveries made in science. Both teams of scientists shared the Nobel Prize for medicine in 1962. Sadly, Rosalind Franklin died from cancer in 1958 and so never lived to see her achievement honoured with the others.

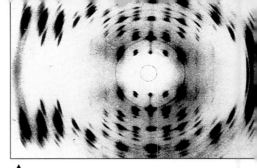

▲
An X-ray crystallography picture of the DNA molecule like those taken by Rosalind Franklin. You can see how hard it is to visualise the whole DNA molecule from this evidence.

▼
Computer-generated model of the DNA molecule.

The structure of DNA

DNA is made from two long threads of chemical, fitting to each other like the two banisters of a spiral staircase. This is the now famous *double helix*.

DNA and genes

The DNA in a chromosome is a coiled double-spiral which coils and coils again. This packs a lot of protein into a small space. The four simpler chemicals (the bases) that make DNA are: adenine, guanine, cytosine and thymine. These are called A, G, C and T for short.

▼
Chromosomes, genes and DNA.

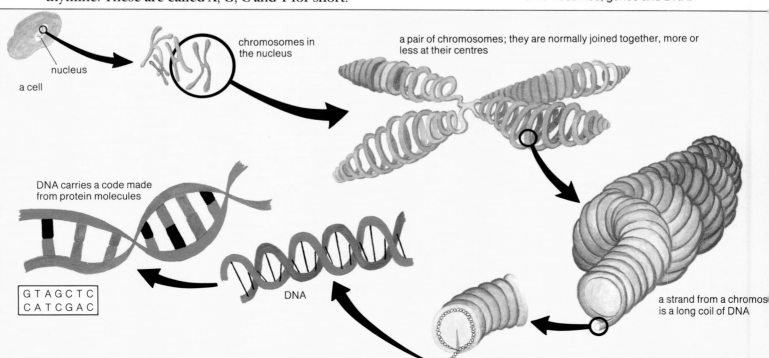

a cell

nucleus

chromosomes in the nucleus

a pair of chromosomes; they are normally joined together, more or less at their centres

a strand from a chromos is a long coil of DNA

DNA carries a code made from protein molecules

DNA

GTAGCTC
CATCGAC

Together, these bases form a protein factory. Different proteins are needed for different jobs. By using the chemicals A, G, C and T in different sequences, they act as a computer program might work in an automatic factory. Computer codes use just two characters – 0 and 1 – in the *binary code*. Genes use four 'letters' – A, G, C and T – to form the *genetic code*.

For example, a sequence like AAGTTCAGATCC might code for some of the amino acids that a protein is made of. A different sequence, AGGTTAACGTTA, for example, will result in a different set of amino acids and so make a different protein. A gene might have a code with as many as 500 000 letters!

The gene doesn't make the proteins directly, it just carries the blueprint that allows other parts of the cell to do the actual work.

When things go wrong

Sometimes a baby is born with a damaged gene, or a gene might be completely missing. *Muscular dystrophy* is a disease in which muscles slowly waste away. Eventually the heart muscle is affected, and the person dies. People with this disease rarely live to be much older than 20. It is caused by a missing gene on one of the X-shaped chromosomes that help to determine whether you are a boy or a girl (see page 84). This gene codes for a protein called dystrophin. Without this protein, children cannot repair damage to an important part of the muscle cell. Only boys are affected. As they grow older, more and more muscle cells gradually die away.

A faulty gene is also responsible for the disease called *haemophilia*. A person with this disease is liable to bleed to death from a simple cut because his blood will not clot. He is missing the gene that makes 'Factor 8', the protein that helps to make blood clot when it is exposed to the air. This is also a 'sex-linked' disease, and again, only affects boys.

Sickle-cell anaemia is another disease of the blood caused by a faulty gene. This time, it affects the making of red blood cells. People with this disease have red blood cells that are mis-shapen and unable to carry oxygen properly. This means that they have difficulty in using the oxygen that they breathe. The fewer red cells makes them *anaemic*. This disease is common in Africa and in people of African descent. However, the sickle-cell gene also gives people extra resistance to malaria.

As you can see, genes are very strongly linked with *heredity*. Children inherit their genes from their parents.

The science of all this is called *genetics*. Genetics is one of the keys to understanding how life on Earth has developed and changed over billions of years. How genes are involved in these things is explained next.

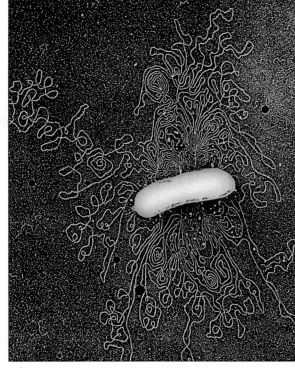

▲
All of the DNA from a single bacterium, stained with gold.

▼
Blood from a person with sickle-cell disease. You can see normal red blood cells and the misshapen ones that are not able to carry oxygen properly.

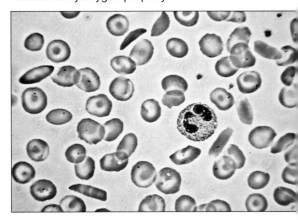

Mendel and Darwin

The two most important discoveries made in biology in the 19th century were made by a monk and a failed doctor. One of these biologists was the clever son of a poor peasant family. He could only get an education by becoming a monk. He was an Austrian called Gregor Mendel. Gregor Mendel discovered the basic secret of the living inheritance, what we now call the 'gene'. But nobody knew this until twenty years after he died.

The second biologist was an Englishman called Charles Darwin. He was a clever but lazy youth from a rich and famous English family. But later he worked very hard indeed, and came up with the theory of *evolution*. He lived at the same time as Mendel, but neither had heard of the other. Darwin kept quiet about his discoveries for twenty years, perhaps because he wasn't confident that he was right; perhaps he knew that his theories would upset a lot of people. There is more about Charles Darwin and evolution later on in this chapter.

The quiet gardener

As a hobby, Mendel bred mice, and was fascinated to see how their different colours were passed on from parents to offspring.

This made him interested in how farmers and gardeners could improve plants and animals by breeding for better qualities. He decided to study heredity properly, not with mice, but with garden peas. For an 'amateur' scientist he had a very good understanding of what it takes to make a good experiment. Years ahead of his time he thought of using a *control* experiment.

He began his experiments in 1857. Farmers and gardeners had been breeding new kinds of plants and animals for many hundreds, even thousands, of years. This is why there are so many breeds of dogs (mostly descended from wild wolves). Cattle and sheep had been domesticated and 'improved'. Gardeners had produced flowers with bigger and better coloured flowers. Scientists call these different forms of the same species *varieties*.

Many people knew *how* to do this. Mendel wanted to find out *why it all worked*.

He was lucky to have made a choice of garden peas. They are simple plants with simple gene patterns compared with other plants. Mendel didn't know this at the time, because no one had even thought of genes. One reason he chose pea plants was because different varieties were easy to get from seedsmen.

Different pea plants have different types of seed – smooth or wrinkly; yellow or green. They have different coloured flowers. Some pea plants are tall, others are short 'dwarf' plants.

Mendel did many hundreds of experiments on pea plants. Let us just follow his experiments with tall and short plants. There are always problems with doing experiments with living things. In this case he had to make sure that when he planted one set of pea seeds the plants were all tall, and not mixed up with some short plants. He had to get a set of plants that *bred true*. He also had to do the same thing with the short plants. He couldn't allow the pea plants to cross-breed too soon. This meant that he had to make sure that the pollen from short plants didn't get into the flowers of the tall plants, and vice versa.

All this took time, but in the end he had 'weeded out' the plants that were in the wrong set. He had 'pure strains' of each type of plant.

Now what would happen if he let the tall plants breed with the short ones? Most biologists of the day already 'knew the answer', but they were wrong. What they, and even Mendel expected, was that the new plants would be an in-between size. They would be shorter than their tall parents but taller than the short ones.

Mendel found that something else happened. When he looked at the new 'mixed breed' of plants, *every single one was tall*. None were short, or 'in between'.

▲ Gregor Mendel (1822–1884), abbott of Brno Monastery.

▼ One *species*, but many *varieties*.

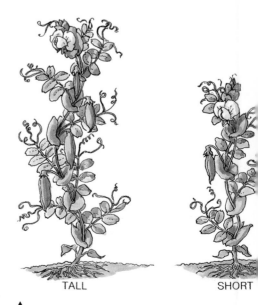

TALL   SHORT

▲ Mendel used tall and short pea plants in his genetics experiments.

Mendel's magic numbers

Mendel investigated further. He let these new plants breed amongst themselves. He planted the seeds that they produced and waited to see what would come up in this second generation.

As he expected, some were now short, and some were tall. There were still no 'in-between' plants. When he *counted* the different types there was a definite pattern in the results. When he repeated the whole experiment again and again, the results were always the same:

- the first generation (called *F1 hybrids*) were all tall;
- on average, a quarter of the plants in the second generation plants (the *F2 hybrids*) were short; and three-quarters were tall. (A *hybrid* is a 'cross' between two pure varieties.)

Mendel wasn't too surprised by this. He already had an idea that something like this would happen. The idea he had was that each plant – or dog, or cow, or sheep – carries a set of 'factors' that decide its characteristics. When two different plants breed together, the offspring share the 'factors' from each parent. We now call these factors *genes*.

But why such regular patterns in the first and second generations? Mendel worked out that this would happen if the gene for *TALL* was somehow stronger than the gene for *short*. Now, it will help if you look at the diagram while reading the rest of this section.

It would work as follows. Suppose all the male part of the new seed came from the *TALL* plants. (You could do this by allowing pollen from the tall plants to get into the female part of the flower on the short plants.)

So, in the first F1 generation each new seed had a gene for *TALLNESS* from the male part of the flower and its own (female) gene for *shortness*. Because *TALL* beats *short*, all the plants grew tall.

Now think about the second generation. One pea plant produces thousands of grains of male pollen. The plant that gets the pollen has lots of flowers and will produce hundreds of pea seeds. This happened in Mendel's experiments with several rows of pea plants all fertilising themselves and each other. The result ought to be chaos, but in fact it produced a pattern.

The *TALL* and *short* genes are mixed together randomly in these seeds. In some seeds there will be a pair of *TALL* genes, in others there will be a pair of *short* genes. Some seeds will have a *short* + *TALL* combination. For a thousand seeds there will be 2000 genes – each seed gets a gene from each parent plant. There will be just as many *TALL* genes as *short* ones.

When you mix the genes up at random you get a result like this.

Parents Genes Seeds	250+250 TALL+TALL 250	500+500 TALL+short 500	250+250 short+short 250

Obviously each *TALL* + *TALL* seed will produce tall plants, and the *short* + *short* plants will all be short. The plants with mixed genes will all grow tall.

So out of a thousand plants in the F2 generation, 250 will be short and 750 tall.

Mendel did not use our modern word 'gene' to explain his results, but he had the basic idea. He did experiments like this for about eight years, using seed type and flower colour as well, the results all followed the same patterns. He had founded the science of *genetics*.

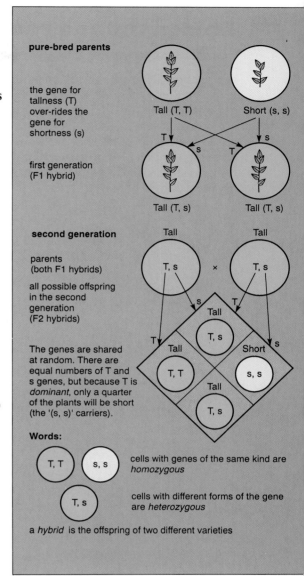

▲
The patterns of inheritance in F1 and F2 hybrids.

Dominant and recessive

In the above example the *TALL* gene is said to be *dominant*. The *short* gene is called *recessive*. Blue eyes in humans are caused by a recessive gene. The gene for brown is dominant. If you have blue-eyed parents you are bound to have blue eyes. But if you have brown-eyed parents you *could* have blue eyes. This is because both of your parents could be carrying the gene for blue eyes, kept 'hidden' by the brown-eye gene that they must also be carrying. Chance will result in some of their children having a pair of blue-eye genes.

▼
Genes decide the colour of your eyes. Brown is dominant to blue.

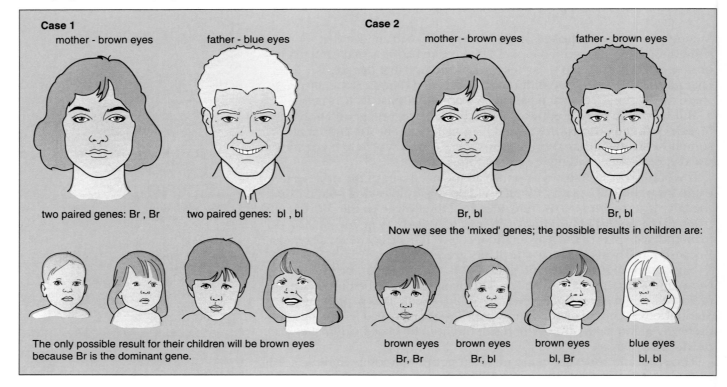

Case 1
mother - brown eyes
father - blue eyes

two paired genes: Br , Br
two paired genes: bl , bl

The only possible result for their children will be brown eyes because Br is the dominant gene.

Case 2
mother - brown eyes
father - brown eyes

Br, bl
Br, bl

Now we see the 'mixed' genes; the possible results in children are:

brown eyes
Br, Br

brown eyes
Br, bl

brown eyes
bl, Br

blue eyes
bl, bl

Mendel rediscovered

In 1900 three scientists, working separately in three different countries, began to do experiments just like Mendel's. They came to the same conclusion about genes and genetics. Then they found Mendel's article in the old scientific magazine, and were very surprised to find that an unknown Austrian monk had beaten them to it by over 40 years!

The living cell as a memory store

The cells of your body don't just keep you alive. They also contain the blueprint that makes you exactly what you are.

Opposite there is a photograph of the chromosomes in a cell at a special time in its life. It is just about to split into two. This, of course, is how you grow. Cells grow and split; then the new cells grow and split again. They do this under the action of growth hormone.

Just before the cell splits into two, the chromosomes also split. Normally a human cell has 46 chromosomes. These split to make 92. These chromosomes then separate, so that 46 go to one half of the cell, and 46 to the other. When the cell splits the new cells each have the right number of chromosomes, which are all identical. This process is called *mitosis*, and is shown in the diagram.

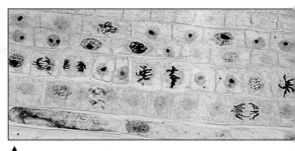

▲
Look at the diagram of mitosis below. Identify the different stages in these cells from a plant root.

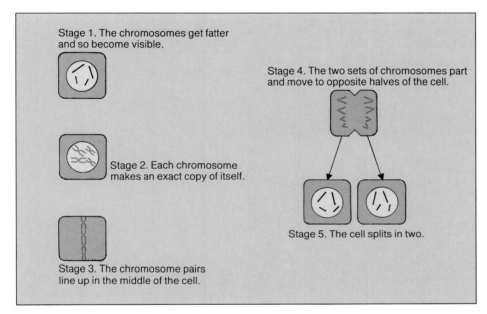

Stage 1. The chromosomes get fatter and so become visible.

Stage 2. Each chromosome makes an exact copy of itself.

Stage 3. The chromosome pairs line up in the middle of the cell.

Stage 4. The two sets of chromosomes part and move to opposite halves of the cell.

Stage 5. The cell splits in two.

◄
The basic process of cell division is called *mitosis*.

How you got to be you

No one is an exact copy of their parents. You began life as a single cell with the 46 chromosomes that carried the information to build *you*. Unless you are an identical twin there is no one else like you in the world. There never has been, and there never will be. Some people you know will be grateful for that fact!

The full story of all this is quite complicated. In simple terms what happens is like this.

The mother's egg cell is *fertilised* when the sperm cell from the father gets inside it. These two cells are different from all the other cells in the body. They are the *sex cells*, and they each contain just 23 chromosomes (half the full number). Your full ration of 46 chromosomes comes half from your father and half from your mother. In fact, it is better to think of your 46 chromosomes as 23 *pairs* of chromosomes.

The dance of the chromosomes!

But the 23 chromosomes you get from each parent aren't exact copies of the 23 pairs in each of their ordinary cells. Before the parental chromosomes separated to become part of the sperm or egg cells, they took part in a complicated dance. The chromosomes broke up into smaller pieces. These waltzed around and then rejoined again, but in a new pattern. Each sperm cell has a *different* pattern, and so has each egg cell.

So not only do you inherit genes from both of your parents, but the genes from both of your *father's parents* got mixed up. The same thing happened when your mother's egg cells were made. So those cells have genes from both of *her* parents. You really are a mixed up person, as far as your genes are concerned. This gene-mixing is part of a process called *meiosis*.

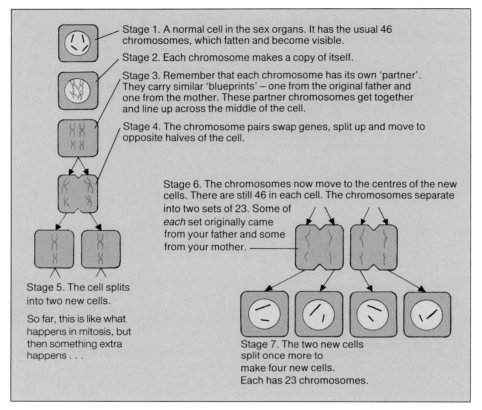

Stage 1. A normal cell in the sex organs. It has the usual 46 chromosomes, which fatten and become visible.

Stage 2. Each chromosome makes a copy of itself.

Stage 3. Remember that each chromosome has its own 'partner'. They carry similar 'blueprints' – one from the original father and one from the mother. These partner chromosomes get together and line up across the middle of the cell.

Stage 4. The chromosome pairs swap genes, split up and move to opposite halves of the cell.

Stage 6. The chromosomes now move to the centres of the new cells. There are still 46 in each cell. The chromosomes separate into two sets of 23. Some of *each* set originally came from your father and some from your mother.

Stage 5. The cell splits into two new cells.

So far, this is like what happens in mitosis, but then something extra happens . . .

Stage 7. The two new cells split once more to make four new cells. Each has 23 chromosomes.

◄ *Meiosis* produces cells that only have half the full number of chromosomes. Can you think why this is needed? Hint: meiosis produces sex cells.

In males, each new cell produced by meiosis is usable. It becomes a *sperm cell*. In females three of the cells are not used. Just one of them survives to become the *ovum*, which is kept in the female ovary.

Boy or girl?

The picture on page 76 shows the 23 pairs of genes found in normal human cells. They have been separated out and put in order. The difference between boys and girls is in just one chromosome. This is the short, stubby Y-shaped chromosome at the end.

This section explains what decides whether a baby will be a boy or a girl. It also explains 'sex-linked' inheritance. For example, why only boys can be haemophiliacs.

We each carry two sets of genes in the nuclei of our living cells. One set comes from the father, one from the mother. The result is that we get *two* sets of instructions for, say, eye colour. Each instruction is coded by a gene. These pairs of genes that tackle the same job are called *alleles*. If both sets give the same instruction, no problem. But if one set is different, what happens?

There are two answers to this question! One answer is that one of the genes takes priority. It is dominant. We saw how this works for shortness and tallness in plants on page 81.

But some genes are equally 'strong': they are called *co-dominant genes*. This means that when two different genes appear in the new nucleus, the result is something in between the effects of the two genes. An example is flower colour in certain plants. If you cross a red flowered plant with one that has white flowers, some of the offspring will have pink flowers. This means that they carry a gene for red and a gene for white. This time the colour is in between white and red – pink.

Just to make things more confusing, some of our characteristics are decided by several genes working together. You can get very complicated results when these genes get mixed up at fertilisation.

Sex

Biological sex is basically an either–or characteristic! The gene (or genes) that decides whether you are male or female is carried by the pair of chromosomes called X and Y. They are called X and Y because of their shapes when they pair up. The Y chromosome contains a set of *dominant* genes which code for male characteristics.

The X chromosome contains a set of *recessive* genes that code for female characteristics. Thus if you inherit a Y chromosome and an X chromosome you will be a boy. To be a girl you have to get a pair of X chromosomes.

This inheritance system gives equal chances for a boy or a girl being born.

Remember that the sex cells contain only one set of chromosomes (23 instead of the normal 23 *pairs*). This is a result of *meiosis*. When the share-out takes place, half the sperm cells will have an X chromosome, and half will have a Y chromosome.

Females only carry X chromosomes, so *all* the egg cells produced carry an X chromosome. Thus if a sperm carrying an X chromosome fertilises an ovum the result is a pair of X chromosomes and the baby will be a girl. If a sperm carrying a Y chromosome enters an ovum the result is an XY pair – and the baby will be a boy. As there are an equal number of sperm with X and Y chromosomes the result is that, on average, as many girls as boys are born. This is shown in the diagram (right).

Two are better than one

Chromosomes come in pairs, and for 22 out of the 23 pairs it is almost impossible to tell them apart. They carry genes designed to do the same job, e.g. make digestive enzymes, decide on eye colour, etc. This is useful because if one chromosome carries a faulty gene, then the other is still there. It carries a healthy gene that can do the same job.

But one pair of chromosomes are not twinned like this. Pair number 23 could be two different chromosomes (X and Y). If something goes wrong with a gene on one of these chromosomes, there is no safety back-up. It is this fact that gives rise to a number of genetic diseases that are *sex-linked*.

Sex-linked inheritance

The X chromosome carries the gene that codes for producing the chemical that makes blood clot when you cut yourself. But in about 1 in a

▲
Genes for skin colour are co-dominant. Co-dominant characteristics can vary a great deal.

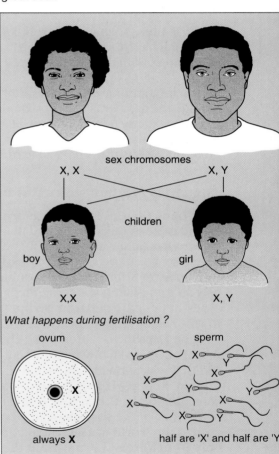

▲
The fertilised egg has an equal chance of being male or female. It depends on which sperm gets there first.

1000 X chromosomes the gene is faulty. This means that if you carry the gene you may have *haemophilia* – your blood won't clot. But it will only affect you in practice if you are male. If you are female the blood-clot gene in the 'spare' X chromosome will take over, so the chemical is produced as normal. Such a female does not suffer from the disease, but is a *carrier* of the disease.

Males don't have a spare blood-clotting gene – their other chromosome is a Y. Y chromosomes don't carry the gene for blood-clotting. So if a baby boy inherits an X chromosome with this fault he will suffer from haemophilia. This also explains why only boys can suffer from muscular dystrophy.

The origin of species

Why are there so many different kinds of animals and plants on Earth? How long have they been here? Have they all been on Earth since the beginning of time? What happened to the dinosaurs? Why can't chickens fly?

You might think about questions like these now and again. For some people, the answer is that God made things the way they are. Others want to know exactly how and when all these things happened. The scientific answers to these questions are part of a theory about how life developed on Earth. This is the *theory of evolution*.

The most famous scientist in the world?

The young Charles Darwin was bright and energetic, but not always in the way that pleased his family and teachers.

Darwin's father was a doctor and he wanted Charles to follow in his footsteps. So, at the age of 16, Charles was sent to study medicine at the University of Edinburgh. The problem was that he had a horror of bleeding and hated watching the operations (this was before anaesthetics). He fled from an operation on a young child, vowing never to enter an operating theatre again.

Then Darwin was offered the chance of a lifetime: to sail around the world on a ship that was being sent to map the coast of South America – and that was to be just the beginning. The ship was the *Beagle* and the captain, Robert Fitzroy. Darwin's job would be to take notes on the birds, animals and plants that they found on the voyage.

The size of the ship shocked Darwin. He had imagined sailing gently around the world in a large and comfortable vessel, but the *Beagle* was only 27 m long and 7 m wide at the widest point!

A voyage round the world

Darwin was 22 years old when he started the five-year voyage. What he learned and saw on that voyage gave him enough work for the rest of his life and changed the way that we think about life on this planet.

No one on the *Beagle* was prepared for the amazing variety of life that they found: not just the plants and animals, but the different people as well. Darwin discovered and named species that no one in Europe had seen before. The animals were all so different from those that he knew

▲
Charles Darwin aged 31, four years after the voyage of the *Beagle*.

▼
The *Beagle*.

▼
Berberis darwinii was discovered by Darwin in South America. It is now one of the most common garden plants in the U.K.

well from home. They lived in different ways, and some even had different body parts. But *why* were they so different?

Darwin began to think that these animals were made like they were because of where they lived. Could *something* alter a species to help it fit in with a changing world?

Just as interesting were the fossil bones. There were bones from huge animals with teeth like mice, and rats that must have been bigger than elephants. Mice pull down ears of corn to eat, but these long-dead 'super mice' must have been strong enough to pull down the tops of trees!

But none of these fossil animals were still alive on Earth. Darwin was able to work out that they had all died out in the fairly recent past, but he could not tell if this was a few thousand or a few million years ago.

▲
Darwin saw fossils of the extinct *Toxodon* in Argentina and started to wonder why some animals lived and others died out.

A secret theory

Returning to England, Darwin had decided that he was going to study science. Gradually, his ideas about *evolution* grew. The new science of geology was beginning to show how old the Earth was. Life had been on Earth for far longer than he had thought before his voyage. Darwin studied worms, pigeons and barnacles to check his new theories. He had to be right before he said anything. Not only did people believe that God had put all living things on Earth, but decided the social order as well: obviously, they thought, people are 'higher up' than animals like apes. Darwin was going to suggest that we were all descended from animals similar to these in the past. Can you imagine what everyone would think about that?

Then, in November 1859, Darwin published his book: *On the Origin of Species by Means of Natural Selection*. The book was an immediate bestseller and the theory of evolution has rarely looked back.

Species can change

For many people, the *Origin of Species* was a worrying book. For some it still is. It explained how different species of animals can change over time. Darwin explained why some species die out (like the dinosaurs) and why others are good survivors. He even explained that human beings were descended from creatures that were also the ancestors of modern animals like apes, chimpanzees and gorillas. This theory was dynamite!

Evolution

Darwin based his theory on three main ideas.
1 Animals and plants have to struggle against each other (*compete*) for the best food, water and shelter.
2 The organisms most likely to survive are the ones that are best 'fitted' to the place where they live.
3 Successful organisms will be well fed and healthy. These will live long enough to reproduce successfully. Unsuccessful organisms will die young, or will have fewer and weaker offspring.

But surroundings change. Over a very long time, the environment becomes colder or warmer, drier or wetter. For example, Britain has had

▼
A French cartoon of Darwin as a circus monkey breaking the hoops of 'ignorance' and 'credulity'.

ice ages, and has been a hot, tropical country. Darwin said that animals and plants could *change* just like their surroundings.

Farmers and gardeners already knew that sometimes a slightly different animal or plant would suddenly appear from 'normal' parents.

Darwin argued that in every new generation there will be a reasonable chance that a new, slightly different plant or animal could appear. It would be just very slightly different from its parents and other members of the species. Most of the time, the change wouldn't make any difference to its life. Sometimes, the change would actually be harmful. But other times, the change would be *helpful*. These unexpected changes are called *variations*.

Suppose a lamb is born with a thicker coat and its environment is getting colder. This sheep will have a better chance of surviving, and so a better chance of breeding. This new feature will be passed on to some of the next generation. These lambs will be better survivors too, and so as time goes on, more and more of the flock will have thicker, warmer, coats.

According to Darwin, this is the kind of thing that has happened to all species.

But changes like this don't happen overnight, they take thousands or even millions of years. Sometimes the changes are successful for a time, and then there are more changes to the environment and the new species dies out. The many different species alive today have descended from older species. These gradually changed to give the plants and animals that are familiar to us. But some older species died out completely and have no successors. Over 99% of the species that have lived on Earth have died out. What we see today is the 1% that have survived.

▲ Animal breeders encourage characteristics that they want to breed prize-winning animals.

Evolution in a nutshell

1 Variations sometimes make an animal or plant better adapted to its environment.
2 The environment will suit some varieties better than others. We say that the better-adapted individuals are *selected* by the environment. This is called *natural selection*.
3 Successful varieties spread throughout a population, so the species changes slightly.
4 Over many thousands (or millions) of years, tiny changes cause a species, or part of a species, to change a great deal. We may get a whole new species.

▼ Dark and light peppered moths on light bark. Which one would be easiest for a bird to see and catch?

Evolution in action

One famous example of an evolutionary change that has happened over a short time-span is the case of the peppered moth.

The peppered moth is common in the U.K. It lives on trees and is a peppery brown colour, which acts as camouflage against the colour of the tree bark. There are two varieties of these moths, one a lighter colour than the other. As you might expect, the light-coloured one is found on light tree bark, and the darker moths on the darker bark.

If you lived in any large city about 100 years ago, you would find very few light moths, but lots of dark ones. This was because of the Industrial Revolution: with tens of thousands of factory chimneys and coal fires, the

city trees were covered in soot. The population of peppered moths changed to mostly dark. Any light ones that hatched out were more likely to be spotted by birds against the dark bark, and eaten. In the countryside, however, where tree bark was not covered in soot, the situation was reversed: there were more of the light moths.

But nowadays, you find more light moths than dark. The Clean Air Acts of the 1950s have made cities a lot cleaner. Tree bark is now its natural colour again, and so the lighter moths are better camouflaged.

The mechanism of variation

A species 'breeds true' because genes carry the information from parents to offspring, which makes sure that the offspring are of the same species. The genes carry the data as a coded series of molecules. It is rather like the sequence of 'pits' that code the music in a compact disc. To read the code and turn it into music you need a lot of complex electronics. In the same way, the gene-code has to be read by the living parts of the cell.

Genes are very small parts of the long-stranded chromosomes that are in the nuclei of cells. Genes are easily damaged. (So are the pits on a compact disc.) But like a compact disc player, the body can make allowances and still read the message.

Anyway, the body has millions of cells, and a few damaged ones shouldn't cause any bother. The same applies to compact discs. Some are always faulty, but if you get a faulty disc you can take it back to the shop and change it. But if the master disc at the factory is wrong, all the discs will be faulty. But remember, you were made from a single fertile cell containing the genetic code from your parents. If one of the really important genes is damaged, it could be serious. All your cells will carry this faulty gene. This is what happens when people have cystic fibrosis or muscular dystrophy.

Changing genes

Every second a few hundred very energetic atomic particles zip through your body. They come from radioactive materials in the ground, in your home, even in your own body. Some come from outer space as 'cosmic rays'. Any one of these particles can alter a gene in one of your body cells. Certain chemicals that you eat or breathe in can also change your DNA in this way.

If the altered gene happens to be in a sex cell, the change could be big enough to alter the code carried by that cell's genes. If that cell is one of the pair that forms a new life, then the child that results will carry that altered gene in every one of his or her cells. It is this changing, or *mutation*, of a gene in a sex cell that is one cause of the variation that gives rise to new species.

There are probably *other* reasons for changes to genes, due to things that happen at a critical time when the cell is dividing to make sex cells like sperm and ova (i.e. during *meiosis*). But it is well known that radiation affects these processes quite dramatically.

Selective breeding or genetic engineering?

New characteristics can appear in plants and animals by accident, as explained above. If a good characteristic appears in a farm animal, say, it can be encouraged to spread through the pollution by *selective breeding*. The animal with the good feature is mated with one or more other animals from the flock or herd.

Some of these first-generation hybrids will not possess the 'good' gene at all. If the gene is recessive you can't tell if they have it or not. The first-generation offspring are bred again, usually with each other. As a result, the chance of the gene appearing in the next generation is increased. After several generations, the good gene is quite common in the herd. There may be an occasional 'throwback', in which the gene doesn't appear, but after a long enough time the new variety of animal will 'breed true'.

The problem with all this is that it takes time. For recessive genes it is quite hard to keep track of what is going on. Very careful records have to be kept.

Variation: what makes things different?

As with any athlete, the winning horse doesn't just need to have good genes, it also needs to be fed well and worked hard and properly in training. The difference between one organism and another isn't just due to its genes. It also depends on its *environment*. You might have all the genes you need to be a world-champion swimmer. But if you never learn to swim nobody will ever know your potential.

▲
The Siamese cat has been bred over hundreds of years to be cross-eyed because people find the expression appealing.

Genetic engineering

Genetic engineering is the latest kind of biotechnology. What it tries to do is simple in theory but hard in practice. Suppose a farmer finds that one of his newly born cows has some very good features. To use this to improve his herd by selective breeding would take many years. Genetic engineers would do the job more quickly.

First, they would find the 'new' gene responsible for the improvement. The scientist could do this by taking just a few cells from the animal's skin. Then they 'transplant' the gene into a host organism. This would be something quick and easy to breed, like a bacterium. The bacteria breed *asexually*, by splitting. Each new bacterium is a perfect copy – a *clone* – of its parent. When there are enough bacteria, each one with the 'good' gene in it, they are mashed up and the genes are extracted. The scientists then inject the genes into egg-cells of a pregnant cow. The new-born cows then will all show the characteristic that the farmer wants. And all done in a few weeks.

It isn't quite as easy as that in practice. But in principle this was how Scottish sheep were made to produce a *human* hormone.

The diagram shows how the process is carried out. It relies on:

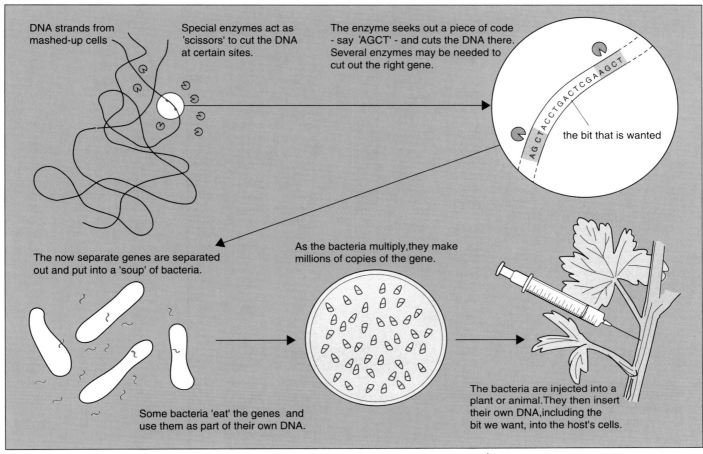

DNA strands from mashed-up cells

Special enzymes act as 'scissors' to cut the DNA at certain sites.

The enzyme seeks out a piece of code - say 'AGCT' - and cuts the DNA there. Several enzymes may be needed to cut out the right gene.

the bit that is wanted

The now separate genes are separated out and put into a 'soup' of bacteria.

As the bacteria multiply, they make millions of copies of the gene.

The bacteria are injected into a plant or animal. They then insert their own DNA, including the bit we want, into the host's cells.

Some bacteria 'eat' the genes and use them as part of their own DNA.

▲
Gene transfer.

▼
Two ears of corn: the one on the left is natural and fertile, but the one on the right has been engineered to be unfertile.

- knowing where exactly on the DNA in the chromosome the wanted gene is;
- being able to cut this gene out and then insert it into the DNA of a bacterium;
- being able to get the gene back from a lot of bacteria that have been allowed to reproduce;
- being able to put the gene back into the DNA of other animals.

During the next 12 years scientists all over the world will spend up to £2 billion to try to map every gene in the human genome. They hope that this will help in:

- treating the 5000 known hereditary diseases, from haemophilia to sickle-cell disease;
- understanding why some people get heart attacks and others don't;
- understanding how people develop from just a single egg;
- understanding a lot more about how the billions of cells in the body are able to work together;
- understanding what happens when the body's cells don't work properly and change into cancer cells.

But in doing all this, the researchers will be experimenting with the human genome — the very basis of what makes us what we are. Should they be allowed to do this? Extension task 2 (part 1) is about this question.

Activities

1 Haemophilia is a blood disease in humans. Find out:
(a) what causes it;
(b) what symptoms it produces;
(c) what treatment patients are given at the moment;
(d) what the problems have been relating to impure blood transfusions and the HIV virus;
(e) what Queen Victoria has to do with the disease.

2 One of the main aims of geneticists is to make a map of all the human chromosomes. This will allow them to find out what each part of the human genome does in making babies grow and develop. Some scientists have claimed that they would like to check the cells in a growing embryo to see if they are all right, and if not, to replace them.
   Find out more about this and make a poster or report giving arguments for and against this work.

3 Twins can be identical — looking exactly the same — or they could be no more like each other than any pair of children from the same family. Find out how twins happen and how a theory of genes can explain the two different kinds of twins.

4 Find out what you can about the fossils found in a bed of rock called the *Burgess Shale*. What do they tell us about the evolution of life on Earth? (Hint: this will take some tracking down; start by looking for books by *Stephen Jay Gould*.)

5 Why do some animals become extinct?
(a) Choose an extinct animal that interests you and find out the possible reasons for it dying out.
(b) Could human beings become extinct? What kind of changes or events could cause this to happen?

6 Think about yourself. Unless you are a twin, you are unique — there is no one else like you in the whole world! Give two important things that you think you have inherited, and two that are mostly caused by your environment. Explain your choices and then give one or two differences that are partly inherited and partly environmental.

Questions

1 Copy out and complete the table by placing the following human conditions in the correct columns: *haemophilia, mumps, measles, having lobed ears, eye colour, jaundice, cystic fibrosis, sickle-cell disease.*

Inherited	Not inherited

2 Match the scientists to what they did. Copy out list A and then add list B in the correct order.

List A	List B
Gregor Mendel	helped discover the double helix of DNA
Charles Darwin	was the founder of genetics
Rosalind Franklin	produced a theory of natural selection
Oswald Avery	discovered that DNA carried the genetic code

3 How many chromosomes are there in each of the following human cells?
(a) Nerve cell.
(b) Sperm cell.
(c) Red blood cell.
(d) Egg cell (ovum).
(e) Cheek cell.

4 Explain the difference between *meiosis* and *mitosis*.

5 Chromosomes are made up of *genes* that carry information in a *genetic code*. The code in a gene is carried by short lengths of *DNA*.
   Explain the terms in italics and draw diagrams to show how the features they describe are related to each other.

6 Explain the following terms used in genetics: *hybrid, monohybrid cross, sex-linkage, dominance, co-dominance.*

Checklist

These are the facts and ideas that you should have learned by studying this topic.

To reach Basic Level you should:

- know that you can inherit features from your parents
- know that animals and plants of one type are often very different from each other, e.g. human beings
- be able to sort plants and animals into groups using simple observable characteristics
- know that some diseases can be inherited, but that others are caused by germs or poor diet

To succeed at Foundation Level you should:

- know that your cells contain genes in their nuclei, and how these genes carry information from parents to children
- understand that in any environment food, light, water and even spaces to live in may be hard to find, so that plants and animals have to compete with each other
- be able to recognise the good points about plants and animals that could be developed to improve the breed
- know that some diseases or disorders are inherited

To succeed at Merit Level you should:

- know that genes
  - control how organisms grow and what they are like
  - contain lengths of DNA
  - work by controlling protein synthesis
  - may be dominant or recessive
- know that the fertilised egg (zygote) contains genetic material from both parents
- know the ways in which living organisms are adapted to survive in the natural environment and that they can adapt both by behaviour and by body structure
- know what *variation* means and that variation can be caused both by genetic changes and by differences in the environment
- know that some genetic changes are caused by ionising radiations
- understand how selective breeding can produce economic benefits and improved yields

To succeed at Special Level you should:

- know how genetic information is passed from cell to cell and from generation to generation by cell division (meiosis, mitosis)
- be able to explain how sex is determined in offspring
- understand how DNA replicates and controls protein synthesis by means of a base code
- understand the principles of a monohybrid cross involving dominant and recessive alleles
- understand the relationships between variation, natural selection and reproductive success in organisms, and the significance of these relationships for evolution
- understand the different sources of genetic variation, including mutation
- understand the basic principles of genetic engineering and selective breeding, and be aware of the social and ethical issues that may be involved

Most animals — and even some plants — give messages. Look at the pictures. Most communication is done by using light and sound. Light is part of a family of radiations, called electromagnetic radiation.

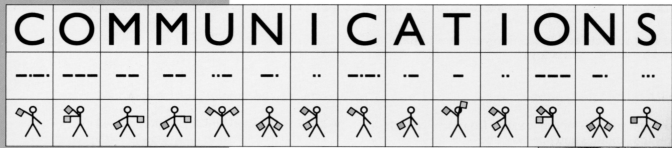

COMMUNICATIONS

▲ Insects' eyes register ultraviolet light. How we see a flower under u.v. is shown left; what the insect sees (right) is much more spectacular. The flower's colours are designed for insects to see best.

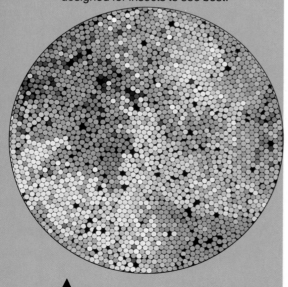

▲ The individual strands running through *one* glass fibre optical cable. Each strand can carry a different message.

Flowers communicate with bees using radiations (ultraviolet rays) that we can't see. A hundred years ago humans also began communicating over long distances using invisible radiation in the form of radio waves. Since then people have invented many new ways of using electromagnetic radiation for sending messages. Some of them are shown in the photographs.

For thousands of years people have recorded information using *codes*. They have made marks on wood, bone, shells, stones, skin and paper. Before that, we had coded our ideas in *sounds*. Even to this day, some writing stands for sounds — like written English and Arabic — and other writing stands for pictures, as in Chinese characters.

▼ Communication with symbols in Egypt, about 1250 B.C.

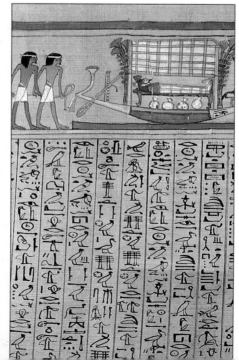

▲ A puzzled expression?

▼ This disc, 30 cm across, contains all of the sound and pictures for a feature film.

We now send both pictures and sounds across the world through space. We use another kind of code that only computers can read. This is the *binary code* of digital signals.

This chapter deals with how modern communication systems work, and the new uses we have found for the simple task of sending and receiving messages. It will also remind you of earlier work you have done, in *Sound and music*, and in your studies of microelectronics and light.

The electromagnetic spectrum

When light travels from one medium to another it is likely to change direction. This is due to refraction (why this happens is explained later). But light may also split up. Different colours are separated to give a *spectrum*.

But the spectrum we see is only a part of the whole spectrum of radiations that come from a hot body like the Sun. The graph shows the radiations coming from the Sun. They are called *electromagnetic radiations.* They all travel at the same speed through space, the speed of light.

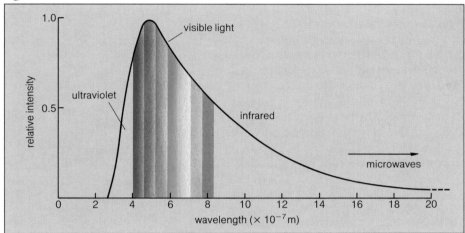

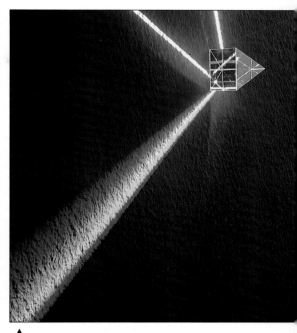

▲
A beam of white light being refracted into a spectrum of visible light. (The second white beam is caused by total internal reflection.)

◄
The radiation from the Sun.

Light is just a small part of this family. It is the part that you are most familiar with, but the invisible rays are important too.

The *infrared* rays are near the red end of the visible spectrum. We can't see them, but we can feel them. This is because they are absorbed in the skin and warm it up. Life can exist on Earth because the infrared rays keep the planet warm enough.

Ultraviolet rays are invisible but they can damage our eyes. They carry a lot of energy and can kill living cells, or alter them so that they become cancerous. Luckily, the oxygen in the atmosphere can absorb ultraviolet. The ultraviolet (u.v.) rays change the normal oxygen (O_2) molecule into ozone (O_3). We get an added bonus when the *ozone layer* that then forms cuts off the most dangerous u.v. rays.

The body protects itself against u.v. rays by changing skin colour: white skins become brown. We can detect u.v. by using the fact that it makes certain chemicals glow (*fluoresce*).

▲
Millions of people expose themselves to high levels of ultraviolet radiation every year.

◄
Some chemical dyes fluoresce under ultraviolet light. Fluorescent dyes have been used in these stage costumes.

The diagram (right) shows the full range of the electromagnetic spectrum. The radiations sometimes behave like a *wave*. We use this idea to design radio and TV sets. But sometimes it is best to think of the radiations as energetic *particles*. For example, we use this idea to explain how u.v. damages cells. This is explained more fully later.

Beaming and trapping

An easy way to control electromagnetic waves is to use curved reflectors. They are used in car headlights, TV satellite 'dishes', microwave transmitters and both radio and light telescopes.

In a transmitter the radiations are given out by a small source. This could be a hot filament, as in a car headlight, or a small 'wave-guide' in a radar transmitter. The source must be at the focus of the curved reflector (you can see why from the diagram). The waves are reflected to form a beam with more or less parallel sides. The idea is to direct the energy to where it is wanted: the *receiver*.

The receiving dish does the same job in reverse. The beam is reflected to a small receiving *aerial* placed at the focus. The electromagnetic waves create an electric current in the aerial which is a copy of the transmitted signal. The rest of the electronic system converts this current into sound or pictures.

All waves are similar

There are many types of wave: water waves, sound waves, radio waves and even light waves. All waves have some things in common.

- they travel (usually at a definite speed in a particular medium);
- they carry energy;
- they have a repeating pattern;
- they have a frequency, a wavelength and an amplitude.

Frequency is the number of repeated patterns occurring per second, and is measured in hertz (Hz).

Wavelength is the length of the pattern, measured in metres.

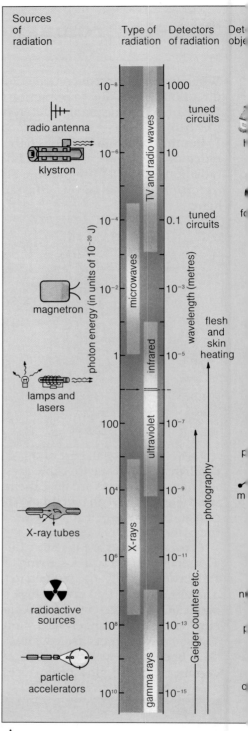

The full electromagnetic spectrum.

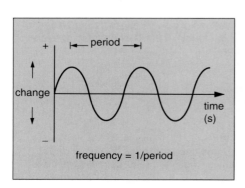

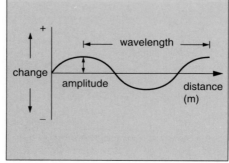

Amplitude is a measure of the maximum change the wave makes. Period is the time taken to repeat a pattern. The wavelength is the distance between similar points on the wave.

Amplitude measures the 'height' of the wave – how much it makes a change above or below normal. The bigger the amplitude, the more energy the wave carries.

How waves behave

To control waves, we have to understand how they behave. The key effects are *diffraction* and *interference*. Some waves can be *polarised*. These effects are explained next.

Diffraction

When waves pass through a gap they spread out again afterwards. This effect is called diffraction. A stream of particles doesn't show this effect.

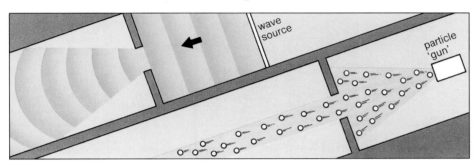

◄
Waves spread out after going through a gap; particles don't.

Diffraction is a problem for communications. It means that it is difficult to keep waves in a narrow beam. So not all the energy transmitted gets into the receiving dish.

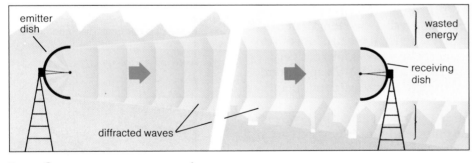

◄
Diffraction makes a beam spread out at the edges. This means that energy is lost.

Interference

Interference occurs when similar waves meet. Particles just collide and bounce off, but waves pass through each other when they meet. The diagram shows what happens when two waves meet.

When a crest meets a crest, the waves add up to give a bigger crest. Two troughs meeting create a deeper trough. But when a crest meets a trough they can cancel each other out. But the waves haven't vanished! When they move on, the original crest and trough reappear.

▼
Waves can pass through each other without being affected afterwards.

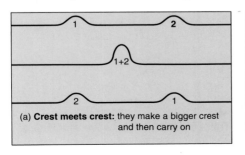

(a) **Crest meets crest:** they make a bigger crest and then carry on

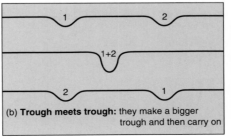

(b) **Trough meets trough:** they make a bigger trough and then carry on

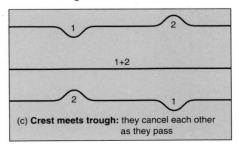

(c) **Crest meets trough:** they cancel each other as they pass

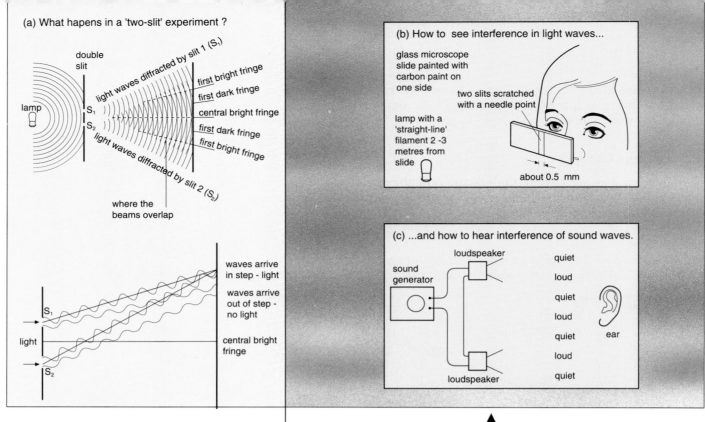

(a) What hapens in a 'two-slit' experiment ?

double slit

light waves diffracted by slit 1 (S₁)

lamp

S₁

S₂

first bright fringe
first dark fringe
central bright fringe
first dark fringe
first bright fringe

light waves diffracted by slit 2 (S₂)

where the beams overlap

S₁

light

S₂

waves arrive in step - light

waves arrive out of step - no light

central bright fringe

(b) How to see interference in light waves...

glass microscope slide painted with carbon paint on one side

lamp with a 'straight-line' filament 2 -3 metres from slide

two slits scratched with a needle point

about 0.5 mm

(c) ...and how to hear interference of sound waves.

sound generator

loudspeaker

quiet
loud
quiet
loud
quiet
loud
quiet

ear

loudspeaker

A sure test to find out if an unknown radiation is made up of waves or particles is to look for interference effects. One of the most common tests is the *Young's two-slit* arrangement. This is shown above.

Diffraction gratings

The effect of two slits is to produce a set of 'fringes' – places of wave and no-wave. Where these regions occur depends on the wavelength of the waves used. White light is a mixture of wavelengths. If we use lots of very narrow slits we get an interesting new effect. The wave-zones get very wide, and the fringes for different colours are separated. We can produce a spectrum. Special diffraction gratings are used to investigate the spectra of light from stars (see page 183).

You can see this effect when you look at a compact disc. The grooves in the disc act like the slits in a grating. The colours of butterfly wings are made by diffraction. Thousands of tiny scales on the wing act as a grating.

Polarised light

Sound waves are push–pull waves. This kind of wave is *longitudinal*. Light and other electromagnetic waves are *transverse* waves. This means they wave from side to side (or up and down), at right angles to the direction of motion.

▲
You will probably do these experiments at school. They let you see and hear interference patterns.

▼
Each scale of the butterfly wing has tiny grooves along it. These diffract light like the surface of a compact disc and give the wing its colours.

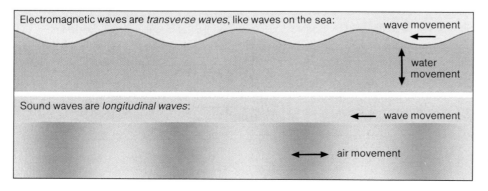

Electromagnetic waves are *transverse waves*, like waves on the sea:

wave movement

water movement

Sound waves are *longitudinal waves*:

wave movement

air movement

◄
There are two types of wave: longitudinal and transverse waves.

ordinary light waves
vibrate in all directions

Polaroid filter

polarised light waves
vibrate in just one direction

◀
Making light polarised.

▼
Looking at a pond. The right-hand side shows the view through a Polaroid filter.

Normally light waves vibrate in all directions. But they can be made to vibrate along one direction only. When they are like this they are *fully polarised*. 'Polaroids' are sunglasses that cut out glare. They do this by making use of the fact that reflected light is often 'polarised'. Light is partly polarised when it is reflected, and also when it passes through certain needle-shaped crystals. These crystals are used to make 'polaroid' filters. These filters only pass light that is vibrating in one direction. Light waves vibrating in other directions are absorbed. In filters and sunglasses the crystals are arranged to absorb the polarised light made by reflections. Using polarised glasses you can see through the reflections in a window. Polaroid filters on cameras let you take photographs of fish underwater. Normally the fish would be hidden by reflections from the water surface.

The speed of electromagnetic waves

Light travels much faster than sound. For a long time people thought that light took no time at all to go from one place to another. In 1676 an astronomer, Olaf Römer, calculated the speed of light.

Scientists and engineers now take the speed of light 'for granted'. The S.I. (*Système International*) unit of distance – the metre – is now defined in terms of the time it takes light to travel that distance.

Very careful measurements have shown that all e.m. waves travel at the same speed. *But they only do so in a vacuum.*

Speed, frequency and wavelength

Imagine a sound wave starting out from a source, a loudspeaker, say. The source has a frequency of 100 vibrations per second. Thus it makes 100 complete waves every second. These waves move away at a speed of 340 metres per second. This is the speed of sound in air.

After 1 second the first wave is 340 metres away, and there are 100 waves following it. How long is each wave?

You should work out that the answer is '3.4 metres'. As a general rule:

$$\text{wavelength} = \frac{\text{wave speed}}{\text{frequency}}$$

As formulae: $\lambda = v/f$, or $v = f\lambda$.

(λ is the Greek letter *lambda*, used as the symbol for wavelength.)

This shows that the sound waves are quite long. Light waves have a very high speed and a very high frequency. Light speed is 300 000 000 m/s, the frequency of green light is 500 000 000 000 000 (5×10^{14} Hz). This gives a wavelength of 0.0006 millimetres (6×10^{-7}m).

The diagram on page 96 shows the frequencies and wavelengths of the main parts of the electromagnetic spectrum.

Refraction

In a transmitting medium like glass or plastic, light waves slow down. This is what causes the change in direction we call *refraction*. The diagram (right) shows what happens.

Light rays

In practice it is easier to think of light as travelling in straight lines along *light rays*. These simply show the direction of the waves. For example, when light goes from air into glass its direction changes as shown in the diagram.

It is useful to draw a line at right angles to the surface between the two materials. This is called the *normal*. We find that when light travels into a denser medium – so that it slows down – the wave direction changes so that it is closer to the normal.

The opposite happens when light leaves the dense material for a less dense one: it moves away from the normal. This produces interesting effects. Water appears less deep than it really is. A pencil in a glass of water looks bent.

Light can get trapped inside a transparent substance by *total internal reflection*. These effects are shown in the diagrams. The new and very important technology of fibre optics is based on the fact that light and infrared waves can be trapped by total internal reflection.

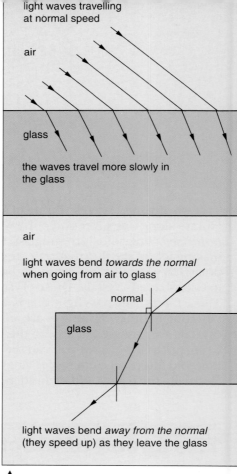

▲
Refraction.

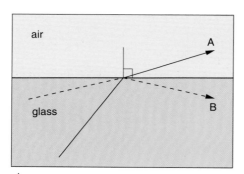

▲
Total internal reflection.

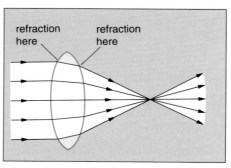

▲
Lenses use refraction to focus light.

What lenses do

Lenses are curved pieces of glass or plastic. The curve is just right for refracting beams of light to a focus. This means that we can use lenses to make *images*. The action of a single lens doing these things is shown in the diagrams opposite.

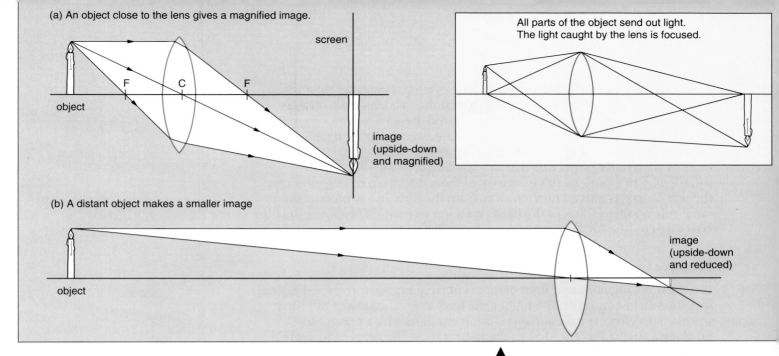

(a) An object close to the lens gives a magnified image.

screen

F   C   F

object

image
(upside-down
and magnified)

All parts of the object send out light.
The light caught by the lens is focused.

(b) A distant object makes a smaller image

object

image
(upside-down
and reduced)

▲
How a lens makes an image of an object.

Strong and weak lenses

The more curved the lens is, the bigger the effect on a beam of light. A 'fat' lens has deeper curves than a thin lens, so it is stronger. This means that a strong lens will make an image closer to itself than a thin, weak lens will. The above diagram shows this for a distant object.

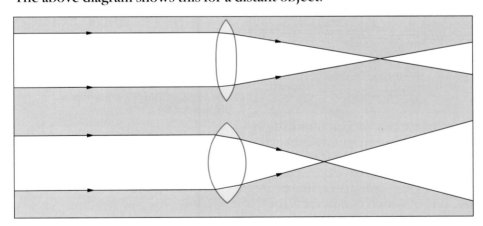

◄
'Fatter' lenses are more powerful because they can bend (refract) the light more.

Making images — the effect of distance

But the position of an image is also decided by where the object is placed. If it is close to the lens, the image will be far away. This is what happens in *projectors*. The image will also be much larger than the object as a result of simple geometry.

Cameras need the opposite effect. The image has to be made on a film which is very close to the lens. In normal use the object being photographed is much further away than the film. This results in an image much smaller than the object.

Focusing the image

An image is clear only when light from any point on the object comes together as a point on the image. For a human eye, the image has to be formed on a screen called the retina. This is always the same distance from the lens. So how does the eye manage to give clear images of both close and distant objects? In fact, it can't — at least not at the same time.

101

When you focus on a distant object, the eye lens is weaker than when you look at a nearby object. This means that the eye lens has to change shape. This is done by a ring of muscle around the lens, which can pull the lens into a thin shape when looking at distant objects, or let it fall into a fatter shape when the lens needs to be stronger.

In *cameras and projectors* the lens is made of glass, which isn't squashable. In a camera, to change focus from distant to nearby objects the whole lens is moved further away from the film. In a projector the same rule applies (think of the light retracing its path). The closer the film is to the lens, the further away the image will be.

Dispersion

In a transmitting medium, light of different frequencies travels at different speeds. As a general rule, the higher the frequency the slower the wave travels. This effect is called *dispersion*. It explains why a prism can produce a spectrum. The slower the light travels, the bigger the angle it turns through when it reaches the prism. Blue light has a higher frequency than red light, so turns through a bigger angle. This is shown in the diagram.

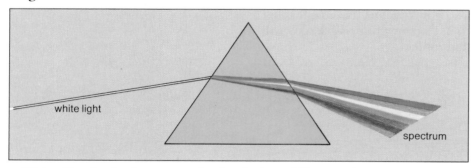

◀

Light slows down in glass, causing refraction. Blue light slows down more then red light, and so it is refracted most. The result is that the white light is dispersed into a spectrum.

This effect is also important in the design of fibre-optic communication systems and camera lenses. Camera lenses have to be designed so that all the colours in the scene are focused properly. If the red light is turned through a different angle than blue light, any image will have blurred edges of different colours! Special *achromatic* (non-colouring) lenses are used. They are made of two types of glass, one of which counteracts the effects of the other.

An *optical fibre* carries a message using pulses of infrared radiation. The pulses are a digital code for the message or music being transmitted. If the infrared contains a spread of frequencies then some will surge ahead of the others. The pulses spread out and mingle with each other. The information is lost. To avoid this the pulses have to be reshaped every now and again using repeater stations.

▼

Digital pulses lose their shape if the signal is carried by a wide range of frequencies.

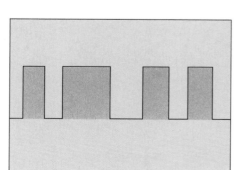

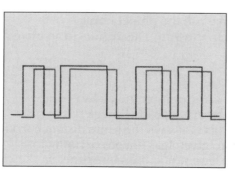

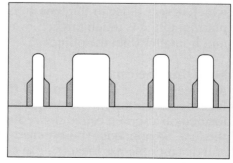

Getting the message across

Most communication systems are complicated. Think of what happens when you hear someone talking to you. There is a lot of complicated biology going on! Even today, no one really understands how the brain controls speech. But all communication systems follow a similar pattern. This is quite simple, as shown in the diagram.

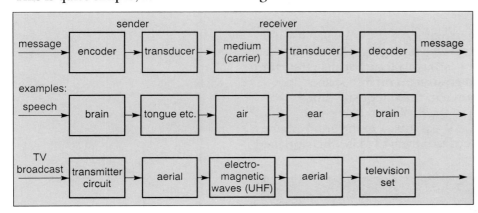

In a TV broadcast the *information source* could be people: talking, dancing, singing or playing tennis. But the information might be a recording, the temperature of the sea, or a set of numbers in a data base.

We often have to use a *transducer* to move the information from one kind of energy carrier to another. For example, speech is changed from air vibrations (sound waves) into a changing electric current in a telephone wire.

The information usually has to be *coded* – into some kind of *signal*. These days, the code may be *digital* (see below). Radio uses what is called 'modulation'. In a radio broadcast the message is carried by a wave of a given frequency, say 90 MHz. 90 MHz is far too high a frequency for an audible sound; the highest note that we can hear is less than 30 kHz. So the audible sounds are coded into slight changes of this carrier frequency. At the receiver, the changes are decoded back into the original frequencies – the 'audio signals'. This form of coding is frequency modulation – FM.

Most signal carriers are waves of some kind: sound, radio, microwaves, infrared, light. The medium may be air, a vacuum, a metal wire or glass. Sound waves are cheap to produce but only travel well through air, and can't travel very far. This limits their use in communication systems.

Transmitted signals have to be *received* by something that can pick up energy from the carrier wave. This may be an aerial, or your eardrum, for example. Finally, the signal has to be changed into an 'energy system' that we can detect. In the ear, the transducer that does this is the spiral tube called the *cochlea*. This changes sound vibrations into nerve impulses which go to the brain. The brain then *decodes* these impulses. No one knows how the brain does this – and in any case it doesn't work if the sounds are in a foreign language that we don't understand!

Signals across the world

The first long-distance communication across the Atlantic used Morse code. This was an early form of digital code. It was sent by undersea cable,

◀
These are the features of an information-transmission system. (Not all systems need 'coding'.)

▼
"97–99 FM", but what does the 'FM' stand for?

THERE'S SOMETHING WRONG WITH THIS COMMUNICATION SYSTEM – I CAN'T UNDERSTAND A WORD!

laid down in 1858. Talking over long distances had to wait until the invention of the telephone, by Alexander Bell in 1876. Both telegraph and telephone systems needed 'boosting stations' to get a signal to cover long distances. It wasn't easy to make these work underwater, so a telephone linking America to Europe had to wait until 1956! For more details about 'boosters', see page 110.

But as long ago as the 1890s many scientists and inventors were experimenting with *radio*. In 1901 the most famous of these, the Italian, Guglielmo Marconi, sent a message across the Atlantic by using radio waves. The message was sent from England to Newfoundland and was simply the letter 'S' in Morse code.

Radio messages are carried by electromagnetic waves. We can use a large range of frequencies. In 1900 scientists knew quite a lot about these waves. They had said that Marconi was wasting his time because the radio waves wouldn't get to America – they'd go straight off into space! The theory was perfectly correct. But unknown to the scientists – and to Marconi! – there was a natural solution to the problem. There just happened to be layer of charged particles – gas ions – in the atmosphere. This layer acted as a mirror for the kind of radio waves Marconi happened to be using.

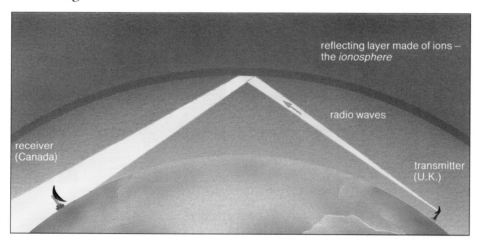

reflecting layer made of ions – the *ionosphere*

radio waves

receiver (Canada)

transmitter (U.K.)

◄
Marconi was lucky – *some* radio waves are reflected by the upper atmosphere.

▼
The original Telstar communications satellite.

Most radio waves do just shoot off into space. Good quality signals – like TV broadcasts – carry a lot of information. This amount of information can only be carried by high-frequency waves. But these frequencies pass straight through the ion layer. Can we put an artificial mirror in space?

Satellite communications

The first communications satellite was just such a mirror. It was called *Echo* and was launched in 1960. It was used for radio and telephone communications. TV requires more information, and so needed stronger signals. This was made possible by the *Telstar* satellite, launched just two years later.

Telstar was more than a mirror. It collected the signals and amplified them before sending them back to Earth. This made it possible to send black and white television pictures across the Atlantic.

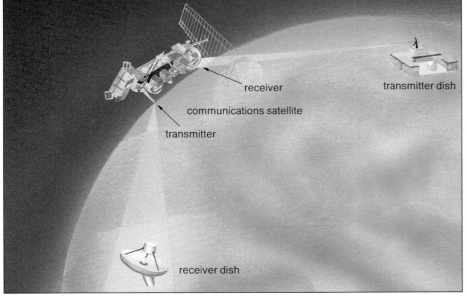

receiver

transmitter dish

communications satellite

transmitter

receiver dish

 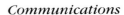

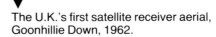
A communications satellite is a mirror in space.

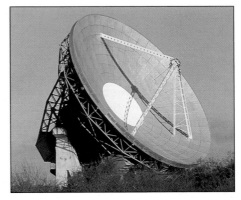
The U.K.'s first satellite receiver aerial, Goonhillie Down, 1962.

Nowadays you can pick up satellite TV with a small aerial fixed to your house. Much bigger aerials were needed to receive satellite signals in 1962.

A communications satellite has to stay in the same place in the sky so that your dish aerial can always point in the same direction. But if a satellite didn't move it would fall down to Earth (see page 173) in Chapter 9, *Space*). How can the satellite move *and* stay in the same place all the time? The mystery is explained by the fact that the Earth is spinning. The satellite is positioned over the equator and orbits in exactly a day, so keeping time with the spin of the Earth. This means that it is always over the same place on Earth. It is called a *geostationary* satellite.

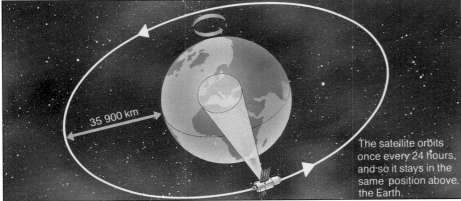

35 900 km

The satellite orbits once every 24 hours, and so it stays in the same position above the Earth.

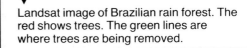
Communication satellites and some weather satellites are in *geostationary* orbits. Meteosat, which gives the pictures that we see on TV weather forecasts, is in an orbit like this.

Landsat image of Brazilian rain forest. The red shows trees. The green lines are where trees are being removed.

Collecting information

The first use of satellites was to collect information. Most satellites were sent into orbit by Russia and the United States as 'spy satellites'. They were used to collect military information. But the same techniques can be used to collect other kinds of information. We use satellites to:

- help forecast the weather;
- check on the growth and destruction of forests;
- check on crop growth and soil changes;
- give accurate data for making maps;
- monitor sudden changes to the environment, like an oil spillage at sea;
- find out how the Earth is changing, under the action of wind, rain, ice and even the movement of continents.

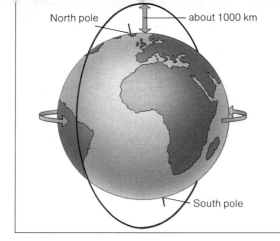

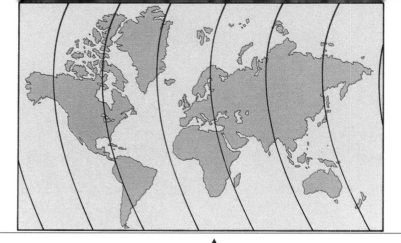

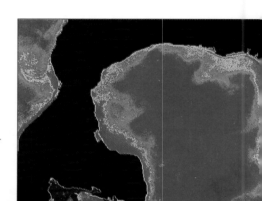

▲
Satellites in a polar orbit can monitor the whole Earth. The satellite travels over all of the Earth as the planet spins beneath.

Keeping an eye on the Earth

The information is collected by the new technology of *remote sensing*. These satellites orbit the Earth across the Poles. As they do so the Earth spins underneath them. This means that in a day or so they can cover the whole Earth.

Sensors in the satellites can pick up a range of electromagnetic radiations. They measure the brightness of the radiation at different wavelengths. The data is recorded as a series of numbers. When the satellite passes over a receiving station the data is transmitted to a *ground station* in a burst of radio signals.

The most useful radiations are the visible (light) and infrared. Sometimes radar is used. Visible light is simply reflected sunlight. The infrared also contains reflected solar radiation, but some is also emitted by warm objects. Infrared is invisible, of course, but the data can be translated by computers into any colours we like. Thus we can get 'false colour' pictures showing the different kinds of infrared radiation coming from the Earth.

Plants are good at reflecting infrared, so it is easy to tell the difference between town and country, forests and desert, and even ploughed and unploughed fields.

The Landsat satellite uses the wavelength ranges shown in the diagram. Lots of images can be combined to show the whole Earth. The picture shows the parts of the Earth that are most active in photosynthesis. On the land, the green shows forests and other vegetation. In the sea the colours show the small floating plants called phytoplankton. Blue areas are low in these plants, red shows where they are plentiful.

▲
The distribution of phytoplankton in the Gulf of Mexico seen from a satellite. Red shows the highest concentration and dark blue the lowest. The streak of light blue at the top is nutrient-rich water flowing 800 km out from the Mississippi delta.

Weather satellites

Weather satellites are geostationary. Five of them are enough to cover the whole Earth. Europe's weather is monitored by *Meteosat*. It provides a new picture of a quarter of the Earth every 30 minutes. Visible light shows where clouds are; the infrared gives information about the temperatures of clouds, the sea and the land.

▼
Meteosat's view of the Earth.

Navigation satellites

The Earth is now covered by navigation satellites. These are also in geostationary orbits. They send out signals that can be picked up by ships and aircraft. A computer on board can use the data to work out where the ship or plane is, to the nearest ten metres or so. The position can be plotted on a map or chart on a computer screen. An 'automatic pilot' can use the information to set and correct a course.

Looking right through you: X-rays

X-rays are one of the most energetic types of electromagnetic radiation. They were first discovered, by accident, by the German physicist Konrad Roentgen in 1895. He was experimenting with streams of fast electrons. He was using a fluorescent plate – like the screen of a TV tube – to detect the electrons. Then he noticed that the screen glowed even when it was a long way from the electron stream. He worked out that some mysterious rays were being produced, which he called 'X-rays'. The amazing discovery was that they passed through human flesh but were absorbed by bones and metal. Roentgen could see the bones of his hand moving when he held his hand between the plate and the X-ray source.

X-rays are produced when a stream of high-speed electrons is suddenly stopped. They are given out by your TV set, for example. To get a strong beam of X-rays special tubes are used, as shown below. X-rays are used in hospitals to see broken bones, diseased parts of lungs or bits of stone or metal that people swallow.

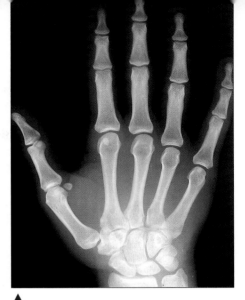

▲
X-ray pictures 'look' straight through skin and muscle.

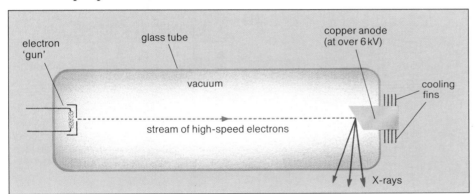

◄
An X-ray tube. Why does the anode need cooling fins?

The particle model of radiation

X-rays are dangerous. They can damage cells. To explain this properly we need to understand something extra about what electromagnetic radiation is like. It is one of the great mysteries of physics: *the radiation can behave both as waves and as particles*. The particles are called *photons*.

The higher the frequency of the radiation, the more energy each photon carries. A typical photon of X-radiation carries 5000 times as much energy as a photon of yellow light. This packet of energy is enough to badly damage or kill a living cell.

Ultraviolet radiation is less dangerous than X-rays. This has a lower frequency and so the photons carry less energy. However, they can still kill cells (think of 'sunburn') and trigger skin cancers. The most dangerous u.v. is absorbed by the ozone layer, as explained in the 'Reference section', page 216.

Gamma rays are similar to X-rays, and can have even higher frequencies and photon energies. Gamma rays are given out by changes inside the nucleus of the atom when radioactive elements decay.

The energy carried by a photon of visible light doesn't affect the skin, but is enough to trigger the specially sensitive cells in the retina of the eye. You can't see infrared radiation because it has a lower frequency than light, so its photons don't have enough energy to stimulate an eye cell. We can see things in colour because we have three types of cell, 'tuned' to the energy carried by photons of red, green and blue light.

Microwaves

The energy carried by microwaves is used in cooking. The first 'microwave ovens' were used in hospitals to sterilise surgical instruments. They work because molecules of water absorb the energy carried by the photons. As a result the molecules move about faster and the water gets hotter. Microwaves used in cookers have a frequency of about 2.45 billion hertz (2.45 GHz). The photons are absorbed in the first centimetre or so of the food. This helps the food to cook quickly (other cooking methods just heat the surface of the food).

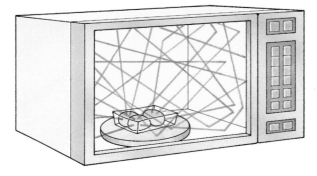

▲
Rescue workers use infrared detectors to check rubble for survivors.

◄
Microwave radiation can pass right through glass and plastic, and carry energy about 1 cm beneath the surface of the food. Water and fat molecules absorb the energy. Microwaves are reflected by metal.

Radar

Microwaves are also used in radar. In fact, the first effective radar transmitters used the microwave ovens from hospitals! Radar uses the wave properties of microwaves. It uses higher frequencies than cooker microwaves, about 10 GHz.

The signal is sent out as a short pulse of microwaves from a dish aerial. This can be reflected by a ship or an aircraft. The echo is picked up by the aerial, and the the time it takes for the pulse to make the journey there and back is measured. Microwaves travel at the speed of light, so the distance between the 'target' and the radar aerial can be worked out.

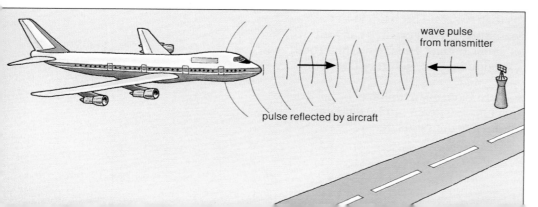

wave pulse from transmitter

pulse reflected by aircraft

◄
How radar works.

What makes electromagnetic radiation?

Electromagnetic waves (or photons!) are produced whenever a charged particle stops, starts, slows down or speeds up. In other words, when charges are accelerated or decelerated.

Radio waves are produced when electrons are made to rush up and down in an aerial. Microwaves are produced when electrons are made to go round in circles (this is equivalent to an acceleration towards the centre of the circle; see Chapter 9, *Space*).

Higher-frequency waves are produced by movements at an atomic or molecular scale. For example, light is made when an electron jumps down from one place to another inside an atom. One jump produces one photon.

Detecting electromagnetic waves

Electromagnetic waves are detected by using the same principles as described above for emitters, but in reverse. An aerial works because the electrons in it are moved up and down as the wave passes through it. The movement of electrons is an electric current, which can be amplified and dealt with by an electronic circuit.

Photography works by using molecules of a silver compound, stuck on a thin plastic film. Photons of the right energy knock electrons out of the silver, causing a simple chemical change. Chemicals called 'developers' and 'fixers' act on the changed chemicals, so that they become insoluble. The untouched chemicals can be washed away. This leaves behind just the chemicals that have been affected by light.

The eye and TV cameras work in a similar way to each other. Both contain a screen covered with tiny cells. The retina of the eye has about 130 million of them and cameras about 300 thousand (pixels). Photons make electrons move about inside special molecules inside these cells, causing other currents to flow through a 'cable'. The cable is a real cable for the TV camera, but in the eye it is the optic nerve. A modern TV camera uses a kind of microchip to detect the light. It is called a *CCD* (charge-coupled device). Photons of visible light trigger electron jumps in millions of tiny pieces of semiconductor. The electrons are collected by complicated circuitry and produce a digitised picture. A CCD chip is about 2 mm square and contains up to 2 million pixels.

▼
A detector for part of the electromagnetic spectrum!

Information and control

Most of the communication devices described in this chapter are controlled by electronics. Even as early as 1846 human beings were found to be too slow to tap out Morse code for the electric telegraph. It was quicker to use paper tape with punched holes.

Boosting a signal

In a telegraph or telephone the message is carried by an electric current. In a telegraph the signal is a series of short or long pulses of current – the dots and dashes of the Morse code. If the wire between stations is too long the current will be too weak to be detected at the receiving end.

The electromagnetic *relay* was invented to boost the signal. The wire for the weak incoming signal was connected to the coil of an electromagnet. When a pulse of current flowed it produced a magnetic field strong enough to pull an iron bar. The bar moved and switched on a battery in the next circuit. As the pulses stopped and started in the first circuit, a copy of the signal was produced in this second circuit. All this was done automatically.

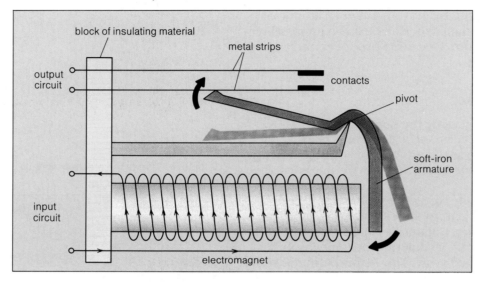

A relay. An incoming pulse energises the electromagnet, which pulls an armature to close the circuits in the output circuit. The contacts are closed as long as the pulse lasts. This means that the pulses in the output circuit are copies of the pulses in the input circuit.

▼
The complicated network of wires, switches (and people) that used to form a telephone exchange.

Boosting a telephone signal isn't so simple. An analogue signal is an alternating current. It is a copy of the sound waves made by the person speaking. The signal is boosted every time by repeater stations using *amplifiers*. These used electronic valves and, later, transistors.

One problem about telephones is making sure that you get the right telephone when you dial a number. This requires complicated switching. For many years this was done by human 'switchboard operators' at the telephone exchange, who did it all by hand, plugging wires into the right sockets. These were then replaced by automatic switching, using huge banks of several thousands relays to make the contacts.

In the last ten years or so the banks or relays have been replaced in turn by electronic switching. The microcircuits take up a tiny fraction of the space of relays, and are quicker and more reliable.

Microelectronics

Microchips are full of tiny current controllers – or switches – called transistors. These are usually arranged in sets to make *logic gates*. A logic gate is what it says: a gate that opens or closes to let a current through, or to stop it. It switches on and off according to the rules of logic.

For example, an *AND* gate has two 'doors' (or input connections). It will let a signal through only if you knock on both doors at the same time! Both *inputs* have to be high.

An *OR* gate will let you through if you knock on *either* of its two doors. A *NOT* gate has one door, and will only let you through if you *don't* knock! If you do knock it closes. Crazy, but useful.

The diagram reminds you of these gates. It also gives the *truth tables* that list the logic of the gates' actions.

logic gate	symbol	is equivalent to	truth table			the gate is 'open' when
NOT	A ▷o▷	INVERTER	input A		output Y	input A is NOT high (output is the input inverted)
			0		1	
			1		0	
OR	A, B	(inclusive) OR	A	B	Y	input A OR input B is high (or both are high)
			0	0	0	
			0	1	1	
			1	0	1	
			1	1	1	
NOR	A, B	OR-NOT	A	B	Y	neither input A NOR input B is high
			0	0	1	
			0	1	0	
			1	0	0	
			1	1	0	
AND	A, B		A	B	Y	input A AND input B are high
			0	0	0	
			0	1	0	
			1	0	0	
			1	1	1	
NAND	A, B	AND-NOT	A	B	Y	input A AND input B are NOT both high
			0	0	1	
			0	1	1	
			1	0	1	
			1	1	0	

▲ How different logic gates work.

Communication systems are now controlled by complicated combinations of logic gates, assembled in their thousands on microchips. One of the most useful combination of gates can be used to 'lock a door' to help make a memory circuit. It is called a *bistable*.

The bistable

A 'bistable' circuit can be put into two states. It stays where it is put. Something that stays where it is put is said to be stable; it is locked there. The two stable states of a bistable are *on* and *off*. A latch can be put on a door to lock it, so a bistable is often called a *latch*. The diagram shows what this means in a simple circuit, where a light is either on or off.

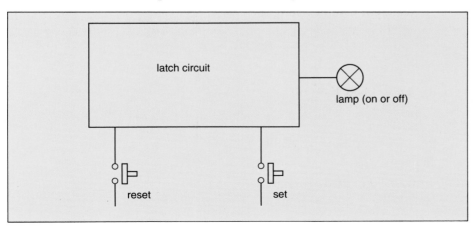

◄ A bistable has two states. The lamp stays on (or off) until the reset button is pressed.

111

Making a bistable

There are various ways of using logic gates to make a bistable. One way is to use two *NOR* gates, as shown in the diagram.

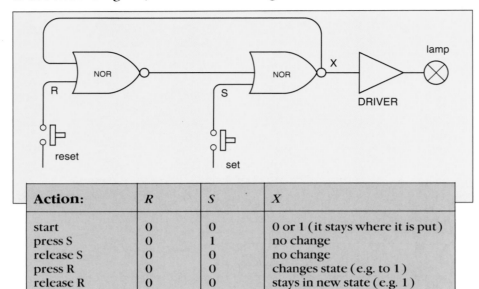

Action:	R	S	X
start	0	0	0 or 1 (it stays where it is put)
press S	0	1	no change
release S	0	0	no change
press R	0	0	changes state (e.g. to 1)
release R	0	0	stays in new state (e.g. 1)

◄
One kind of bistable is made by using two NOR gates.

The diagram on page 111 gives the truth table for a *NOR* gate. Its output is ON (or 1) only if *neither* input is ON (or 1).

In the bistable circuit (above) when both S and R are OFF, the output X stays in whatever state it happens to be in. Pressing S doesn't change anything. Pressing R puts its input ON for a short time. It goes back to OFF when you release it. When you press R, X changes from ON to OFF, or from OFF to ON. X stays as it is after each change.

Memories

A bistable can be used to store information. It can't store much, it just 'remembers' whether it is ON or OFF. It keeps on remembering it until the R switch is pressed. We can call ON and OFF the numbers 1 and 0. These are all the digits you need for a *binary code*. One binary digit is called a *bit*, so an '8-bistable stystem' can store 8 bits of memory. This is called a *byte*. A computer connects lots of bistables together to give a lot of memory: thousands of bytes.

The very first personal computer (PC) had just eight bistables in it. It was built in 1975. With 8 binary digits you can count up to 256 (2^8). Computers use an alpha-numeric system with an 'alphabet' of 256 different letters or symbols. Each one of these is a *byte* of information. So the computer had a memory of just 256 bytes.

A single microchip can have enough gates on it to make 8 million bistables. This means that a chip with 8 million bistables can store 1 million letters or bytes of data. It has one *megabyte* of memory.

Symbol	ASCII code	Binary code (8-bit)
1	1	00000001
4	4	00000100
8	8	00001000
A	65	01000001
X	88	01011000

ASCII is the code used to program symbols into computers

Binary stores

Data can be numbers, letters, points on a graph, colours, shades of light and dark and many other things. All of these can be changed into an electric voltage, by using a transducer.

The voltage can then be coded into numbers on a scale and stored in a binary memory. The scale normally used is 0–256, which will fit into an 8-bit memory system. Newer computers, and the data-handling parts of a compact disc player, may use 16-bit memory systems.

The data that you feed into a computer memory will be stored in bistables. They usually lose the information once the computer is switched off. To store it for longer you can change the data back into a pulsed voltage and use this to drive a current to make a magnetic field. The magnetism is then stored on a magnetic tape or disc. Alternatively, you can store the bits of binary code as tiny pits burned by ultraviolet light in a shiny surface. This is the principle of the compact disc. One compact disc can store 650 megabytes – roughly equivalent to 250 000 typewritten pages of A4 paper!

◀

Twenty volumes of the Oxford English Dictionary on one compact disc.

Activities

1 Look around your home. How many communication devices does your family own? (Don't count ordinary speaking.) List them under the headings:
    one-way devices (e.g. television); *two-way devices* (e.g. the telephone), and *recording devices*.
    Some items may be put into more than one list.

2 Find out on which frequencies you can receive television and radio broadcasts in your home.

3 Plan experiments to show that sound waves:
  (a) can pass through each other;
  (b) can be diffracted;
  (c) can interfere with each other.

4 Look around your home, your school and in shops to find out where mirrors are used and what they are used for. Write a short essay, or draw a poster, with the title: *the importance of mirrors*.

5 Design an experiment to show that light travels faster than sound. Do the experiment and explain what happened.

6 Borrow some Polaroid sunglasses. They are supposed to cut down glare, which is due to reflection from shiny objects. Investigate the glasses to see how they work. Find out what you can about *polarised light*.

Questions

1 What is the difference between *reflection* and *refraction*?

2 Draw diagrams to show what happens to a beam of parallel light (a) when it is reflected by a curved mirror (like the one in a torch) and (b) when it passes through a positive (convex) lens.

3 Use the wave theory of light to explain how refraction happens.

4 Give one use for each of the following types of electromagnetic radiation:
(a) X rays;
(b) infrared;
(c) ultraviolet;
(d) microwaves;
(e) UHF waves.

5 Use the formula: *wave speed = frequency × wavelength* to calculate the following. (Where necessary, take the speed of electromagnetic radiation to be 300 000 000 metres per second and the speed of sound in air to be 340 metres per second.)
(a) Find the speed of a water wave that has a wavelength of 20 metres and a frequency of 0.2 Hz.
(b) Calculate the speed of sound in iron, given that sound at a frequency of 2000 Hz produces a wavelength of 2.5 metres.
(c) What is the wavelength of a radio wave of frequency 600 kHz (600 000 Hz)?
(d) An organ pipe is 1.3 metres long. It produces a sound wave four times its own length. What is the frequency of the note it produces?
(e) Ultraviolet light has a wavelength of 4×10^{-7} metres. What is its frequency?

6 What are the differences between analogue signals and digital signals? Why are digital signals preferred for both long distance telephone messages and for recording music?

7 Explain how total internal reflection works, and why it is so important for modern information transmission.

8 'Where ignorance is bliss, 'tis folly to be wise' (Alexander Pope, 18th century poet). Explain why Guglielmo Marconi was feeling blissful in 1901.

9 A microelectronic system will use input and output devices. If they are *digital*, their logic state will be either 0 or 1, depending whether they are OFF or ON.
   The table shows the logic states of some devices. Use it to answer the questions below.

Input devices	logic 0	logic 1
light sensor	when dark	when light
dampness sensor	when dry	when damp
temperature sensor	when cold	when hot
Output devices	*logic 0*	*logic 1*
room heater	off	on
electric motor	off	on
warning buzzer	off	on
TV set	off	on

(a) What is the weather like if a temperature sensor is at logic 0 and the dampness sensor is at logic 1?
(b) The processor (decision-maker) will only switch the TV set on if the room is dark, warm and dry. (This is to keep the children active during the day and stop them catching cold.)
(i) What sensors would be used?
(ii) What logic states would they be at for the TV to work?
(iii) What other output device(s) should the processor also be able to control to do its job properly?

10 Design a system of logic gates that could be used to do the following:
(a) let you know if plants need watering on a hot day (they don't need watering on cold days);
(b) let mum know if her greedy children are raiding the refrigerator;
(c) warn a gardener if the greenhouse heating needs to be turned on at night;
(d) switch on a light over the front door if someone rings the bell at night;
(e) sounds a buzzer to let you know if the water in the hot water tank is hot. (You don't want the buzzer on *all* the time the water is hot!)

These are the facts and ideas that you should have learned by studying this topic.

To reach Basic Level you should:

- know two examples of communication systems
- know the important differences between sound and light
- know how to reflect light and sound
- be able to use mirrors to solve problems or make a model
- know that we can use the following in communication: light, radio, infrared, microwaves
- know one use of Earth satellites (e.g. weather forecasting, communications, mapping)

To succeed at Foundation Level you should:

- know how we can use sound and electromagnetic waves in communications and in other applications
- understand how useful the reflection of light is for seeing things and when using plane and curved mirrors
- understand how useful the refraction of light is in optical fibres and lenses
- know the main types of electromagnetic waves, and that they all travel at the same, very high speed in air or a vacuum
- know that sound travels much more slowly than light
- know how switches, relays, sensors and logic gates can be used to solve problems
- know that Earth satellites are used to give us useful information (i.e. weather pictures) and in communication (TV satellites)

To succeed at Merit Level you should:

- know the basic plan of a communication system
- know what happens to rays of light when they are refracted, and be able to explain refraction using the wave model of light
- know the uses of the main parts of the electromagnetic spectrum, and be able to place them in order
- be able to recognise logic gates connected to make a bistable, and know what the bistable can do and be used for
- know the main uses of Earth satellites

To succeed at Special Level you should:

- know that modern communication systems will also contain some coding and decoding devices
- know the differences between, and the uses of, analogue and digital signals and instruments
- be able to explain total internal reflection and other optical effects dependent upon refraction
- know how the following devices work: optical fibres; lenses used to make images in cameras, the eye and projectors
- be able to relate the physical properties of the main areas of the electromagnetic spectrum to their uses and effects
- be able to explain what happens when electromagnetic waves show interference, diffraction and polarisation
- be able to recognise feedback in a system and describe its effect
- understand the social and economic significance of using Earth satellites

CHAPTER SEVEN

EXCLUSIVE!

CHEMICAL INDUSTRIES RUINED

Government bans all chemical industry activity

Mounting pressure from voters worried by the safety of operations of the new chemical industry have forced the new Government to close down the entire operation.

'We are not here to discuss balanced arguments,' a Government official stated and assured the public that they would now be able to feel safe from accidental spillages from container lorries and pollution into rivers and the atmosphere.

The official added that the public would not be inconvenienced in any way, only feel healthier and more 'natural'.

Memo number 1
The Government regrets the closure of all public swimming baths.

Chlorine is now unavailable for disinfecting purposes.

Memo number 2
The Government regrets that no more paint can be manufactured. New treatments for bicycles, cars and home decoration are to be investigated.

Memo number 3
The Government regrets that the sufferers of headaches and indigestion will no longer find relief. It also regrets the loss of all High Street pharmacists.

Memo number 4
The Government denies responsibility for the closure of all hospitals and the cancellation of all operations. It assures the public that alternatives to disinfectants, anaesthetics and other necessary pharmaceuticals should soon be found.

Memo number 5
The Government assures the public that they will soon get used to uncoloured cotton garments and plain-wool carpets again and that colour photography will not be missed.

It also regrets that no plastic material of any kind will ever be made again but assures the public that the safety and efficiency of the electrical supply will be maintained.

Car interiors, cassette tapes, compact discs, computers and many household goods will either be made from other materials, as they used to be, or they will not be missed.

Memo number 6
The Government regrets that bread is to be rationed. The wheat supply has fallen dramatically due to cuts in fertiliser production and the lack of pesticides.

Memo number 7
The Government is fully aware that many people are now without a job following the closures. It also regrets that this large industry has had to go. This, said a spokesperson, 'is a price well worth paying considering what is at stake.'

ICI produces 1 million litres of paint every week.

The U.K. chemical industry produced £9000 million worth of pharmaceuticals in 1990.

The U.K. industry produced £1364 million worth of dyes and pigments in 1990.

In 1990, world usage of plastics was 350 million cubic metres.

Total U.K. production of fertilisers in 1990 was worth £546 million.

- The chemical industry is Britain's 4th largest manufacturing industry.
- It is industry's number 1 export earner – £13.2 billion in 1990.
- It employs 300 000 people.

Raw materials

All of the goods that we take for granted, clothes, carpets, fridges, washing machines, bottles, bags, records and books, are *manufactured*. All of these goods are made from a few basic chemicals.

We get these chemicals by processing basic raw materials. The raw materials used in manufacturing processes are: *rocks*, *oil*, *air*, *sea*, *plants* and *animals*.

These different raw materials are used in many ways by a huge chemical industry. Rocks are quarried, trees chopped down (and hopefully others put in their place); wells are sunk deep into the Earth. Even air is used as a raw material. It can be liquefied and separated into its component gases.

Processing the raw materials

Many raw materials were formed million of years ago as part of geological processes. The materials have to be extracted from the ground and then changed to make the best use of them. This is usually done by chemical processing. It is like making a meal from raw food, but raw materials are processed on a huge scale. The 'cooking' is done by the tonne in 'pots and pans' that are larger than the average house. But the basic processes are the same: heating, stirring, dissolving, waiting for reactions to happen; evaporating and condensing.

The basic chemicals produced then have to be treated even further to produce the building blocks of useful products. At each stage the materials have 'value added' and are sold at a higher price than at the stage before. For instance, crude oil can be changed to naphtha which is eventually made into plastics for making washing up bowls.

What does the chemical industry do?

The chemical industry is the fourth-largest industry in Britain.
The first three are:

- food, drink and tobacco;
- mechanical engineering;
- electrical engineering.

The chemical industry manufactures a wide range of products, from fertilisers to plastics to printing inks.

washing-up liquid bottles £1800 per tonne

polythene £500 per tonne

ethene £300 per tonne

naphtha £100 per tonne

▲
Chemical processes have to produce something that is more valuable than the raw materials. The finished product is worth much more than the chemicals that it is made from.

◀
The chemical industry divided up by annual sales figures.

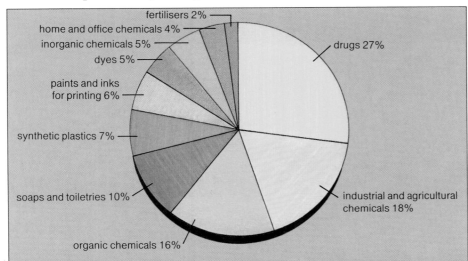

fertilisers 2%
home and office chemicals 4%
inorganic chemicals 5%
dyes 5%
paints and inks for printing 6%
synthetic plastics 7%
soaps and toiletries 10%
organic chemicals 16%
industrial and agricultural chemicals 18%
drugs 27%

The bigger chemical companies extract the raw materials and convert them into a few *basic chemicals*. A great deal of money is needed to buy machinery and to build plants to do this. This is called *capital investment*. So only the largest companies are able to convert the chemicals on a large scale; only they are able to transport the raw materials to the central locations where the work is done efficiently on a large scale.

The major source of raw material for the chemical industry today is oil. It used to be coal and may, one day, change again. Perhaps you can think of a reason why. The problem with using either coal or oil is that they take millions of years to create. They are *finite* resources.

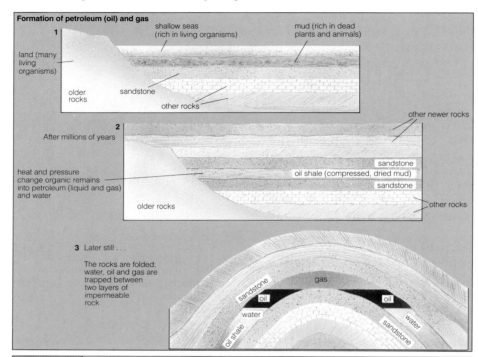

◄
The formation of oil and gas.

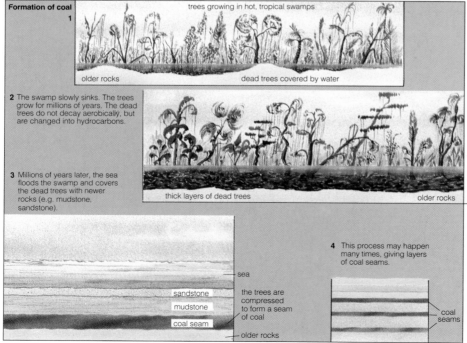

◄
The formation of coal.

Refining oil

Look at the map and notice where the oil refineries are located.

Perhaps you can suggest why the refineries are situated there. Think about the effects that large industrial developments have had on areas like these. What do you think happens to employment prospects, transport links, housing, schools, hospitals and shops when big industrial plants are built in an area? And what about the countryside, the river systems, and the air that people breathe?

Separating crude oil

Crude oil is a mixture of hydrocarbons, with some dissolved impurities. Hydrocarbons are compounds of hydrogen and carbon, made from the remains of the living materials that went into making the oil.

The different hydrocarbons in crude oil are separated by fractional distillation. The oil is heated and different compounds boil off at different temperatures. The 'lighter' compounds boil away first, and the crude oil is separated into its fractions. The crude oil is heated by super-heated steam at the bottom of the column. The different compounds are drawn off at different levels. The boiling points are determined by how big the molecules are in each fraction.

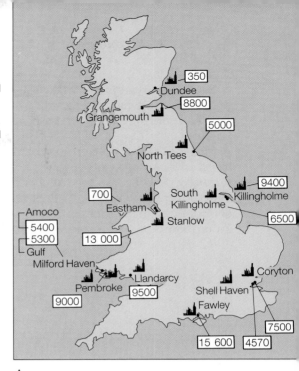

▲ Where the main oil refineries are in England and Wales, and their annual capacities (1990), in thousands of tonnes.

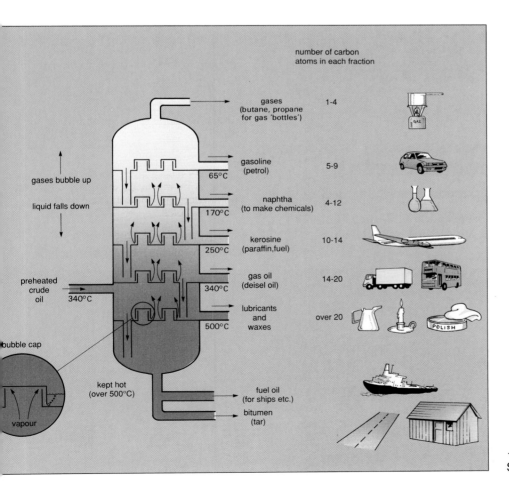

◀ Separating the fractions in crude oil.

119

Each carbon atom can make four bonds with other atoms, and each hydrogen atom can make a single bond. This means that the simplest structures formed between carbon and hydrogen are those in the figure (right).

Most of the fractions from the distillation are used as they are, for fuels, lubricants and waxes. The key fraction for making new chemicals is *naphtha*. This is a mixture of chemicals, essentially the same ones that are in gasoline and kerosine. As these are not all needed for fuel, it is economic to make them into new substances. Naphtha makes up about 20% of crude oil. Most of the hydrocarbon molecules in naphtha have 4–12 carbon atoms.

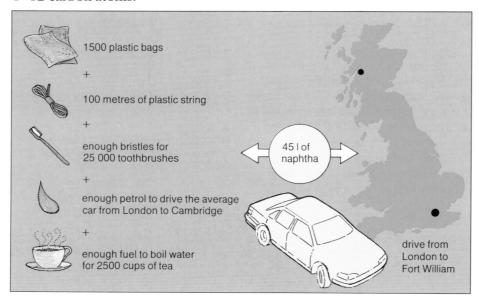

1500 plastic bags
+
100 metres of plastic string
+
enough bristles for 25 000 toothbrushes
+
enough petrol to drive the average car from London to Cambridge
+
enough fuel to boil water for 2500 cups of tea

45 l of naphtha

drive from London to Fort William

▲
What you can get out of a chemical depends on how you use it.

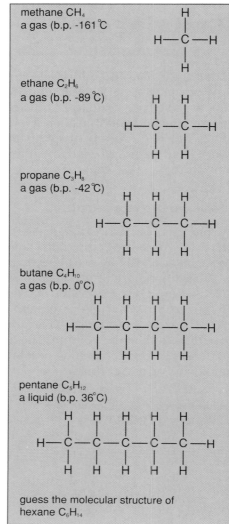

methane CH₄
a gas (b.p. -161 °C)

ethane C₂H₆
a gas (b.p. -89 °C)

propane C₃H₈
a gas (b.p. -42 °C)

butane C₄H₁₀
a gas (b.p. 0°C)

pentane C₅H₁₂
a liquid (b.p. 36°C)

guess the molecular structure of hexane C₆H₁₄

▲
The common organic molecules in crude oil. These are mostly alkanes. The diagram does not show the actual shapes of the molecules.

▼
Some of the alkane molecules in naphtha.

Making molecules more useful

The simple hydrocarbons in the fractions of crude oil form a family of chemicals, called the *alkanes*. They are built from hydrogen atoms attached to a back-bone of carbon atoms.

To make these molecules more useful, they have to be broken apart. This is called *cracking*. The process needs high temperatures and pressures, and a catalyst to speed up the reactions. This is called *catalytic cracking*.

'crack'

butane → ethane + ethene
(an alkane)   (an alkene)

C_4H_{10} → C_2H_6 + C_2H_4

◄
Making ethene in a 'cat-cracker'.

The most useful chemical produced by the cracker is *ethene*. The diagram shows how a long hydrocarbon molecule is split up to make ethene. The process actually produces many different small molecules, but ethene is the smallest and it evaporates easily. It is collected by fractional distillation.

Ethene is a member of another family of hydrocarbons, the *alkenes*. In ethane, each of the carbon atom's four bonds joins to a different atom. In ethene, however, the carbon atoms are joined by two of the bonds, not one. This is called a *double bond*.

The double bond between the carbon atoms is almost exactly twice as strong as a single bond. But even so, the alkenes are very reactive molecules. This is because once the double bond *is* broken open, the other bonds link eagerly with other atoms. Ethene breaks up when its molecules are squashed together at a temperature of about 200 °C. The pressure has to be 2000-times normal air pressure!

Ethene is one of the six 'building-block' chemicals that are made on a large scale. Two others are also alkenes. The other three are carbon ring structures called *aromatics*.

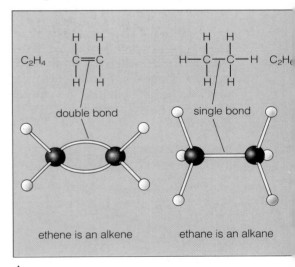

▲
The difference between ethene and ethane.

Combinations

Petrochemicals are mostly made from six building blocks:

- ethene;
- propene;
- butadiene;
- benzene;
- toluene (methylbenzene);
- xylene (1,3-dimethylbenzene).

One or more of the building blocks may be combined with other chemicals. There are four of these:

- oxygen (O_2);
- water (H_2O);
- chlorine (Cl_2);
- ammonia (NH_2).

These building-block chemicals are rarely sold directly to the public. They are sold on to other chemical companies that make them into more everyday chemicals. These smaller companies usually specialise in certain types of chemicals and make products which are sold directly to the consumer.

These products may be made in very small quantities but have tremendous added value, for example *medicines* and *pesticides*. Some may be manufactured in large quantities but have lower added value, for example *plastics*.

Plastics

In 1938, an ICI chemical plant was suffering from clogged pipes. Pipes for carrying ethene were filling with a white, gooey mess. The conditions in the pipe had broken the double bonds in the ethene molecules, and because there was nothing else to react with the molecules had joined together in long chains. The plant had accidentally produced what is now one of the most useful materials to be made from ethene–polyethene, or polythene.

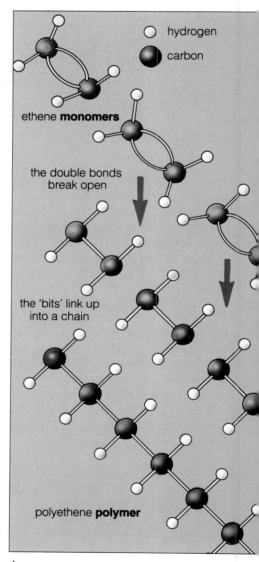

Making polythene from ethene. The reaction needs a low temperature and pressure, and a catalyst. The ethene molecules join up in chains about 10 000 molecules long.

◄

What we can make from ethene.

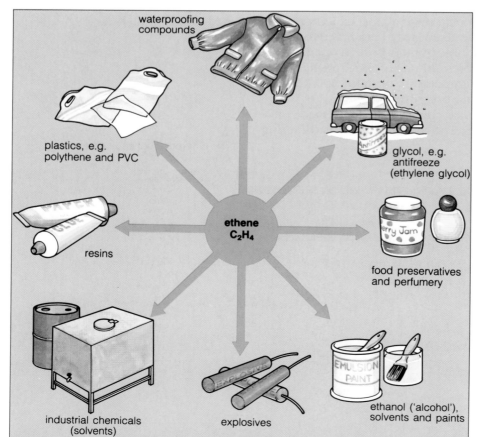

Plastics are made of these long-chain molecules. They usually begin as an alkene. So, we can think of polythene as a long chain of ethene molecules. Each link in the chain is called a *monomer*. A long chain of monomers is called a *polymer*. The reaction is simply breaking open the double bond and adding molecules to a bond that already exists, hence it is called *addition polymerisation*.

More plastics – addition polymerisation

Ethene can also be converted into alkanes. These can be made into other plastics. They are all addition polymers like polyethene – adding to the double bond.

Polymer	Plastic of fibre	Monomer		Examples of uses
Polyethene	plastic	ethene	$\begin{array}{c} H \\ \\ H \end{array} C = C \begin{array}{c} H \\ \\ H \end{array}$	plastic bags, squeezy bottles, washing up bowls
Polypropene	plastic, fibre	propene	$\begin{array}{c} CH_3 \\ \\ H \end{array} C = C \begin{array}{c} H \\ \\ H \end{array}$	milk-bottle crates, carpet, plastic rope
Polystyrene	plastic	styrene	$\begin{array}{c} C_6H_5 \\ \\ H \end{array} C = C \begin{array}{c} H \\ \\ H \end{array}$	plastic toys, expanded polystyrene for insulation
Polyvinyl chloride (PVC)	plastic	vinyl chloride (chloroethene)	$\begin{array}{c} Cl \\ \\ H \end{array} C = C \begin{array}{c} H \\ \\ H \end{array}$	guttering and pipes, electrical insulation, floor covering
Acrylic fibre	fibre	acrylonitrile (cyanoethene)	$\begin{array}{c} CN \\ \\ H \end{array} C = C \begin{array}{c} H \\ \\ H \end{array}$	fibre for clothing

Even more plastics – condensation polymerisation

Plastics can also be made from monomers by using a different chemical process. Instead of molecules being added at the double bond, the two molecules join and lose bits of themselves. Usually, they lose hydrogen and oxygen atoms in the form of water. The process is called *condensation polymerisation*, as water is condensed out.

▼
Making polymers by taking bits away: condensation polymers.

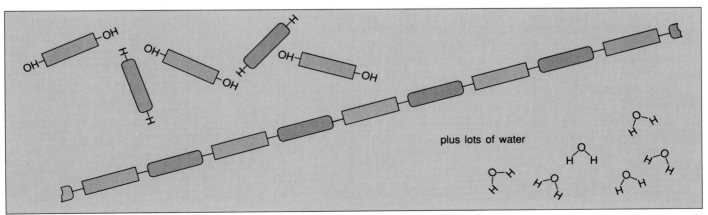

plus lots of water

Nylon and polyester are manufactured in this way, but it is also the method by which natural polymers are made. Starch is a natural polymer made from monomers of glucose. Plants carry out the polymerisation without high temperatures and pressures – they use an enzyme catalyst.

Wood fibres and most plant and animal proteins are natural polymers. They can be incredibly strong. Muscle fibres and tendons are some of the strongest. The first plastics were made from plants. Celluloid and Rayon were made from the plant polymer, cellulose. Rubber is another example of a natural polymer.

Making fibres

To make polymer into a fibre the chains have to be lined up. This is done by drawing the molten plastics through a lot of very fine holes. Fibres are strong along the direction of the polymer chains, but they can be pulled apart 'across the grain'.

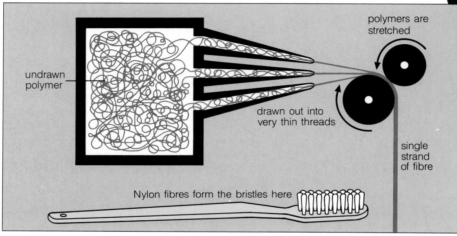

- undrawn polymer
- polymers are stretched
- drawn out into very thin threads
- single strand of fibre
- Nylon fibres form the bristles here

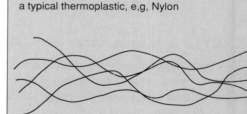

▲ Making nylon in a school laboratory.

◀ Drawing a nylon polymer.

Making plastics stiff — cross-polymerisation

Polythene, nylon and Terylene are examples of plastics that can be made as textile fibres. They are strong and hard wearing, but they are flexible. Also, they melt quite easily. This makes them useful because they can be moulded into different shapes. The snag is that they are not very stiff, and are easily damaged by heat. They are sometimes called *thermoplastics*.

Sometimes we need plastics that are stiff and do not melt when they are heated. These are called *thermosetting plastics*. You will find them in car fittings, electrical plugs, many toys, the cases of computers, TV sets, etc.

The different behaviour of these plastics is decided by their internal structure. The long-chain molecules of a thermoplastic are intertwined but quite separate. The polymer chains can slide across each other, or straighten out. The material is flexible and stretchy.

But in thermosetting plastics, atoms from one chain have linked with atoms in other chains. This linking is called *cross-polymerisation*. It stops the molecules moving so easily, and the material is stiffer and resistant to melting. Instead, it chars or burns.

▶ The differences between molecules in a thermoplastic and a thermosetting plastic.

a typical thermoplastic, e.g, Nylon

a typical thermosetting plastic, e.g. melamine

the cross links make the plastic stiffer, and give it a higher melting point

Ethanol

Ethanol is another basic chemical made from ethene. It is used in all kinds of industries and is also converted into other chemicals. You have heard of it by another name – alcohol.

Industrial alcohol (ethanol) is made by adding water to ethene. But the water has to be added as super-heated steam at high pressure – remember the strength of that double bond.

Ethene + water → ethanol,
$$CH_2=CH_2 + H_2O$$
$$→ C_2H_5OH.$$

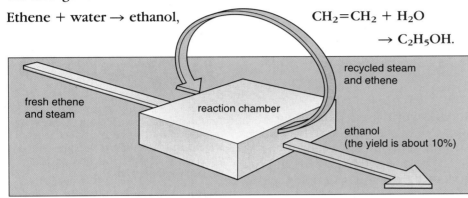

◄ Making ethanol from ethene.

The reaction is carried out in a large, steel pressure vessel. It is done continuously, with fresh ethene and water injected at one end and the ethanol coming out at the other. But, as with most chemical reactions like this, not all of the ethene is changed at one go. So the material is *recycled* through the reaction chamber. A catalyst boosts the rate, but not the yield. Only about 10% of the ethene is converted at each pass through the reaction chamber. This is called the *yield*. The ethanol is taken out after each pass, and the unreacted material put back through to join fresh material added.

The chemical industry needs to make a profit. It has to arrange a process so that neither chemicals nor energy are wasted, and the process doesn't take too long. It is sometimes cheaper to have a small yield and a lot of recyling.

Biotechnology

Biotechnology is the use of living things to make useful chemicals.

Microbes can make ethanol

Yeasts feed on sugars. As waste products the yeasts produce carbon dioxide and ethanol. These 'wastes' are the basis of the brewing and baking industries. The process is called *fermentation*. (See Chapter 4, *Controlling chemical reactions*.)

Ethanol is important as an industrial chemical. Most of it is made by the petrochemical industry. By the middle of the twenty-first century most of the world's known oil reserves will be used up. Can we use plants to make the basic chemicals that we now get from crude oil?

Chemicals from plants

The largest experiment in getting raw materials from plants took place in Brazil in the 1980s. Brazil is a tropical country and grows a lot of sugar cane. When the sugar is extracted a lot of waste pulp is left behind.

The sugary pulp was fed to yeasts and they made many tonnes of ethanol. Mixed with petrol it made a good fuel for cars, and became known as 'Gasohol'. Unfortunately, the price of crude oil fell and the ethanol was more expensive than the petrol.

However, using *biomass* as a raw material is still worth thinking about. Biomass is mostly plants – trees, bushes, crop wastes or plants specially bred for a particular purpose. Some industrial oils are now made from plants instead of crude oil. Biomass can be used to make fuel and other basic feedstocks for the chemical industry. The main advantage is that biomass is renewable.

Degradable plastics

Plastics are very useful materials; in 1990 the world used 350 million cubic metres of them. Unfortunately, plastics last too long, and this causes pollution problems. Waste plastics stay in the soil for many years. In the countryside, they are a hazard to wildlife. Plastic bags trap animals and can poison them. Plastic waste is not nice to look at in woods and fields, and on beaches.

Scientists wanted to make plastics that would rot away just like dead plant materials do. They mixed polyethylene with small amounts of starch. The starch was attacked by soil microbes and so the plastic fell apart, leaving a plastic dust. But the plastic has not really degraded – it is still there, but in smaller pieces.

The first truely biodegradable plastic is *Biopol*. It is made from glucose by a strain of bacteria. Bacteria found in sewage works and compost heaps can break down the polymer chains of Biopol. The plastic can therefore be recycled naturally.

▲
An American Gasohol pump. Corn syrup is fermented with yeast to produce alcohol, which is then purified. It can be blended with petrol or the pure alcohol used in specially adapted cars.

▲
Bottles made from Biopol in various states of decay.

Minerals as raw materials

The useful materials found in rocks are called *minerals*. Most of these are compounds of metals. These charts show the most common elements found in the Earth's crust and the elements most used.

By comparing the charts you can see that some of the most useful and important metals seem to be very rare. Many rocks may contain copper, or even gold, but this will only be as tiny traces. It is far too expensive to get the metals out of such rocks.

A rock containing a metallic mineral is called an ore. Mining companies have to decide whether or not it is economic to work a 'low-grade ore'. Gold is an expensive metal, not necessarily because it is so useful, but because it is rare and does not corrode. Gold is usually found as the 'native metal' – it isn't combined chemically with other elements. This makes it easier to extract. It is worth mining, even if there is very little in the rock.

Copper ore is worth mining if there is only 0.08% in the rock, but this amount is too low for direct chemical extraction. The basic ore first has to be *processed* to increase the concentration of the metal.

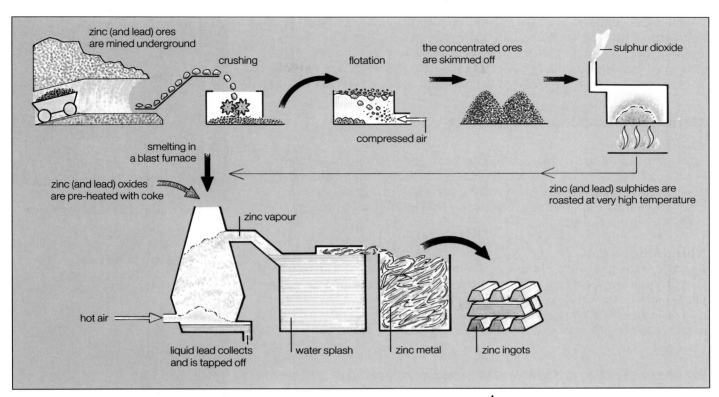

The ores of zinc and lead are usually found together. The rock containing the ore is quarried and crushed. The material is then put in water and high-pressure air blown through it. The ore attracts air bubbles and is carried to the surface. Here, it is scraped off as the *concentrate*.

▲
Zinc and lead are extracted in the same process.

◄
What do we get out of the Earth's crust? (Figures are in millions of tonnes per year.)

▼
What is in the Earth's crust?

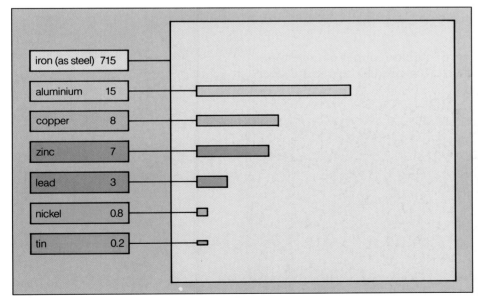

iron (as steel)	715
aluminium	15
copper	8
zinc	7
lead	3
nickel	0.8
tin	0.2

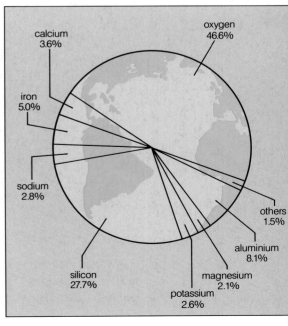

Chemical concentration

Another natural chemical process relies on rain being slightly acidic. This dissolves certain minerals in rocks. It does this over a wide area, and then can concentrate the metal as a different compound. The most important mineral formed this way is iron ore.

The most common ore of iron is called *haematite*. Most of the haematite found on Earth was laid down in warm shallow seas over 600 million years ago. It is an oxide of iron (Fe_2O_3). Iron compounds were dissolved out of even older rocks and carried to the warm sea. As these seas slowly evaporated the iron was deposited as large beds of iron oxide.

Natural chemical reactions

China clay
Most of the high-quality plates, cups and saucers in Britain have been made from china clay. This started off as granite, deep underground. Hot gases from deep inside the Earth were forced up through the granite, changing it into a soft mineral, *kaolinite*. This is quarried by using high-pressure water jets.

Aluminium
Bauxite is the ore of aluminium. It is mostly impure aluminium oxide. Bauxite was formed when warm tropical rains attacked soils rich in clay. Clay is mostly various types of aluminium silicate. The warm water took away ('leached') chemicals from the soil, leaving the bauxite behind. It is much easier to get aluminium out of bauxite than out of clay.

▲ Nodules of haematite are kidney-shaped.

▼ A kaolinite quarry in Cornwall.

Minerals from living things

Living things have produced minerals. Chalk and some forms of limestone were formed from the shells of countless millions of sea creatures.

The limestone industry

Limestone is the basis of a huge industry: 65 million tonnes of limestone are used a year in the construction industry. It is used to help make steel in blast furnaces and to make glass.

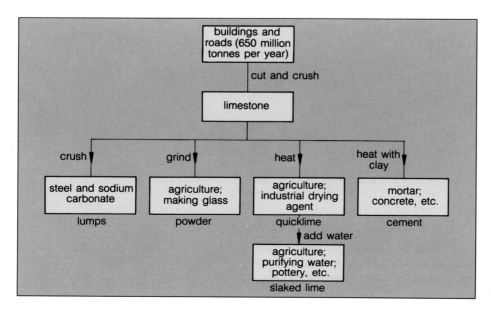

◄ The uses of limestone.

Limestone and chalk are mostly calcium carbonate. When limestone is heated it changes to *quicklime*, calcium oxide:

calcium carbonate $\rightarrow$ calcium oxide + carbon dioxide,
$$CaCO_3 \rightarrow CaO + CO_2.$$

Quicklime is used in agriculture as a quick way of making soil less acid. It is also used in industry to dry air and other gases. It attracts water, making *slaked lime* or calcium hydroxide when it does so:

calcium oxide + water $\rightarrow$ calcium hydroxide,
$$CaO + H_2O \rightarrow Ca(OH)_2.$$

You have probably used a dilute solution of calcium hydroxide as a test for carbon dioxide. The solution is known as lime water. This reacts with carbon dioxide to make solid calcium carbonate again. This doesn't dissolve in water so you get a 'milky' precipitate:

calcium hydroxide + carbon dioxide $\rightarrow$ calcium carbonate + water,
$$Ca(OH)_2 + CO_2 \rightarrow CaCO_3 + H_2O.$$

This reaction is also the basis of the cement industry. A good-quality limestone is heated with clay to make cement. The result is a mixture of quicklime with a clay 'filler' to give it body. This is mixed with water and the slaked lime now reacts with carbon dioxide in the air to make a strong, solid artificial rock. Adding aggregate (pebbles and sand) makes concrete.

Most upland areas in Britain contain limestone. These are often areas of beautiful scenery. There is a great demand for limestone and this causes environmental problems. People don't like having such places spoiled by industrial wastes, gaping holes in the hills and the extra traffic on quiet country roads.

▲
Quicklime being added to an acidic lake in Sweden, to increase the pH of the water so that plants and fish can survive.

Chemicals from the sea

The sea is salty, and most of the 'salt' in it is the chemical that you can put on your food. Its chemical name is sodium chloride, and you may be surprised to learn that it is basic raw material of a whole industry – the chlor–alkali chemical industry.

◄
Salt lagoons in Thailand. As the water evaporates, the salt crystals are raked into piles.

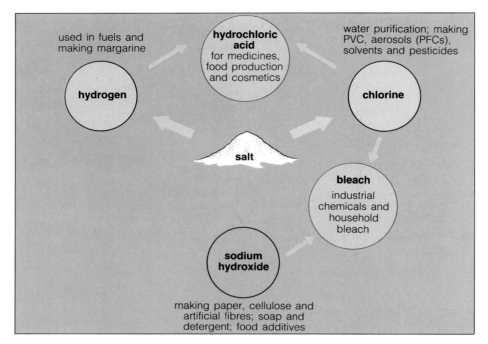

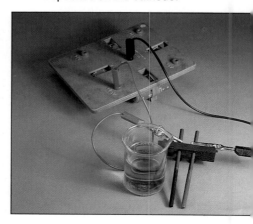

◄ What we can make with salt: the chlor-alkali industry.

Sea salt is produced in countries where the sun shines a lot. The table salt we use, like the salt used in industry, comes from salt mines. There are salt mines in Cheshire, Siberia, Germany and many other parts of the world. The Cheshire salt beds are the remains of warm tropical sea that evaporated away about 200 million years ago.

Salt dissolves easily in water, and the salt is extracted by pumping water down to the salt beds and then pumping it back up as a strong solution of salt, called *brine*.

Sodium chloride is an ionic compound. When salt dissolves in water, the positive ions of sodium and the negative chloride ions are released:

$$Na^+Cl^-_{(s)} \rightarrow Na^+_{(aq)} + Cl^-_{(aq)}.$$

This means that we can pass electricity through a solution of sodium chloride to produce more useful chemicals. This process is called *electrolysis*.

The electrolysis of brine

▼ A solution of copper sulphate that has been electrolysed. You can see the copper metal deposited on the cathode.

In electrolysis, two metal plates called *electrodes* are put into the solution. One is kept positive and is called the *anode*. The negative plate is the *cathode*. Positive ions are attracted to the cathode and negative ions go to the anode.

When we electrolyse brine, chloride ions go to the anode and chlorine gas bubbles off.

At the cathode things aren't so simple. When a solution of copper sulphate is electrolysed, the copper is plated onto the cathode. But sodium is a very reactive element and cannot be simply plated this way. Instead, hydrogen gas bubbles off. The salt solution changes to an alkaline solution of sodium hydroxide (a strong alkali). This is why it is called the chlor–alkali industry.

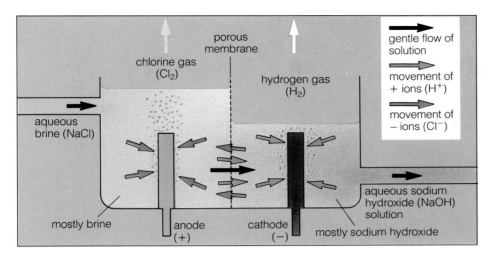

The electrolysis of brine in a membrane cell.

The net result of some complicated chemistry is:

sodium chloride$_{(aq)}$ + water$_{(1)}$ → sodium hydroxide$_{(aq)}$ + chlorine$_{(g)}$ + hydrogen$_{(g)}$,

(aq, solution in water; l, liquid; g, gas)

$$2NaCl_{(aq)} + 2H_2O_{(1)} \rightarrow 2NaOH_{(aq)} + Cl_{2(g)} + H_{2(g)}.$$

Hydrogen is not very valuable. But the process gets £125 worth of sodium hydroxide and £90 worth of chlorine from £25 worth of salt. (Of course, the industry has to pay for the energy and running of the plant.)

Hydrogen can be combined with chlorine to make hydrochloric acid. This is very useful in industry. Hydrogen is also used to turn edible oils into solid margarine.

Chlorine is a poisonous gas. It kills germs and is used to purify drinking water and to keep swimming pools free of germs. It is also used to make plastics (e.g. PVC – polyvinylchloride), solvents, in fire extinguishers and pesticides (PFCs).

Combined with sodium hydroxide, chlorine makes household bleach and other kinds of cleaning chemicals used in industry. Sodium hydroxide is a strong alkali. It is used to help make paper and other artificial fibres. It is the basic chemical used in soaps and detergents.

Chlorine is a very reactive non-metal. It belongs to a group of elements called the halogens. There is more about these in Chapter 5 of GCSE book 1, *Chemical patterns*.

The nuts and bolts of chemistry

There are 2 000 000 grains of sugar in a bag! But you would never go into your local store and ask for this number of grains, you ask for a kilogram bag. It is easier to measure.

If you bought a kilogram bag of nuts and bolts instead, you would get the same *mass* of these as the sugar. But would you get as many nuts and bolts as grains of sugar? Of course not. Because each individual grain of sugar is much lighter than a nut and bolt.

If we now separated the nuts from the bolts, and put them into two bags, the bag of bolts would be heavier. But even though the bag of nuts is lighter, each nut would match up with each bolt. There would be the same number of each.

Working out how much we need to start with

But what would happen if we measured out 1 kg of bolts and 1 kg of the smaller nuts? When we paired them up, we would match all of the bolts to a nut, but we would have some nuts left over. We would have wasted our money! The leftover nuts are useless on their own.

We face the same problem in chemistry. Let's compare 'bags' of sulphur atoms with 'bags' of iron atoms. We would get many more sulphur atoms in a kilogram bag of sulphur than we would get iron atoms in a kilogram of iron. This is because an atom of sulphur is lighter than an atom of iron. If we reacted the iron with the sulphur, each atom of iron would 'join' with an atom of sulphur, but some sulphur would be left over. This is wasteful. We need some method of making sure that when a collision takes place between molecules and a reaction happens, that we have the right number of 'particles' to match up.

Matching the masses

We tackle this problem by using the idea of *relative masses*. A sulphur atom is 32 times as heavy as a hydrogen atom, which has a relative mass of 1. So we say that sulphur has a relative mass of 32. The relative mass of the atoms of each element is given in the periodic table on page 239.

HYDROGEN
1

SULPHUR
32

IRON
56

◀ Relative atomic masses.

Hydrogen is the lightest atom, so let's say that a certain number of hydrogen atoms has a mass of 1 g. The same number of sulphur atoms has a mass 32 times as much, so they have a mass of 32 g.

From a data book of the periodic table, you would see that the same number of iron atoms would have a mass of 56 g. This number of atoms is a special number called the *Avogadro number*. (Perhaps you could find out why.) This number is very large: 6.0×10^{23}.

Nowadays all elements are compared to ^{12}C, which is said to have a relative mass of exactly 12.0. The Avogadro number is the number of *atoms* in 12 g of pure ^{12}C. This huge number is also called a *mole*.

Relative molecular masses

We can work out the relative mass of a *molecule* by adding up the relative masses of the atoms in it. So iron sulphide (FeS) has a relative molecular mass of 88.

A collection of 6×10^{23} molecules of iron sulphide has a mass that is the sum of the two types of atom in it:

56 g for iron and 32 g for sulphur, totalling 88 g:

$$Fe + S \rightarrow FeS,$$

$$56 g + 32 g \rightarrow 88 g.$$

If we started with 56 g of iron and enough sulphur, we should get 88 g of iron sulphide. If we put more than 32 g of sulphur with the iron, the *excess* sulphur will not be combined.

Real-life calculations

In practice, we might find it hard to get *all* the iron atoms to meet and react with all of the sulphur atoms (the chemical industry deals with many tonnes of chemicals in a single reaction vessel). But we can still use our method of calculating masses to predict the *expected* yield of product. This tells us how much we should finish with, given the amounts that we started with.

In real reactions, we never get as much as we predict. Some product is lost, or the starting materials do not all react. The amount we get is the *actual yield*. It is not usually as much as the *theoretical yield*.

$$\text{Percentage yield} = \frac{\text{actual yield}}{\text{theoretical yield}} \times 100\%.$$

In industrial reactions, chemists work hard to get the right conditions to give the best possible percentage yield. They have to solve a lot of problems to do this, using the skills of chemical engineers.

Making sulphuric acid

Sulphuric acid (H_2SO_4) is one of the most important 'feedstocks' of the chemical industry. It is used in the manufacture of many other chemicals, from fertilisers to plastics.

Sulphuric acid is made from air, water and sulphur. Sulphur is, in fact, a waste product from the oil industry. Most crude oil is contaminated with unwanted sulphur.

Sulphuric acid is made in three main steps.

1 Sulphur is burned in air to make sulphur dioxide:

sulphur + oxygen → sulphur dioxide,
$$S + O_2 \rightarrow SO_2$$

2 The sulphur dioxide is heated to 450 °C in air, with a vanadium (V) oxide V_2O_5 catalyst, to make sulphur trioxide:

sulphur dioxide + oxygen → sulphur trioxide,
$$2SO_2 + O_2 \rightarrow 2SO_3.$$

3 The sulphur trioxide reacts with water to make sulphuric acid:

sulphur trioxide + water → sulphuric acid,
$$SO_3 + H_2O \rightarrow H_2SO_4.$$

This reaction is done in two smaller steps because the reaction is almost explosive if you did it all at once. Some sulphuric acid is needed there to start with:

first, $SO_3 + H_2SO_4 \rightarrow H_2S_2O_7$ (disulphuric acid),

then, $H_2S_2O_7 + H_2O \rightarrow 2H_2SO_4$ (sulphuric acid).

The sulphuric acid acts as its own catalyst!
A flow chart of the processes would look like this:

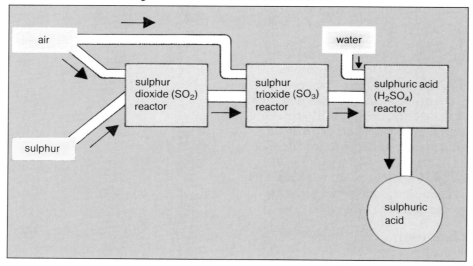

As explained above, the important question that has to be answered about a chemical process is: *how much does it yield?* In other words: what mass (weight) of product can the reaction make from a certain mass of the raw materials?

The engineers try to work this out in advance from the chemical formulae. Sometimes this is easy to do – sometimes quite hard.

We start by making sulphur dioxide, burning sulphur in air. The word equation is simply:

sulphur + oxygen → sulphur dioxide.

The formula equation is:

$S + O_2 \rightarrow SO_2$.

We are going to calculate how much sulphur dioxide we produce if we burn a certain mass of sulphur. This is the first stage in the process of making sulphuric acid.

The chemical *formula* tells us how many atoms of each element are in a molecule (or particle) or the different substances.

The periodic table gives the *relative atomic mass* (RAM) of each element.

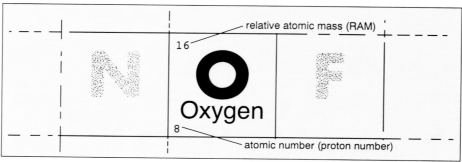

The data for oxygen taken from its entry in the periodic table.

The relative atomic masses given in the periodic table begin with hydrogen (RAM of 1); the oxygen atom is 16 times heavier than the hydrogen atom, so has an RAM of 16.

The process equation tells us that we need one atom of sulphur for every two atoms of oxygen: S – one atom of sulphur (RAM 32) = 32 units; O_2 – two atoms of oxygen (RAM 16) = 32 units.

So, 32 units (of mass) of sulphur combine with 32 units (of mass) of oxygen. These are added together, so the mass of sulphur dioxide produced is 32 + 32 = 64 units. We could have worked this out directly from the formula for sulphur dioxide, of course:

SO_2 is 1 sulphur atom (32 units) and 2 oxygen atoms (16 units each).

We have worked out the 'relative formula mass' of each formula (for sulphur, oxygen and sulphur dioxide).

The 'units' are whatever we measure the mass in. If we burn 32 tonnes of sulphur we will produce 64 tonnes of sulphur dioxide. If we burn 32 milligrams of sulphur it makes 64 milligrams of sulphur dioxide.

Balancing the equations

In effect, to make sulphuric acid, we add oxygen to sulphur, then add water. So we have:

oxygen + sulphur → sulphur dioxide,

sulphur dioxide + water → sulphuric acid.

The overall equation for the production of sulphuric acid has to 'balance'. This means that we can't get more atoms out than we put in. We can't get something for nothing – and we can't lose anything. The number of sulphur atoms on the left of the equals sign has to equal the number of sulphur atoms on the right of it. The same applies to all the other kinds of atom. The balancing can be shown as:

$3O_2 + 2S + 2H_2O \rightarrow 2H_2SO_4$.

Remember:
- O_2 means '2 atoms of oxygen';
- S means '1 atom of sulphur';
- H_2O means '2 atoms of hydrogen, 1 of oxygen';
- H_2SO_4 means '2 atoms of hydrogen, 1 atom of sulphur and 4 of oxygen'.

As described above, this is a multi-stage reaction, and this balanced equation is really a 'book-keeping' equation, so that we get the sums right. Check the equation to see that the number of each kind of atom is the same on both sides. There should be:
- 2 atoms of sulphur (each of RAM 32);
- 4 atoms of hydrogen (each of RAM 1);
- 8 atoms of oxygen (each of RAM 16).

The formula for sulphuric acid (H_2SO_4) tells us that we should have a product mass of:

H_2	2 units (2 times 1);
S	32 units (1 times 32);
O_4	64 units (4 times 16);
total, H_2SO_4	98 units.

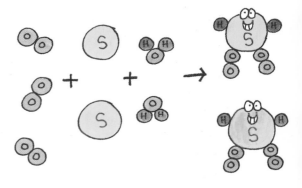

▲
You need to balance equations so that they make sense.

Yield

The equation for the process tells us that we get 'two lots' of sulphuric acid. The yield (what we get) is 2×98, that is 196 units.

This needs an input of:

- 3 molecules of oxygen, $3O_2$, giving $3 \times 32 = 96$ units;
- 2 atoms of sulphur, $2S$, giving $2 \times 32 = 64$ units;
- 2 molecules of water, $2H_2O$, giving $2 \times (2 + 16) = 36$ units.

This lot should add up to 196 as well – or we've lost or found some extra atoms!

In a school laboratory experiment, it might be enough to make 19.6 grams of sulphuric acid. In this case we'd need:

- 9.6 grams of oxygen;
- 6.4 grams of sulphur;
- 3.6 grams of water,

a total of 19.6 grams of raw materials.

If you want to make some enormous quantity like 25 000 tonnes of sulphuric acid, you just have to scale-up these figures accordingly.

Percentage yield

But all of these figures are assuming that everything goes perfectly. In real life there may be wastage. There is also the annoying chemical fact that a reaction doesn't usually 'go all the way'. This means that some of the raw materials don't actually react, or that some of the product breaks up and changes back again to the raw materials. This means that the actual yield is only a fraction of the theoretical yield, say 80%. This is such a common effect that most chemical plants recycle the materials through the reaction vessels to give the raw materials 'another go' at reacting. The design has to allow for many 'passes' through the vessels.

These extra 'passes' cost more money, and so chemical economics is all about balancing the yield with the cost, to produce something more valuable than what you started with, and make a profit.

Activities

1 Find out if there are any chemical industries in your locality.
- What products do they make?
- What basic chemicals are used?
- Where do they get their basic chemicals from?
- What raw material is it derived from?

2 Find out what the nine biggest chemical companies in the U.K. produce, and where they operate. They are:

ICI	Ciba-Geigy	Exxon
BP chemicals	Shell chemicals	Boots
Glaxo	Unilever	Procter & Gamble

3 Collect some paper clips and use them to make a model that explains what a polymer is. Your model should form part of a poster. Use the model to show the differences between an ordinary polymer and a cross-linked polymer.

4 Collect a selection of different packaging materials. Design a series of investigations to test the properties of these materials. First, decide what *kind* of materials they all are. Then plan some simple tests. You could try:
- strength
- 'tearability'
- is the material biodegradable?

Get your plans checked by your teacher. Write a report, including a table of your results, saying why the materials could cause environmental problems.

5 Use any sources of information that you can find to present balanced arguments for and against *one* of the following:
- 'Oil is too valuable to be used as a fuel.'
- 'All raw materials are too cheap because we don't count any environmental costs.'
- 'Artificial fertilisers should be banned. All our food should be produced organically.'

Questions

1 Look up and write down the formulae for the following chemical compounds:
(a) ammonia, (b) sodium hydroxide, (c) hydrochloric acid, (d) calcium carbonate, (e) sulphuric acid, (f) calcium oxide and (g) calcium hydroxide.

2 Write balanced equations for the following reactions. You can look up any formulae you don't know in the 'Reference section' (page 238):
(a) zinc + oxygen → zinc oxide;

(b) carbon + oxygen → carbon dioxide;

(c) calcium carbonate $\xrightarrow{\text{heat}}$ calcium oxide + carbon dioxide;

(d) nitrogen + hydrogen → ammonia;

(e) sodium chloride + water $\xrightarrow{\text{electrolysis}}$ sodium hydroxide + chlorine + hydrogen.

3 Choose any pure metal and describe how it can be obtained from its ore.

4 Explain how crude oil can be separated into its different components by using fractional distillation.

5 The following table gives the boiling points and formulae of different components of crude oil. They are all alkanes.

Compound	Boiling point (in kelvin)
methane CH_4	112
ethane C_2H_6	185
propane C_3H_8	231
butane C_4H_{10}	273
pentane C_5H_{12}	309

(a) Plot a graph of boiling point against the number of carbon atoms in each compound.
(b) Is there any pattern relating boiling point and the number of carbon atoms in a compound?
(c) Another alkane, hexane, has the formula C_6H_{14}. Use your graph to estimate its boiling point. If you can, check your answer with the actual boiling point (which you will find in a book of tables). Comment on the comparison.

6 (a) Instead of plotting boiling points against the number of carbon atoms, draw a graph of boiling points against the relative molecular mass (RMM) of the compounds. You can work this out by taking the relative mass of hydrogen to be 1 and that of carbon to be 12. Thus the RMM of methane is 16 (C + 4H = 12 + 4). Then answer the same questions from question 5.
(b) Does this plot give a more reliable pattern?
(c) Use your knowledge of the kinetic theory of matter to explain why you would expect liquids with more massive particles to boil at a higher temperature.

7 How does electrolysis work? Explain what happens when you plate a metal with copper using copper sulphate. Use the following key words: *electrode, anode, cathode, ion, electrolyte, positive, negative*.

8 What are the differences between thermoplastics and thermosetting plastics? How do their structures cause these differences?

9 Explain how polymers may be made into fibres. What are the structural differences that cause the difference between a bulk sample of nylon and a nylon fibre?

10 The biggest oil companies operating in Britain are Shell UK, Esso, Texaco, and BP Oil. The two biggest oil refineries are located at
• Fawley in Hampshire (Esso) with a production capacity of 15 600 thousand tonnes, and;
• Stanlow in Cheshire (Shell) with a production capacity of 13 000 thousand tonnes.
Find them on the map of Britain in the chapter (page 119). Why do you think they are located there?
Draw a bar chart showing the relative production capacities of the major oil refineries in Britain.

11 When copper carbonate is heated, black copper oxide and carbon dioxide are formed:
$CuCO_3 \rightarrow CuO + CO_2$.
• What is the relative molecular mass of copper carbonate?
• What is the relative molecular mass of copper oxide?
• How many tonnes of copper oxide should be formed from 62 tonnes of copper carbonate?
• During the process only 30 tonnes of copper oxide were formed, what was the percentage yield of copper oxide?

12 Chemical companies want to get the highest percentage yield when they produce chemicals. But percentage yield may change with a change in temperature or with a change in pressure. Construct a graph using the table below, for a reaction which was followed at different temperatures, but keeping the pressure constant.

Temperature (°C)	0	100	200	300	400	500
Percentage yield	82	54	34	22	14	8

• Which temperature must you operate at to get a 60% yield?
• If the plant operated at 250 °C what would be the percentage yield?

Checklist

These are the facts and ideas that you should have learned by studying this topic.

To reach Basic Level you should:

- know some useful things that are made from chemical factories (plastics, medicines, pure metals)
- know where we get the raw materials to make useful chemicals (i.e. oil from the ground to make plastics, ores from rocks to make metals)
- know that we can change and purify chemicals using electricity
- be able to give three things that must be paid for when making new chemicals (e.g. raw materials, wages, transport, energy, plant)
- be able to recognise bad as well as good effects of making chemicals on a large scale

To succeed at Foundation Level you should:

- know that solutions and metals conduct electricity because they contain charged particles and that chemical changes can occur when this happens in solutions
- be able to calculate the formula mass of a substance
- know that chemical reactions can change raw materials into new, useful products and understand the idea of 'yield'
- know that the more raw materials you start with the bigger the yield – but you might not get all you expected
- know the main factors that decide the cost of making a new material
- know that recycling can reduce the cost of a product

To succeed at Merit Level you should:

- know what happens in electrolysis and how electrolysis is used in metal extraction
- be able to describe and explain the chemical changes involved in some important manufacturing processes (production of aluminium, copper, chlorine, ethene and sodium hydroxide)
- be able to make up simple word equations for reactions
- be able to calculate percentage yield
- know that some chemical processes are reversible and how pressure, temperature and concentration affect the equilibrium state

To succeed at Special Level you should:

- be able to use symbolic equations to describe and explain a range of reactions including ionic reactions and electrolysis
- be able to interpret chemical equations quantitatively, i.e. in calculating yield, making equations balance, in electrolysis
- be able to use scientific information from a range of sources to evaluate the social, health and safety, economic and environmental effects of a major manufacturing process
- be able to work out formulae for compounds, given experimental or other data

CHAPTER EIGHT

Managing the Earth

THE DAILY GLOOM

FRIDAY 13 AUGUST 2010

Will even more trawlers be forced out of business in the future?

Famine spreads

The Sahara desert is growing. The rains have failed again in Burkina Faso and severe famine is predicted.

Do you remember the devastating famine in Ethiopia that led to Band Aid and Comic Relief?

Now the tragedy is about to strike another African country, still further west.

Oxfam say that massive amounts of aid are needed to avoid huge loss of life; the cycle of malnutrition and disease will continue until the rains return on a regular basis, but this may never happen.

Against all the odds, the size of herds of grazing animals in Burkina Faso has increased in recent years. Grass and bushes are removed by overgrazing and the soil is eroded.

Villagers stripping the flesh from a tiger.

Fishing port closes
Haddock have had it!

Hull, once the largest fishing port on the east coast of England, has seen the last catches landed there.

The decline in North Sea fishing began over 20 years ago when consumer demand led to huge catches being made. Many countries fished the waters after talks on European Community fish quotas collapsed in the mid 1990s.

Experts maintained that fish stocks could only be maintained if only the adult fish were caught, and even then, not during the breeding season. This advice was ignored. Nets with mesh small enough to catch even the youngest fish were used with the result that stocks have fallen. Shoals of fish are now so difficult to find that the business is no longer economic.

Many other countries bordering the North Sea are experiencing the same problems and other major fishing ports are expected to close soon.

The hunters are hunted

The last refuge of the Royal Bengal Tiger, the Sunderbans National Park in Bangladesh, is slowly being poisoned by sea water as ocean levels rise. The tigers have begun to range beyond the park boundary. They are threatening the local villages and many are being hunted and killed as a result.

The World Wide Fund for Nature has warned that if the killing continues, there will be no tigers left in five years' time. Already, breeding success has been reduced by human disturbance and by the tigers not being able to find enough food.

Elephants safe

The African elephant survey has presented its latest report. This was set up to study the decline of the African elephant due to ivory poaching. The elephant was close to extinction because of this illegal trade.

The report shows a further increase in elephant numbers within the national parks. A senior biologist with the project said, 'The elephants are now safe and future looks brighter. We hope to reintroduce the animals to parts of Africa where they haven't been seen for 20 years.'

DAILY HOPE

SATURDAY 14 AUGUST 2010

▲ Reforestation project in Brazil.

▲ African elephants are social animals.

UN appoints rain forest chief

Daniel Agoons has been given overall control of 20 rain-forest conservation projects around the world. These include the massive Brazilian undertaking that has all but halted logging in the central Brazilian rain forest. Dr Agoons said of his appointment: 'There is a lot to be done, and I intend to be the one who gets things moving.'

▼ The small mesh of this trawler net even catches very small animals and fish that are too young to have bred.

Acid rain falls

For the fifth year in succession, the World Acid Rain Project has reported a fall in sulphur dioxide concentrations in the air over central Europe. Forest regeneration has taken hold.

New trees are being planted in vast numbers and there have been reports of older trees actually recovering and sending out new shoots. A spokeswoman for the German Ministry of Environment has said that their policies have helped to lead Europe into the clean air.

The introduction of 'scrubbers' to all European power stations began the decline in acid-rain levels. The modifications were expensive but carried out after mounting pressure from environmental groups.

The spokeswoman said that consumers had accepted the large increase in electricity costs despite some initial hardship. The need for economy with energy has led to improvement in house design through the latter half of the 1990s. Today we take for granted that all homes have solar heating for water.

Even the building trade has accepted rules making it illegal to build a house without proper insulation.

▲ Monitoring levels of sulphur dioxide in air near a smelting plant in Botswana.

Herring catch up

North sea herring fishers have had another excellent season. Fish stocks have again shown an increase on the previous year. This is thought to be due to a combination of factors. These include new net sizes, rigidly applied quotas with fixed prices and a halt to fishing during the breeding season.

The new nets will only catch adult fish. The smaller ones escape through the large mesh. The 'closed' breeding season has also encouraged a rapid recovery of stocks.

Why does the Earth need managing?

Magazines, newspapers and television keep telling us about the bad things that are happening to the Earth. There are worries about the climate, the plants and animals that are dying out, the pollution that affects all life, including human life. But you will also read of governments, industrial firms and many other groups of people trying to make the world a better place to live in.

Is there a crisis? What has happened in the past twenty or thirty years to cause these problems? Are the problems really serious? How can science help us to look after the environment?

Before we can begin to answer these questions we have to know something about:

- the key ideas of *ecology*;
- the Earth as an *ecosystem*;
- how the activities of *human beings* affect the ecosystems in which we live.

The most important thing that we have to recognise is that we are part of the Earth's ecosystem. *We are not on the outside looking in.*

Ecology

You have already studied the ecology of a field, a wood, a stream or a pond. You have learned that the plants and animals living there affect each other.

Some animals prey on each other. Owls eat mice, small birds and voles. Small birds eat insects and worms. Some animals compete against each other for the same food. Owls and hawks, snakes and weasels all like to eat mice. Voles compete with birds for seeds and fruit. Plants compete for chemicals in the soil and light.

Some animals work together directly. Ants will feed on some kinds of insects (aphids) and milk them for the sugary fluid they produce. Some help each other indirectly. For example, worms live on the remains of dead plants and animals. As they dig through the soil they improve it, so that plants find it easier to grow. The many animals that live by eating plants are helped by this. In turn their droppings return chemicals to the soil, manuring it for the plants, and providing food for worms.

◀
Ants 'milking' aphids.

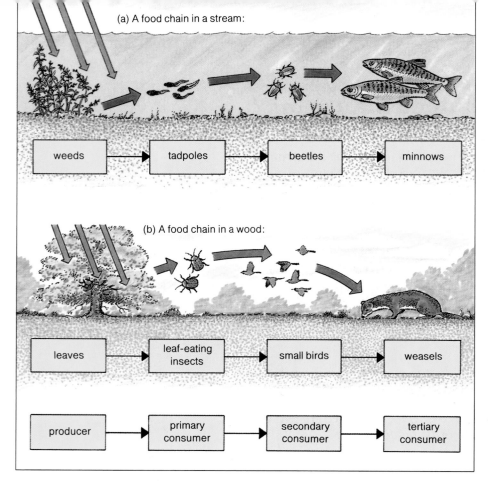

(a) A food chain in a stream:

| weeds | → | tadpoles | → | beetles | → | minnows |

(b) A food chain in a wood:

| leaves | → | leaf-eating insects | → | small birds | → | weasels |

| producer | → | primary consumer | → | secondary consumer | → | tertiary consumer |

◄ Sample food chains.

The diagram shows a simple *food chain* for both a wood and a small stream. It shows us that even the animals that don't eat plants rely on them to feed the animals that they do eat. All life on Earth depends on plants because they are starting points of the food chain.

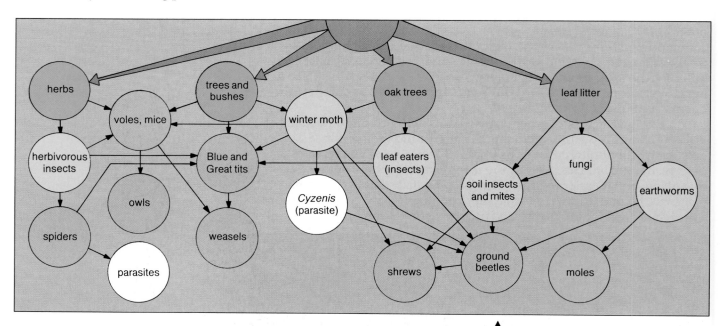

But what really happens is a lot more complicated. This is just a part of the *food web* for a wood. It shows how the organisms in a wood are linked in the way that they get and provide food. Each living thing has a role to play. The key roles are:

▲ Food web for an English oak wood. The decomposers have been omitted.

- *producers*: the green plants that can use the energy of sunlight to make food from water and the gas carbon dioxide;
- *consumers*: animals that either eat plants or eat other animals that eat plants (some animals do both – like us);
- *decomposers*: bacteria and fungi that live off the dead remains of plants and animals, turning these into soil nutrients, especially the nitrates essential for plant growth.

Flows and pyramids

Ecologists show the main features of ecosystems using *flow diagrams* and *pyramid diagrams*.

▼
A pyramid of biomass for a small wood.

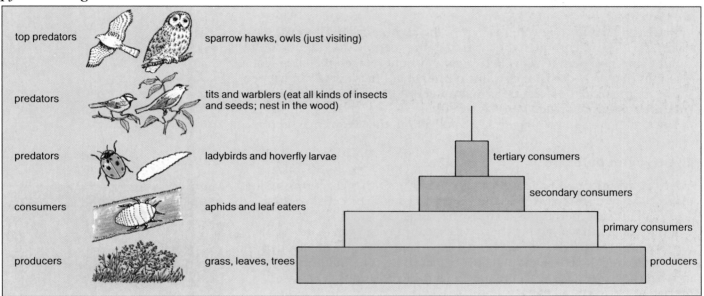

top predators	sparrow hawks, owls (just visiting)	
predators	tits and warblers (eat all kinds of insects and seeds; nest in the wood)	tertiary consumers
predators	ladybirds and hoverfly larvae	secondary consumers
consumers	aphids and leaf eaters	primary consumers
producers	grass, leaves, trees	producers

The whole-Earth system

The energy balance

Every day the Earth receives 15 thousand terajoules of energy from the Sun (1.5×10^{22} joules). Most of it is reflected by clouds, or radiated back again by the warm sea and the land. On average, year by year, the Earth loses as much energy as it gets from the Sun. This means that the Earth shouldn't get hotter and hotter (or colder and colder).

The plants of the Earth trap a very tiny fraction of this solar energy. They need some to keep alive. Plants have to pump water and grow; their cells need energy. Plants also store energy in wood, seeds, leaves and fruit. On average, plants store about 0.02% of the total yearly supply of solar energy.

Grazing animals will mostly eat just the leaves, so can get only about a tenth of the energy stored in a typical plant. The result is that all of the animals of the Earth make do with just two thousandths of one percent of the energy that arrives from the Sun! And all they do is 'borrow' it for the time that they are alive. (See the diagram on page 215 in the 'Reference section'.)

Cycles

Energy isn't the only thing that living things just borrow. This also happens with the chemicals of life, living things are made almost entirely of proteins and carbohydrates. Proteins are very complicated chemicals made of smaller 'bits' called the amino acids. In turn these are made largely from the elements oxygen, hydrogen, carbon and nitrogen. They all contain the combinations COOH and NH_2. There are 23 important amino acids. They are made by plants, but on the whole they can't be made by animals. Animals need to eat plants or other animals.

When animals die and aren't eaten, by worms or vultures, say, the decomposers get to work. The nitrogen from their protein ends up as soil *nitrates*. These are then re-used by plants. All this is the main part of the *nitrogen cycle*.

Similarly, carbon is recycled as part of the *carbon cycle*. This cycle makes great use of carbon in the form of the gas carbon dioxide.

But plants also help to recycle *oxygen*. Without oxygen the chemical reactions that provide the energy for most living things could not happen. These are the oxidation reactions that power *respiration* in living cells. They are sometimes called *aerobic* reactions.

The cycles are shown on pages 218 and 219 in the 'Reference section'.

The oxygen balance

Some organisms can do without oxygen. They use other reactions, called anaerobic reactions, to provide the energy to keep their cells working. Yeast can use this method, as do many bacteria.

When the Earth was young there was hardly any oxygen in its atmosphere. The Earth's atmosphere was a mainly mixture of nitrogen and carbon dioxide. It is thought that 'life' began about 3000 million years ago, and that the earliest forms of life used anaerobic reactions to release energy. At this time, all life was in the sea, in the form of very simple single-celled organisms.

But then some of these tiny organisms began to use light energy from the Sun. They used it to make an energy store – starch. Starch is made from water and carbon dioxide with the aid of the green chemical *chlorophyll*, which 'traps' the energy from sunlight. Oxygen was the 'waste' product from this reaction:

$$\text{carbon dioxide} + \text{water} \xrightarrow{\text{light}} \text{starch} + \text{oxygen}.$$

The starch was a handy 'building brick' for the plant bodies. It could be used to make strong fibres – the first polymers – and it became easier for larger, many-celled organisms to exist. The *green plants* could grow strong enough to survive on land. They no longer needed to be supported by water to counteract the force of gravity.

The atmosphere becomes rich in oxygen

It took over 2000 million years for the oxygen 'waste' to build up in the atmosphere. As it did so a completely new kind of life could evolve: the animals. Animals are much more active than plants. They need to get energy quickly. They do this by combining oxygen with chemicals from the bodies of plants or other animals.

About 400 million years ago there was a 'plant explosion' as green plants spread rapidly over the land. This raised the oxygen content of the air to its present level.

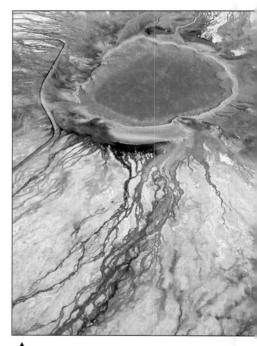

▲
Grand Prismatic Pool, Yellowstone Park, U.S.A. The deep blue–green is caused by algae that grow on the chemical nutrients in the spring water. At the edges are colours caused by anaerobic bacteria that feed on sulphur. These were some of the first forms of life on Earth.

Patterns of life

The main ecosystems of the world are decided by two simple things: *climate* and the pattern of *sea and land*.

Climate

Climate is the day-to-day pattern of weather measured over many years. Roughly speaking, climate is decided by how far a place is from the equator. Places near the equator get much more energy from the Sun than places near the North and South Poles. But winds and ocean currents carry energy north and south from the equator.

The main climate zones of the Earth are shown on the map. As a rule the lands near the equator are covered with thick *equatorial rain forests*. Next to these we often find regions of mainly *grassland*. Further out again and we find drier lands that we call *deserts*.

These zones are determined by the circulation of hot air rising from the tropics. The air carries water vapour, picked up from the sea and the millions of forest trees. But as the vapour rises, it cools, condenses and falls as heavy rain to help keep the forests wet. The grasslands get some of this water at certain times of the year. Grasslands are too dry for many trees, but there is enough water for the grass. Further away from the equator the air is even drier, and we find deserts.

Eventually the equatorial air comes down to ground level again. It is still warmer than the air it now meets. Cold air seeps away from the North and South Poles. The warm air will pick up water vapour from the sea. As it battles against cold air it causes jet streams and the westerly winds that blow around the world at around 40° from the equator. These 'Westerlies' and the water that they carry create the cooler *temperate* wet lands where trees can grow so well. These are the cool forests that covered a lot of Northern Europe and North America for millions of years, before the arrival of human beings.

▲
Tropical rainforest, Papua New Guinea.

▼
Savannah grassland supports a large amount of wildlife. (Tsavo National Park, Kenya.)

◄
Desert vegetation, Namibia. 'Desert' doesn't just mean miles of sand!

▼
Temperate forest, like this in Hungary, once covered all of Northern Europe.

▼
Natural pine forest. Pine trees can grow further north than other tree species.

◀
There are no trees in tundra landscapes. Here, all of the vegetation is very low-lying.

▼
The climate in Arctic Greenland does not allow any plant life to survive.

Moving closer to the Poles, the air becomes drier and colder. There is less sunshine. It is still a good climate for trees, especially *conifers*. These trees do not shed their leaves in winter. They can stand cold weather. The leaves are thin and needle-shaped to cut down water loss.

Eventually it gets too cold and dry even for these trees. Only shrubs and grasses survive in this cold semi-desert called *tundra*.

Land and sea

Climate zones are affected by the pattern of sea and land. The tropical seas soak up energy from the Sun, and warm-water currents flow away from the equator. You should know about the *Gulf Stream*, which carries warm water from the Gulf of Mexico across the North Atlantic and helps to keep Britain warm (and wet) through the winter.

This water has to get back to the tropics, which it does as a current of water – now cold – which flows down the coast of North Africa as the Canary Current.

▼
The major ocean currents in the Atlantic. The fastest-moving water is shown red. You can see the Gulf Stream very clearly.

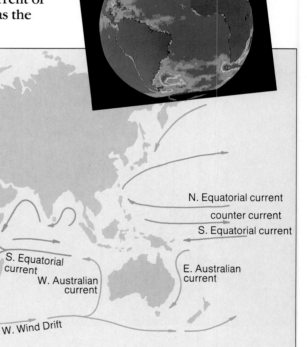

Labrador current
North Atlantic Drift
Gulf Stream
Canary current
N. Equatorial current
N. Equatorial current
counter current
S. Equatorial current
N. Equatorial current
counter current
S. Equatorial current
Guinea current
S. Equatorial current
Brazil current
S. Equatorial current
W. Australian current
E. Australian current
W. Wind Drift
W. Wind Drift
W. Wind Drift

▲
The world's main ocean currents.

These currents cause some parts of the land to be warmer than they otherwise would be, and other parts to be cooler.

Parts of the continents far from the sea may be warm, and have plenty of sunshine. But they will have less rain. Trees find it hard to grow. But grass can survive, so we have the prairies of North America, the pampas of South America, and the grasslands of Ukraine.

Three important ecosystems

In the past 100 000 years or so people have spread around the world and now live on every continent and in every climate zone. People have become an important part of the ecosystems of all these regions, which have become *managed ecosystems*.

We shall look at just three of these main ecosystems: grassland, tropical rain forests and the sea.

Ecosystem 1: the grasslands

The first recognisably human-type creatures emerged in the tropical grasslands of Africa. They walked upright (perhaps to see better over the tall grass, or perhaps to keep cooler). They ate anything: seeds, fruit, insects, birds, small animals. They were also scavengers, eating the remains of large animals killed by the giant cats like lions. They were small and weak, but intelligent. The oldest fossils of these creatures are about 3 million years old. Everything we know about these people has been learned from these fossil remains.

Hunters

As time went on the human beings became good hunters. They learned how to trap large animals like deer and elephants. They developed stone tools for cutting and digging. By this time, over a million years ago, people were hunting animals not just in Africa but also in China, southeast Asia and northern Europe.

◄
Cave painting from the late Stone Age in Swaziland. An ox, deer and bison are shown, with tribal 'healers' in a trance-like state.

Later, people learned how to tame the grazing animals instead of just hunting them. When the great Ice Ages came, they learned to find shelter in caves. In Europe the hunters followed the migrating reindeer as they moved north in summer and south in winter.

Farmers

But in the Middle East people were changing their habits and altering the behaviour of wild goats and sheep as well: they trained and bred the animals to become quiet grazing flocks. Wild dogs were tamed to help control the flocks.

So human beings were mainly creatures of the grasslands. They lived on the animals that lived by eating grass. The next revolution was to live off the grass itself. People did this by discovering how to grow grasses that gave lots of food in the form of *seeds*. They bred better and better seed-grasses, like barley, millet, wheat and rice. They became farmers.

This meant that they had to stay in one place, waiting for the crop to grow. They built villages, towns and, eventually, cities. This happened first about 10 000 years ago.

Since then, the history of people on Earth has been about changing forests into grassland. Eating grass seeds is a very efficient way of getting energy. The world lives on bread and rice.

The discovery of iron about 3000 years ago allowed farmers to cut down forests more easily, and to plough heavier, wetter soils. In 500 B.C. England was covered in forest. It is now mostly grassland. The same change has happened to much of Europe, Asia and North America.

The ecology of a natural grassland is quite simple.

▼
A simple food web for a tropical grassland.

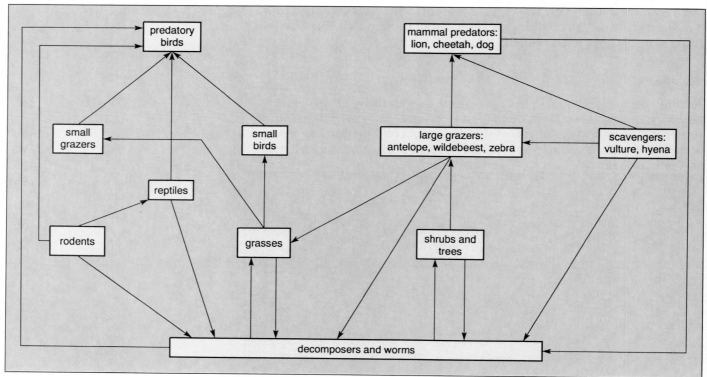

Grass is *adapted* to being grazed. It grows very quickly in a warm, wet spring (faster than the grass-eating herbivores can eat it). Eating the parts above ground does the grass no harm. If it is able to make seed, all well and good. If not, it can reproduce itself vegetatively, by runners that creep along or just under the ground. Its main competitor would be shrubby bushes, which would keep the light away. But the animals that eat grass are also happy to eat young bushes. And bushes can't survive this experience as well as grass can.

The animals produce plenty of droppings from the grass they eat. This is recycled by the grass and soil bacteria in the nitrogen cycle. The grassland animals don't live for ever, and their dead bodies are also recycled. The grassland animals – both herbivores and carnivores – live off the grass and also help it to survive. Grasslands are very efficient: a square kilometre of grass can support 18 tonnes of animal life.

The human impact

But when human beings take over a grassland ecosystem they change it. First of all, they get rid of the predators. The herbivores are 'farmed'; this means that *we* become the top predators. The wastes of the herbivores may not return to the soil. Also, the 'grass' is improved by breeding so that it makes bigger and better grain seeds. We either eat these seeds or feed them to meat and dairy cattle. Again, the wastes may not be recycled properly.

The main part of the grass plant is also waste. If the straw from the plants is burned the valuable soil nutrients vanish in smoke.

Fertilisers

But the soil has to be kept productive. This is done by using 'artificial fertilisers' made from phosphate rocks and the nitrogen in the air. The energy to make the fertilisers comes from the dead remains of tropical plants and animals that died 300 million years ago – fossil fuels.

Modern farmed grasslands are so efficient that they produce too much food! In Europe in 1992 farmers were being paid to let some grassland go to waste. It is cheaper to do this than pay the costs of storing the surplus grain or milk.

But there may be other costs that we have yet to pay. The artificial fertilisers wash out of the soil easily. The nitrates build up in rivers, seas and even in the underground stores of water that people drink. The nitrates in the drinking water are harmful to young children; in hot summers the lakes and streams grow a poisonous 'bloom' of algae.

Disappearing grasslands

The huge natural grasslands of North America – the *prairies* – produce more grain per head of population than anywhere else in the world. But they are no longer natural. They are no longer places were buffaloes and native Indians roam. They are ploughed every year. If the rains are late, the soil dries out and turns to dust. They are windy places, and the dust blows away. It has been calculated that the prairies lose 5 billion tonnes of soil a year. Even in Britain, the fens of East Anglia are losing soil.

▲ Grass is very productive: 1 km² can support 18 tonnes of animal life.

▼
Algal growth makes it to the newspapers!

Algae 'bloom' threat to Australia's Darling

From Robert Milliken in Sydney

OUTBACK Australia is facing an environmental disaster from drought

could penetrate the giant Murray River which supplies water to 16 urban

Ecosystem 2: the tropical rain forests

The ecology of rain forests is very complicated. They contain the biggest variety of plants and animals of any place on Earth. Every year biologists discover new species of plants or insects. It was the rich life of the Amazonian rain forest that started Charles Darwin thinking about the origin of species and led to his theory of evolution (see Chapter 5, *The living inheritance*).

Energy enters the ecosystem via the *tree canopy*. A 'canopy' is a sheet of leaves. The trees are up to 30 metres tall. Underneath this are smaller, thinner trees fighting their way to the sunlight. There may be large areas of even taller trees, up to 50 metres tall.

The layer of leaves in the tree canopy is thick and shuts out most of the sunlight, trapping it for the energy it carries. Monkeys, birds and insects live off the leaves and fruit.

The ground is covered by smaller plants that need less light, such as ferns and fungi. Fungi can also get energy from the decaying leaves that fall from the tall trees. But the lack of light means that the forest is usually very open and easy to walk through. Some plants save energy by not having to grow strong stems. They are the jungle creepers that twine around tree trunks to lift themselves up to the sunlight.

The only areas open to the sun are the rivers. Even here plants will cover the surface where the current isn't too strong. It is likely that flowering plants first appeared on Earth in tropical forests. They evolved to attract the insects that helped to pollinate the flowers.

Plants and insects have evolved together in this ecosystem. This means that some plants will die out if a single species of insect dies and vice versa. Humming birds play the part of insects for some plants, transferring pollen from one flower to another.

◀
A view through a tropical rain forest.

The rain forests do not have large herbivores. But there are large numbers of small ones like monkeys (which *mainly* eat plants). There are also countless species of insect that feed off leaves, seeds and fruit. These are prey for the insect-eating animals like birds, bats and ant-eaters. Small rodents (like mice) eat seeds as well as insects. These medium sized animals are preyed upon by snakes, birds (like hawks and owls), crocodiles and the felines – the large cats like tigers and jaguars.

In the trees there will be many kinds of *simians* (or monkeys). The apes are the largest simians, and are now mostly found in central Africa and southeast Asia.

Tropical farming?

Tropical soils are thin. This is because fallen leaves decompose rapidly in the heat. Recycling is quick. One effect of this is that people could not become farmers at all easily. The rain quickly washes chemicals needed for plant growth out of bare soils.

In some tropical forests people survived as hunters, but growing some crops in temporary 'gardens'. They made these by cutting down trees to make small clearings in the forests. After a few growing seasons they had to move elsewhere, when the soil had lost its nutrients.

Rain forests and the atmosphere

The tropical rain forests play a large role in global ecology. They 'manage' the rainfall to sustain their own life. They also play a large role in managing the atmosphere.

Plants take carbon dioxide out of the air and replace it with oxygen. Since the year 1800 or so there has been a great increase in the human population. The extra people and the extra fossil fuels that they burn have led to a steady increase in the carbon dioxide content in the air. This has led to the theory known as the *greenhouse effect*.

▼
The amounts of carbon dioxide and methane in the Earth's atmosphere have increased rapidly since the industrial revolution.

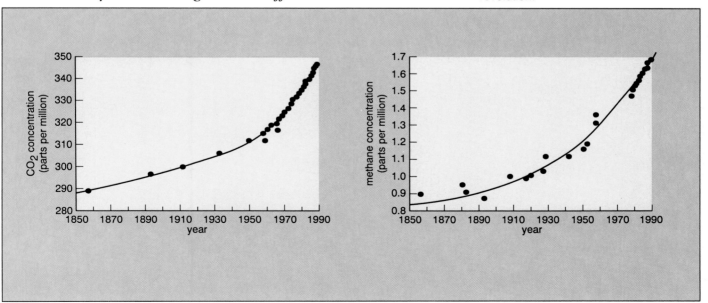

No one really knows what will happen if the carbon dioxide in the air keeps on increasing. The world should get warmer. This could make the polar ice caps melt. The sea levels would rise, flooding coastal cities and much good agricultural land. There would be an unknown effect on sea life. There could be an even greater effect on plant life because carbon dioxide is their main food. This may help better crops to grow, or make it easier for weeds to take over.

Will these changes be good or bad for people? This is hard to predict, even if we knew what changes would occur!

But some things are certain: the loss of tropical rain forest speeds up the increase in atmospheric carbon dioxide. Over the very long term the loss might cut down the amount of oxygen in the air. The atmosphere would reach a new balance, possibly less suitable to animal life.

Why cut down rain forests?

People are cutting down rain forests in many tropical countries. If they replace them with grass or other trees the result may not be very damaging. But this needs careful management, which is not happening at present in South America. Here, the trees *are* being replaced by grasses. The aim is to produce beef that can be sold abroad for cash. The wood can also be sold, but many shops no longer sell things made from these *tropical hardwoods*.

Without tree roots to hold in soil nutrients and the soil itself, these get washed away. This is already happening. Once the soil is gone, not even the smallest trees can grow back again. The loss is irreversible.

Similar things are happening in the semi-tropical forests of eastern India. The soil is being washed down to the sea by the great rivers that end up as the Ganges. The soil eventually settles out to form mud-islands in river mouths, which are then made shallower. The soil forming these islands is very fertile. Millions of people are attracted to live on and to farm these islands. They are at risk every year when storms build up in the monsoon season and the land floods.

▼

Brazil: once the trees are gone, rain water washes the top soil away. When the soil has gone, a new balance will be reached. What might this be?

▼
Much of the Ganges delta floods in the monsoon season.

Ecosystem 3: the sea

Two-thirds of the Earth's surface is covered by salt water. Most of this area is deep ocean. This is not as rich in living things as the shallow seas because life in the seas, like life on land, depends on plants. In their turn, plants depend on sunlight. Water absorbs sunlight, so the bottom of deep seas is very dark and plants cannot live there.

As the sea gets deeper, there is less light for water plants. Sea animals rely on plants not only for 'grazing' but also for oxygen. As the plants photosynthesise, the oxygen they make dissolves in the water.

Shallow seas are some of the richest ecosystems on Earth. This is especially true in tropical seas where *corals* grow. A coral reef is a 'rock' made by colonies of tiny animals. They build the reef to live in, and keep building so that it is always close to the surface. Thus even if the sea level changes with time, the reef is always in a good position to receive sunlight. This encourages plant life, and this in turn forms a basis for the lives of millions of species that are found in warm coral seas.

◄
Coral reefs are extremely rich ecosystems. The water is dense with plankton, which attracts thousands of fish and other animals.

Nearly all sea plants belong to one group: the *algae*. These are plants without true roots or leaves. The familiar *seaweed* is a form of algae. It anchors itself to rocks, but doesn't get its nutrients from these but from the sea water.

But there is a group of sea plants that can live in water of any depth. They are *floating* plants. Most of them are small single-celled plants. They are the first step in a food chain that extends to the largest animal on the Earth, the whale.

These small floating algae are eaten by equally small, single-celled animals. Both groups are called *plankton*, which literally means 'the drifters'. The plants are *phytoplankton*; the animals are *zooplankton*.

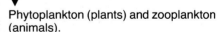
▼
Phytoplankton (plants) and zooplankton (animals).

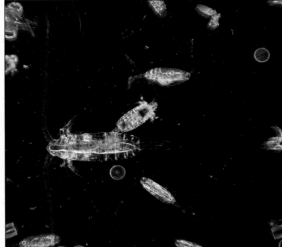

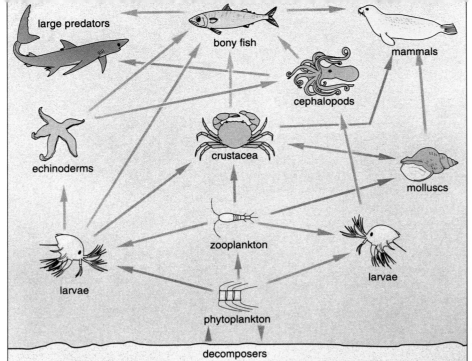

▼
Salmon being harvested from pens.

▲
One factory ship can support a fleet of smaller vessels. Here, a whaling boat is delivering its catch to the factory ship for processing.

▼
Productivity of the seas.

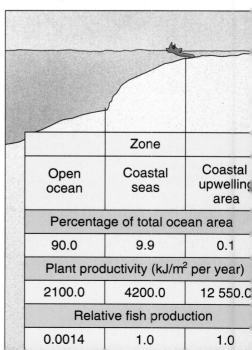

Plankton are found all over the world, in fresh as well as salt water. The picture (above) shows the food web for a sea that is rich in plankton.

Farming the sea

On the whole, humans are still hunters as far as sea life is concerned. You can get 'farmed fish', but fencing the sea isn't as easy as fencing the land. It is easier if the land has long narrow inlets. So, many fish farms are found in Scotland and Norway. This costs a lot of money and so you can only farm fish that have a high price in the shops, like salmon or lobsters.

Fish farms can cause problems. The fish may have to be given chemicals to keep them healthy in unnatural surroundings, or growth hormone so that they grow more quickly. These chemicals can pollute the surrounding sea. Good fish farming doesn't use chemicals.

Of course, shellfish have been farmed for many hundreds of years. They stay where they are put, which makes things a lot easier!

The main problem with sea fishing, however, is that we are getting too good at it. Modern techniques include:

- Factory ships: these can freeze and process the catch at sea. The small fishing boats don't have to keep returning to port every two weeks or so, but off-load their catch onto the factory vessel.
- Sonar: sound is used to detect shoals of fish deep under water that would otherwise escape.
- Drift nets: nets up to 30 *kilometres* long, which hang down into the sea. They catch everything, and kill it, so unwanted fish can't be thrown back into the sea. These nets have damaged the ecosystem so much in many fishing areas that they have now been banned.

All this has resulted in overfishing. This means that there is a strong danger that the population of a fish species gets so small that it is unable to reproduce. For fish, reproduction is a very hit-and-miss affair. The female lays eggs in shallow water, and the male squirts sperm all over them — if he can find them. As more and more adult fish are caught there aren't enough left to breed.

	Zone		
Open ocean	Coastal seas	Coastal upwelling area
Percentage of total ocean area			
90.0	9.9	0.1
Plant productivity (kJ/m² per year)			
2100.0	4200.0	12 550.0
Relative fish production			
0.0014	1.0	1.0

The graph for question 6 on page 158 shows the effect of overfishing mackerel in the seas near Britain. Fewer and fewer fish are caught each year. This isn't helped by the fact that European countries have been using the North Sea for waste disposal for so long. Many of the fish that are caught are unhealthy, due to the chemical pollution from large rivers such as the Rhine.

Globally, large scale 'industrial' fishing caught 84 million tones of fish in 1986. About a third of the fish is used for animal feed, the rest for human consumption. Scientists estimate that the total *sustainable* catch is 100 million tonnes per year. This total would have been reached in 1992. But governments from many fishing nations are taking action to see that this doesn't happen.

▼
The world distribution of primary production in major ecosystems. Some ecosystems are much more productive than others: oceans are practically deserts! (Data in grams of biomass per m².)

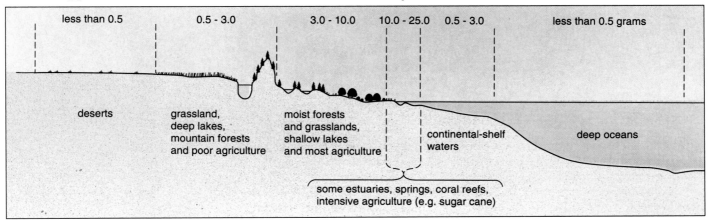

| less than 0.5 | 0.5 - 3.0 | 3.0 - 10.0 | 10.0 - 25.0 | 0.5 - 3.0 | less than 0.5 grams |

deserts

grassland, deep lakes, mountain forests and poor agriculture

moist forests and grasslands, shallow lakes and most agriculture

continental-shelf waters

deep oceans

some estuaries, springs, coral reefs, intensive agriculture (e.g. sugar cane)

The Gaia theory

In 3.5 billion years life has changed the Earth. Plants have created an oxygen-rich atmosphere. They have also preserved soils that would otherwise be continually washed into the sea. Small animals have taken the small amounts of carbonates dissolved in sea water to make their shells and skeletons. When they died, their remains produced layers of chalk and limestone rock many hundreds of metres thick. These new rocks kept the seas shallow and also took away excess carbon dioxide. It seems that on the whole, life has changed the Earth to suit *itself*.

Life hasn't had everything its own way. Every so often many of the species alive at that time seem to die out. This has happened about every 30 million years or so. Sometimes, nearly all the species disappear, to be replaced by completely different ones.

The most famous of these 'great dyings' happened about 65 million years ago at the end of the Cretaceous Period. This ended the 'Age of the Dinosaurs'. Dinosaurs were reptiles – cold-blooded animals. For 135 million years they were the dominant life-form on Earth.

There were hundreds of species of dinosaur. They ranged from tiny ones not much bigger than cats to huge 'monsters' 30 metres long with a mass of 80 tonnes. The dinosaurs didn't die overnight. They simply 'faded away' over a period of about 5 million years. There is some evidence to suggest that their decline began with a 'triggering event'. One theory has long been that the Earth was hit by a very large meteorite. (Some astronomers think that there is a risk of this kind of disaster happening at regular intervals!)

◄
A reconstruction of Late Jurassic times, western U.S.A.

A large meteorite would have caused some devastating earthquakes and probably some tidal waves. But the worst effect would have been the production of a thick layer of dust, high in the atmosphere.

This would have cut down the energy received from the Sun. The Earth would have grown darker and cooler. The cold-blooded dinosaurs would have become sluggish and less able to fend for themselves. Warm blooded animals – the early mammals and birds – would have had the edge.

Whatever the cause, the dinosaurs died out and the dominant (but not the largest) animal group on Earth is now the mammals.

The dinosaurs weren't the only animals to suffer. Other reptiles died out too. In fact, about 75% of all living species living in the Cretaceous era didn't survive into the next era (the Paleocene).

Events like this are hard on the species alive at the time, but the Earth carries on. Dr James Lovelock called this the *Gaia theory*.

Gaia

'Gaia' was the name the ancient Greeks gave to the goddess who was the mother of Earth and Sky. The Gaia theory says that the Earth itself adapts to any changes that happen, however serious or damaging they appear to be. Earth 'looks after itself'. But Greek gods were pretty ruthless, and the Gaia theory doesn't say that the Earth looks after any particular species, such as human beings, for example.

Chapter 5 describes how life changes, very, very slowly, because of random changes in genes. It is changes like these that allow living species to adapt to changes in their environment. It may take many generations for these changes to become effective, and so produce new, 'better-adapted' species. And it doesn't always work; after all, in the history of the Earth *most* species have died out!

We assume that the laws of physics, chemistry and biology can't be broken. Human beings may pollute the Earth, make it warm up by increasing the greenhouse effect, or destroy the ozone layer. The Earth will change. Life will adapt to the new conditions. But it may not be so friendly a place for people, or dolphins, or giant pandas.

If we think of the Earth as being a day old, life has been on it for about 16 hours. Human beings have been around for about 10 millionths of a second! On the timescale of the Earth, humans are very new and could disappear quickly, without much of a trace. The Gaia theory says that the 'whole-Earth system' is what is really important. Not single species. The system balances itself out, whatever is done to it.

Managing the Earth

We want to keep the Earth as friendly a place for humans as it has been for most of the past million years. We have been a very successful species. The human population has grown tremendously, especially in the past two hundred years or so. This is mainly due to highly developed brain-power, allowing us to use resources. It is also due to our ability to use other organisms very effectively for our benefit (usually on farms). For example, in 1991 all the food that we need in Britain could be produced on its farms by just 1% of its population.

If we want to manage our lives on Earth well, we must think about some rules for 'good behaviour'.

What do you think about the following?

1 Keep learning more and more about the Earth by using the tools of science; satellites taught us about the ozone layer; computers can model the possible effects of different policies; research into apparently useless 'pure chemistry' taught us about the effects of aerosol chemicals on the ozone layer. There is a need for knowledge.

2 Reduce waste. Learn from people who have lived in one place for many hundreds of years, like the rice farmers of Indonesia; try to recycle the metals and plastics that we tend to throw away.

3 Respect all life. Ecosystems are complicated; we do not know what might happen if we kill off 'pests', for example; even weeds have genes that might be vital for our human needs one day; unthinking cruelty is wrong.

4 Be realistic. We must be realistic about things like the *cost of pollution* because sooner or later we shall have to pay for it.

5 Save energy. Energy from fossil fuels has been so cheap that we have probably come to rely on it too much; we shall have to make plans for when these fuels run out, and should start doing this now: examples are the energy cost of farming, individual transport (cars versus trains or buses).

6 Slow down the growth of the human population. This is easier said than done! But more people means that more resources and energy are being used. This means more pollution, and fewer resources left for the future.

We all have different opinions about these 'rules'. The important thing is to understand what each of them means for the places where we live, and how science can be used for the benefit of the Earth system.

▲
There are more people alive today than have ever lived.

Activities

1 The opening of this chapter suggests the worst and best states the planet may be in by 2010. The true situation will probably be somewhere in the middle. How old will you be in 2010?

Prepare a 'newspaper' poster with a series of short articles covering both local and global issues that you think will relevant then, using *genuine* newspaper or magazine photographs if you can.

2 You have been asked to speak for a group of Amazonian Indians whose forest homeland is under threat. A group of beef farmers are planning to burn the forest and raise cattle on the land when grass has grown.

Write a speech that you would deliver to the public inquiry to be held to discuss the matter. To convince the board you must give good scientific reasons why the forest should be left and the trees should not be felled.

3 As a group exercise discuss the issue of eating meat. With your teacher's help set up a debate in your science lesson. You can either use a motion of your own or use one of the following.
(a) 'The slaughter of animals for human consumption cannot be justified in a modern world.'
(b) 'Using land to grow meat results in famine in the Third World.'
(c) 'A vegetarian diet lacks important vitamins.'
(d) 'Human beings are omnivores who have always eaten meat and plants. They must do this to stay healthy.'

4 Look at your school environment. Suggest ways in which:
(a) pollution could be cut down;
(b) valuable resources could be recycled;
(c) energy could be saved.
Prepare a series of posters to encourage fellow pupils and staff to implement your ideas.

5 There are three main areas of pollution: air, water and land. Study your local environment. Draw an outline map and mark in places and types of pollution.

Suggest sensible ways in which the greatest problems could be reduced. You need to take into account the economic well-being of any industry that you include in your account. Prepare a report to present to your class.

Questions

1 (a) What is the difference between catching a fish by trawling and using drift nets? (A drawing will help)
(b) Apart from fish, what other marine species are likely to be caught and killed by these two types of nets?
(c) How does the size of the mesh affect the age of the fish caught?

2 Give a simple explanation of the following words or phrases:
(a) *ecosystem;* (b) *predator;* (c) *decomposer;* and (d) *food web.*

3 '*Recycling* is important in nature.' Describe (in writing or by using a labelled diagram) one example of natural recycling. Why is the example that you have chosen important?

4 (a) What was the American 'dust bowl'?
(b) How have the problems that created it been prevented form happening again?

5

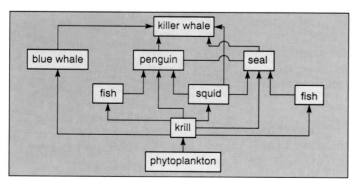

Look at the simplified Antarctic food-web above.
(a) 'Factory' ships catch krill to turn into animal food. Explain why the over-harvesting of krill by 'factory' ships is so damaging to the ecosystem.

(b) Why is the blue whale in more danger than the killer whale?
(c) Suggest what might happen to the web if the *squid* population was seriously affected by disease.

6 Catches of fish:

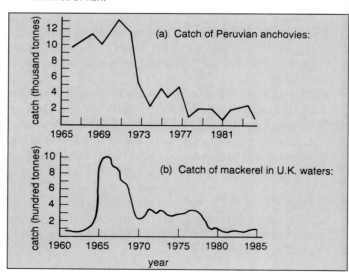

(a) Catch of Peruvian anchovies:

(b) Catch of mackerel in U.K. waters:

(a) In which years were the largest catches of the two species, Peruvian anchovies and mackerel, made?
(b) Which species was caught in the greatest numbers?
(c) Can you suggest a reason for this?
(d) Which species declined most rapidly?
(e) What similarities are there in the shape of the two graphs?
(f) What measures should have been introduced to enable the fish stocks to provide a sustainable catch? When should this have been done?

These are the facts and ideas that you should have learned by studying this topic.

To reach *Basic Level* you should:

- know an example of pollution of the soil, of the air and of water
- know one example of how changes in the environment affect people, plants or animals
- know two ways in which people cause pollution
- be able to give an example of what ought to be done to help stop or cut down pollution
- know that the world population is increasing

To succeed at *Foundation Level* you should:

- know how pollution can affect living things
- know that the human population is increasing very quickly, and that people make a lot of changes to the environment
- be able to describe where extra carbon dioxide in the atmosphere comes from
- be able to name important pollutants and important raw materials
- understand why farmers use nitrogen fertilisers, but that this can cause pollution
- know that plants get their energy from the Sun, but that only a small part of the energy supplied can be harvested as food

To succeed at *Merit Level* you should:

- know how population changes depend on resources in the environment
- know the main effects of human activity on the environment, and that these effects are fairly recent
- understand the flow of nitrates through a mixed (animals and arable) farm ecosystem
- know why plants can only use a part of the energy provided by solar radiation

To succeed at *Special Level* you should:

- understand the factors affecting the size of human populations, and how in turn this affects the impact of human activity on the environment
- understand the basic scientific principles associated with a major change in the biosphere (e.g. the greenhouse effect)
- know some of the important waste products that are disposed of into the sea, the soil and the atmosphere
- be able to use scientific knowledge to evaluate data about good and bad environmental practice in farming and other managed ecosystems
- understand how food production involves a careful and responsible management of ecosystems to improve the efficiency of energy transfer

CHAPTER NINE

S P A C E

This is part of the night sky. The photograph was taken on a clear winter night. With good eyesight and a lot of patience you could count about 5000 stars over your head on a night like this. You'd see fewer than this if you lived in a town, or if it was a moonlit night. You would only see the brighter stars, which are shown in the drawings in the 'Reference section' (page 248–9), and in the diagram on the next page.

Constellations

But when you can't see too many stars it actually makes it easier to see the main star patterns. We call these the *constellations*. They are usually named after Ancient Greek heroes or heroines, most of whom came to a sticky end — like Hercules, Orion, Castor and Pollux, Andromeda and Cassiopeia.

Others are named after animals, like Aries (the ram), Capricorn (the goat) and Cancer (the crab). These were named a very long time ago, before the time of the Ancient Greeks.

It takes a lot of imagination to see the shapes of these people or creatures in the sky. But it helped people to remember the star patterns.

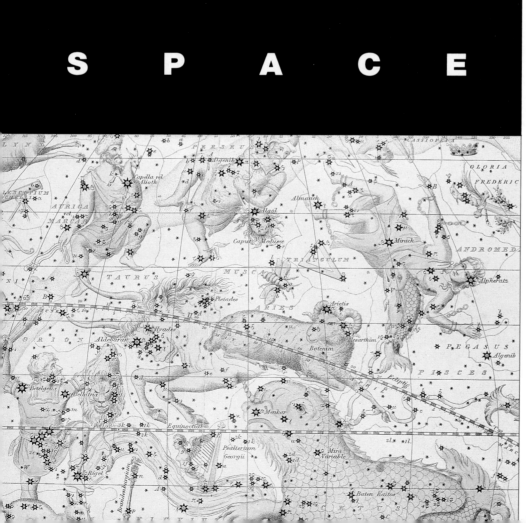

◄

The main stars (shown in red) and constellations (blue) that you can see in the picture (opposite).

Star	Apparent magnitude	Constellation	When best seen
Sirius	−1.4	Canis Major	winter
Canopus	−0.73	Carina	—
Alpha Centauri	−0.27	Centaurus	—
Arcturus	−0.06	Bootes	spring
Vega	0.04	Lyra	summer
Capella	0.09	Auriga	all year
Rigel	0.15	Orion	winter
Procyon	0.37	Canis Minor	winter
Acherna	0.48	Eridanus	—
Betelgeuse	0.8	Orion	winter

The *magnitude* of a star is a measure of its apparent brightness. It used to be done by eye, but now we use instruments. A star of magnitude 1 gives out 100 times as much light as a star of the 'sixth magnitude'. The bigger the number, the fainter the star.

Star names

Most of the names of the stars themselves are in Arabic. A thousand years after the Greeks had lost interest in astronomy the Arabs had become a rich and powerful civilisation. They were excellent doctors, scientists, poets and astronomers. They started where the Greek astronomers had finished and took the trouble to name individual stars, like the 'Devil Star', *Algol*, in the constellation of Perseus, and *Deneb* in the swan (Cygnus).

The brightest stars in the sky are given in the table. The Ancient Greeks and Arabs could see all of these.

Is astronomy useful?

People have always been interested in the stars and the night sky. In the first place, a starry sky on a clear sky is so beautiful. It was easy to imagine going to such a nice place as 'the heavens' when you died. But another and very important reason was seriously practical. The movement of the stars can measure the passing of *time* very accurately.

You can also predict the changing of the seasons, so that you know when to plough and when to sow seeds. Ancient peoples believed that the stars could tell them even more than that; they believed that the stars could tell them their own futures — *astrology*. Many people still believe this, which is why there are horoscopes in some newspapers and magazines.

Stars can be used to help you find direction, especially at sea. Even today, the computers in space probes use the bright star *Canopus* as a marker to get their direction right.

◄

Our own galaxy, the Milky Way. When you look through the galaxy at its densest areas, you see this mass of light coming from countless stars.

◄
With a fixed camera, and the shutter left open for a few hours, you can see the 'trails' of stars as the Earth spins. The Pole Star at the centre of the trails does not appear to move.

The moving sky

When you look up at the stars in the night sky they seem to be perfectly still. In fact, they are all moving. The two pictures show some of the stars around the Pole Star. They show that in two hours the star groups seem to have moved in an arc of a circle around the Pole Star. They move like the hands of a clock, making a complete circle in just under 24 hours (23 hours 56 minutes actually).

But the stars move together; the star *patterns* stay the same. We can always recognise the same constellations, night after night, year after year. This is why they are sometimes called the 'fixed stars'.

The wandering stars

A few 'stars' are not fixed into constellations. If you know where to look – and when to look – you can see five stars that slide very slowly through the fixed constellations. These are the 'wandering stars' called *planets*. They look like stars, but in fact they aren't stars at all (see below). Some planets can be much brighter than real stars, and their brightness changes as they wander through the sky.

The planets that you could see with the naked eye have been known for thousands of years. They were named after the old Roman gods: Mercury, Venus, Mars, Jupiter and Saturn. We now know that there are three others: Uranus, Neptune and Pluto, too faint to be seen without a telescope.

The zodiac

These planets don't just wander anywhere. They all move through a belt of twelve constellations that make a complete circle in the sky. The Earth is in the centre of this circle, which is known as the belt of the *zodiac*. Most people will recognise the names of the constellations (or 'signs') of

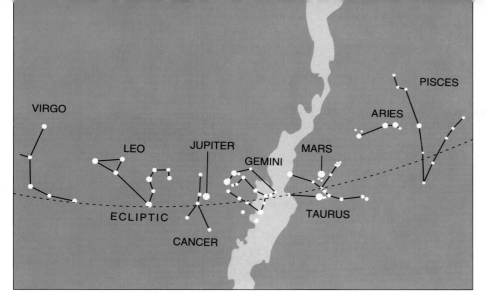

◄
Part of the zodiac with Gemini overhead.

the zodiac. The star map shows the zodiac groups as we could see them from Britain in winter. At least half of them are hidden from us, as they are on the other side of the Earth.

The Sun

Like the stars, the Sun also rises and sets. The length of the day compared with the night changes depending on the time of year. But the Sun makes a complete circle in the sky in about 24.00 hours, taking 4 minutes longer than the stars do. Our clocks are set to 'Sun time', but astronomers work to 'star time' (called *sidereal time*). This helps them to find where the stars are on any night.

But the Sun seems to have another movement. Like the planets, it moves through the constellations. Again, the constellation the Sun is in will always be one of the 'signs' of the zodiac. In June, the Sun is in the constellation Gemini (The Twins). In December, it is in Sagittarius (The Archer). This means that you can't see Gemini in June or Sagittarius in December because they are in the sky in broad daylight.

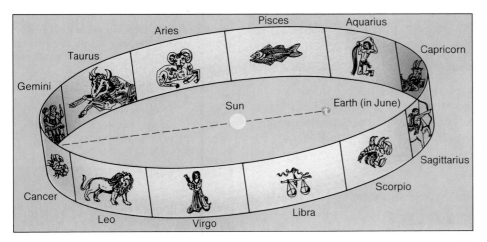
◄
The zodiac. In June, the Sun appears to be in the constellation of Gemini.

The Sun travels through all the constellations of the zodiac and gets back to where it started in the same time. This is what we call a *year*. Actually, it takes 365.25 days, which is an awkward quarter of a day too much. If we did nothing about this we'd end up having December in midsummer. (Which they do in Australia — but that's another story — see page 167). So we save up these quarters and add them to the year every four years. Each *leap year* we get an extra day in February.

Space

163

The Moon

The Moon has its own timing. It rises and sets like the Sun, but to a different pattern. It also changes shape as it goes through its *phases*.

The Moon completes its cycle of changes in a month. But it is a *lunar month* of 29.5 days. This is the time from, say, new Moon to new Moon. Also, like the Sun and planets, the Moon slides against the background of the fixed stars through the zodiac. It does this very quickly, completing its trip through the zodiac in just over 27.25 days: less than a lunar month.

Eclipses

The Moon's path is very close to that of the Sun. Sometimes it crosses the Sun's path and there is a chance of an *eclipse*.

Eclipses and the ecliptic

The Sun's path through the zodiac is called the *ecliptic*. (This is marked on the star maps in the 'Reference section'.) If the Moon happens to cross the ecliptic just when the Sun is there we get an *eclipse of the Sun*. This doesn't happen very often.

The fact that the Moon can eclipse the Sun shows that the Moon is nearer to us than the Sun. Sometimes the Moon gets eclipsed. This always happens in the early evening or at night. It has been known for thousands of years that it happens because the Moon has passed into the Earth's shadow.

Observing and explaining

These are the basic facts about what we see happening in the sky. The reasons for all these *observations* have interested human beings for many thousands of years. This section deals with the *explanations* for what we see happening.

Eclipses of the Sun used to terrify people as the daylight faded away. Now, we can explain the eclipse quite simply.

▼
The Moon in its first quarter.

▲
The Moon, almost in full phase.

◄
A sequence showing a total eclipse of the sun. At left, the Moon's disc can be seen gradually covering our view of the Sun. Centre, shows the halo of light from the Sun, and then (right) the Moon moves away again.

▼
An eclipse of the Moon. The Earth's shadow is being cast over the Moon. The very bright area is where sunlight is still reaching the Moon's surface.

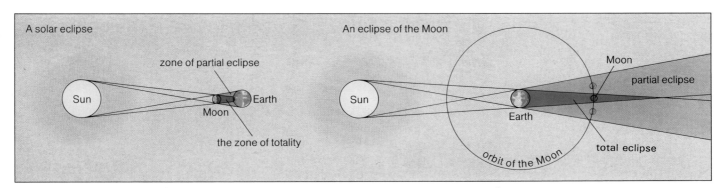

| A solar eclipse | An eclipse of the Moon |

zone of partial eclipse

Sun

Moon

Earth

the zone of totality

Sun

Earth

orbit of the Moon

Moon

partial eclipse

total eclipse

But it took many thousands of years for this view of the Earth in space to be accepted.

▲
How the Earth casts an eclipse on the Moon, and the Moon casts its shadow over the Earth.

Sky theories

The simplest way to think about the movements of the Sun, Moon, stars and planets is that they move in circles around the Earth. Let us imagine a fixed, round, solid Earth. As the Sun goes around it from east to west it rises and sets. It is dark at night because the Sun has travelled to the other side of the Earth. The Moon and the stars do the same.

This is what good astronomers believed for over two thousand years. It gave sensible explanations of what they saw, and even allowed them to make very accurate calculations. For example, Babylonian astronomers were able to predict eclipses of the Moon; a Greek astronomer, Thales of Miletus, predicted the eclipse of the Sun in 585 B.C. As a 'model', it is still used by astronomers, navigators and calendar-makers to make quite detailed calculations of the positions of heavenly objects, and the times at which they rise and set.

But this simple theory couldn't explain the strange movement of the wandering stars, the planets.

A mathematical universe

Claudius Ptolemy was a Greek astronomer and geographer who lived in the city of Alexandria in Egypt. He did his work there between A.D. 130 and A.D. 170. Ptolemy became so famous that he is credited with the discoveries of astronomers that lived before him. In Ptolemy's time, Alexandria had the biggest library in the world. It held records of hundreds of years of astronomical observations.

Ptolemy used these past records to make tables which could predict the future movement of the planets, the *Syntaxis mathematike*. This needed a more complicated model of the universe. Ptolemy said that the stars were fixed to a huge sphere that surrounded the Earth. The planets moved across further glass-like spheres between the Earth and the stars. The whole model was incredibly complicated, but it did explain what the astronomers could see in the sky.

Unfortunately, the model made holes in the theory – all the extra circles would have broken the crystal spheres! Ptolemy had to explain that they weren't 'real' spheres; they were just mathematical ideas to get the right answer.

Nevertheless, ordinary people (and many astronomers) believed that the spheres were really there.

There were other things that the old Earth-centred theory couldn't

▼
Ptolemy's universe: the small sphere with the planet attached to it is carried by the larger sphere. The spheres turn at different speeds. The dotted line shows the resulting movement of the planet. Also, the large sphere turns once every day on another axis!

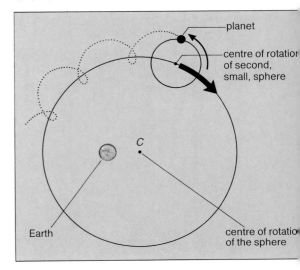

planet

centre of rotation of second, small, sphere

C

Earth

centre of rotation of the sphere

explain. One was the appearance of *comets*. These swept through the sky and must also have broken through the crystal spheres. But the theory was good enough to last more than a thousand years.

The need for a new theory

Five hundred years ago the world of astronomers was shaken up. After a thousand years of ignoring astronomy, Europeans began to learn from the Arabs, who then dominated the eastern Mediterranean lands. The Europeans learned how to use astronomical instruments to make careful measurements, to help navigate ships in unknown seas. They learned about Greek astronomy (from Arabic translations). Europeans also wanted a share of the world trade that the Arab countries had developed.

The world was bigger than European people had thought. In 1492 Christopher Columbus set out to find a new route to India, and 'discovered' the West Indies and America by mistake. In that same year, in Poland, a 19-year-old boy was studying astronomy. He may already have had the idea of a revolutionary new theory: that the Sun and not the Earth, was at the centre of the universe. His name was Nicholas Copernicus (1473–1543).

Copernicus had worked out his theory by 1509, when his first small book was being passed around amongst interested astronomers and mathematicians. He argued that:

- the Earth was in fact very small, compared to the distances to the fixed stars;
- the stars must be a long way away: if it was the stars that moved, they would have to move impossibly fast to get all the way round in one day, and so it must be the Earth that moves;
- night and day, and the rising and setting of Sun, Moon and stars were caused by the Earth spinning once a day;
- the odd movements of the planets could be explained more sensibly by saying that the planets and the Earth went around the Sun;
- the Moon was the only object in the sky that actually went around the Earth.

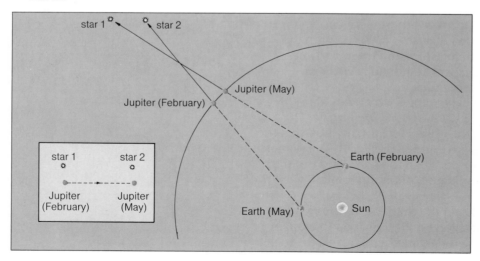

◄
The Earth moves faster than Jupiter. When we overtake it, it *looks* as if Jupiter is moving backwards against the background stars, even though it is still moving forwards. This is just like overtaking a car on the motorway: the car that you overtake seems to be moving backwards.

Copernicus was also able to give the correct order of the planets. Up until then no-one was certain where Mercury and Venus actually were, compared with the Sun and the Earth.

All this might be obvious to us now, but in the sixteenth century it was a difficult theory to understand. It took a hundred years for most astronomers to take this Sun-centred system seriously.

By then the telescope had been invented, and there were also much more accurate measurements of the movements of the planets. This information was vital for sailors who were by now sailing around the world. The old methods of Ptolemy could no longer give the accurate results that navigators wanted.

Galileo and Newton

In 1610 the Italian scientists Galileo Galilei first used a new invention, the telescope, to look at the night sky. He saw the mountains of the Moon. He saw sunspots. He also discovered that the planet Jupiter had four moons in orbit around it. This, he said, was just like Copernicus's *solar system*, on a smaller scale.

Bigger and better telescopes were invented. More and more evidence was produced to support the Copernican theory. In 1665 the 23-year-old Isaac Newton produced a theory that *explained* the movements of Earth, Moon and planets. It was the *theory of gravity*. (There is more about this below.) The solar system is shown on pages 246 and 247 in the 'Reference section'.

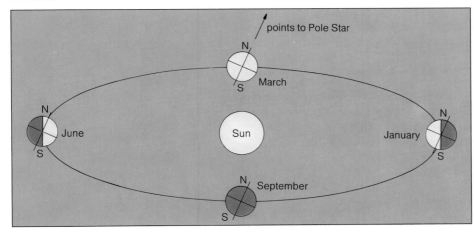

◀ The seasons are caused by the fact that the Earth's axis is tilted. In June, the northern hemisphere is tilted towards the Sun; the Sun is higher in the sky, giving more energy per square metre.

Moving in a gravity field

The force of gravity attracts objects to each other. Gravity produces a very tiny force. The gravity force between you and someone sitting next to you is about a millionth of a newton. The Earth has a large mass, so the force between you and the Earth is much larger, and is called your *weight*.

Field strength

Just like a magnet has a magnetic field, we can think of the Earth as having a gravity field. The strength of the field tells us how much force it exerts

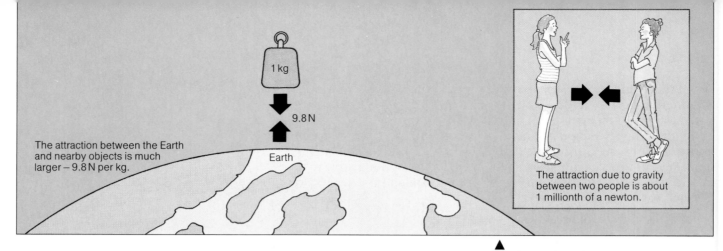

The attraction between the Earth and nearby objects is much larger – 9.8 N per kg.

1 kg

9.8 N

Earth

The attraction due to gravity between two people is about 1 millionth of a newton.

▲ The force of gravity.

on a standard object: a mass of 1 kilogram. The strength of the Earth's gravity field – *on the surface of the Earth* – is 9.8 newtons per kilogram.

This means that every kilogram of mass in an object will have a gravity force of 9.8 newtons acting on it. Mathematically:

$$\text{gravity force} = \text{mass} \times \text{field strength},$$
$$\text{or, } F = mg.$$

The gravity force on different masses

Mass (kg)	1	2	5	10
Force due to gravity (N)	9.8	19.6	49	98

▼ Will the rate of the elephant's fall be any faster than the mouse's?

The acceleration of free fall

When you jump off a wall, or dive from a diving board, the force of gravity makes you fall towards the centre of the Earth. According to Newton's laws of motion, the force produces an acceleration, called the *acceleration of free fall*. All objects, whatever their mass, will be accelerated at the same rate. How can this be?

First, remember that:

$$\text{force} = \text{mass} \times \text{acceleration}.$$

This means that to get the same acceleration, the bigger the mass the bigger the force we need to apply.

Secondly, the force is due to gravity. This means that the bigger the mass, the bigger the force (see above). This automatic increase in force just matches the extra force we need to get the same acceleration.

Mathematically:

Gravity rule: $F = mg$, (g is the field strength);
Newton's Law: $F = ma$, (a is the acceleration produced by force F);
so, for acceleration due to gravity:

$$ma = mg,$$
so, $$a = g.$$

This is true whatever the value of m. Because of this equality, you will sometimes see g written as $9.8\,\text{m/s}^2$, and sometimes as $9.8\,\text{N/kg}$.

168

Measuring *g*

The most accurate way to get a value for *g* is to measure the acceleration of free fall. This can be done by using an accurate timer to time how long it takes for an object to fall a given distance. This is best done electronically. There are different kinds of equipment for doing this and your teacher will explain how to use the one you have in your school.

You need to use one of the equations of motion given in the 'Reference section' to work out the result.

The basic equation is: $d = u + \frac{1}{2}gt^2$.

(d = distance in metres moved in time *t* seconds by a mass with an acceleration *g*; *u* is the velocity at the start of the timing.)

In most experiments, $u = 0$ (the object falls from rest).

So $$d = \frac{1}{2}gt^2,$$
or, $$g = \frac{2d}{t^2}.$$

Diving and sky diving

Have you ever dived off the top board at a swimming pool? If you have, you'll know that you hit the water at a high speed. This means you have to make a good entry into the water (belly-flops are very painful indeed). How fast are you going when you hit the water?

We can work this out by using the idea of energy transfer. We also need to know the height of the diving board and the fact that you are in a gravity field of strength 9.8 N/kg.

When you climb the steps to the top of the board you are doing work against the force of gravity. You gain *gravitational potential energy*. When you dive off, this potential energy becomes *kinetic energy* as you go faster and faster.

Suppose the diving board is 10 metres above the water, and that your mass is 50 kg. When you climb out of the pool and go up to the board you increase your potential energy:

energy transferred = work done = force × distance
$$= 50 \text{ kg} \times 9.8 \text{ N/kg} \times 10 \text{ m}$$
$$= 4900 \text{ Nm (or } joules\text{)}.$$

When you dive off, this energy is transferred into kinetic energy. The formula for kinetic energy is $\frac{1}{2}mv^2$, where *v* is the speed that you gain.

So, $\frac{1}{2} \times 50 \text{ kg} \times v^2 = 4900$ joules
$$v^2 = \frac{4900 \times 2}{50} = 196; v = 14 \text{ m/s}.$$

(The speed limit in towns is 13.4 m/s (30 mph)!)

Keen mathematicians might have noticed that we have done some extra calculations here that aren't necessary. The algebra shows this:
potential energy transferred $= mgh$,
kinetic energy gained $= \frac{1}{2}mv^2$.
As these are equal: $\frac{1}{2}mv^2 = mgh$
and, $\frac{1}{2}v^2 = gh$
or $v^2 = 2gh$
$$v = \sqrt{2gh}$$

m has cancelled out: so we could have gone straight to the last formula to give $v = \sqrt{2 \times 9.8 \times 10} = 14$ m/s.

▲
Diving from a 10 m high board, you hit the water at 14 m/s (over 30 mph)! That's why it is important to break through the water surface very cleanly.

Getting into space

Blow up a balloon. Let it go. It flies off at speed, but you can't tell which way it will go. It works by using the same principle as a rocket. But rockets are a lot bigger and have to be better controlled.

Momentum

The air in a balloon is under pressure. When you let the balloon go, air rushes out. At the same time, the balloon moves in the opposite direction to the air. Newton used the idea of *momentum* to explain this effect.

A moving object is said to have momentum. This is a combination of the object's *mass* and its *velocity*. Both of these words have careful definitions in physics.

Mass depends on the amount of material in an object. It is measured in kilograms: 2 kilograms of iron has twice as much mass as 1 kilogram of iron. Compared with a mass of 1 kilogram, a 2 kilogram mass is twice as hard to get moving (and twice as hard to stop). This feature of matter is sometimes called its *inertia* (or *inertial mass*).

Velocity is *speed in a given direction*. An object moving north at 10 metres per second has a different velocity than an object moving south at 10 metres per second! They both have the same speed: 10 metres per second, but to show their velocities we'd have to draw a diagram.

To start with, let's keep to objects moving along a single straight line. As with graph axes, we can say that going left is going negative, and that going right is going positive.

Momentum is important because it keeps turning up in physics, from explaining the pressure in gases to explaining the solar system:

$$\text{momentum} = \text{mass} \times \text{velocity},$$
$$p = mv.$$

Thus the object going right has a momentum of $+10000$ units, the other, going left, has a momentum of -10000 units.

Back to the balloon

Before you let the balloon go it was still. It didn't have a velocity, so it didn't have any momentum either. When you let go, the air had momentum in one direction, and the balloon had momentum in the opposite direction. Newton showed that these two 'momenta' (plural of momentum) were equal in *size*. But they were opposite in *direction*, which meant that they were opposite in *sign*.

Added together, they cancel each other out. The total momentum is still zero. *The total momentum hasn't changed.*

The box (opposite) explains the reasons for this, using Newton's Laws of Motion (see also Chapter 8, *Movement and forces* in GCSE book 1).

This discovery of Newton's was one of his most important. It applies to everything, everywhere in the universe. It works with stars colliding with stars, with quarks hitting quarks, and in a game of marbles. It applies whenever there is a collision or an explosion, whenever a force acts to change an object's movement.

Always remember: the total momentum before (something happens) equals the momentum afterwards.

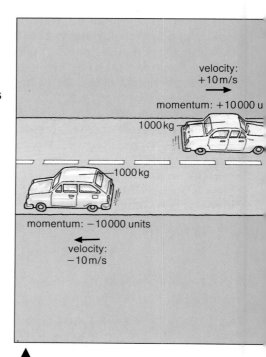

velocity:
$+10\,\text{m/s}$

momentum: $+10\,000$ u

$1000\,\text{kg}$

$1000\,\text{kg}$

momentum: $-10\,000$ units

velocity:
$-10\,\text{m/s}$

▲
These cars have the same *speeds* but different *velocities*.

The conservation of momentum

Think of two equal trolleys squashing a spring between them. When you let the trolleys go, the force of the spring pushes on both. They both move away in opposite directions, gaining opposite momenta.

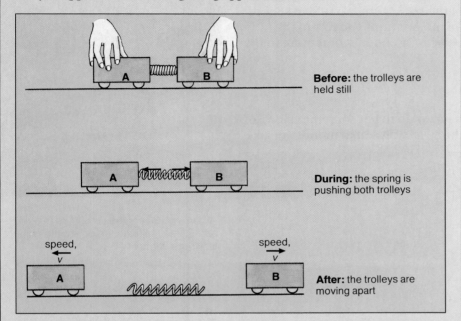

Before: the trolleys are held still

During: the spring is pushing both trolleys

speed, v

speed, v

After: the trolleys are moving apart

◀
What would happen if trolley **A** was twice the mass of trolley **B**?

The force of the spring is the same for both trolleys, and acts for the same time. Its effect on the trolleys must be exactly the same (apart from being different in directions). So the trolleys reach the same speed, and have the same quantity of momentum.

But, of course, one trolley has positive momentum, the other has negative momentum. The total momentum is still zero. Mathematically:

$$\text{Force} = \text{mass} \times \text{acceleration} = \text{mass} \times \frac{\text{change of speed}}{\text{time taken}}.$$

For trolley A: $\qquad F \quad = \dfrac{\overleftarrow{mv}}{t}$ (the arrow shows which way the trolley is moving),

or $\qquad\qquad\qquad Ft \quad = \overleftarrow{mv}$

For trolley B: $\qquad Ft \quad = \overrightarrow{mv}.$

Notice that Ft is the same for both, and equals the *change in momentum* of each trolley. So the momentum gained by each trolley is the same in size, and opposite in direction.

So, $\quad \overleftarrow{mv} = \overrightarrow{mv}, \quad$ or $\quad \overleftarrow{mv} + \overrightarrow{mv} = 0.$

Total momentum is still zero, as it was when the spring was still squashed.

This rule applies even when the masses of the trolleys are different, but the speeds will change so that the momentum changes are still equal:

$$Ft \quad = \overleftarrow{Mv} \quad = \overrightarrow{mV}$$

'*Ft*' is called *impetus*.

Rockets

Large rockets are needed to get an Earth satellite into orbit. Most of the rocket is going to be thrown away. It will be ejected backwards at a very high speed. It is, in fact, fuel and oxygen. When these react they produce very hot gases. They leave the nozzle of the rocket engine at high speed.

As they go, the hot gases carry a lot of momentum. The rest of the rocket – unburnt fuel and payload – gains just as much momentum in the opposite direction. We have 'lift-off'.

Getting into orbit

Newton worked out what you would have to do to get something into an orbit around the Earth. He imagined a huge gun on a high mountain.

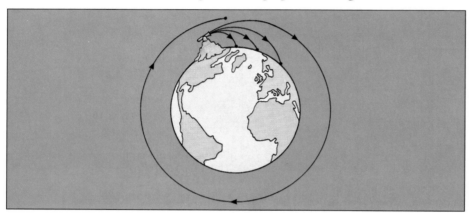

To get into orbit the object would have to travel at a high speed. If it moved too slowly it would simply fall back to hit the ground. Newton saw that even in orbit the new 'satellite' would still be falling. But at a high enough speed, the satellite would 'run out of ground' as the Earth curved away beneath it. The speed needed to do this is 8 *kilometres per second*.

Satellites reach this high speed gradually, in up to three stages, as shown.

▲ All five rocket engines must fire at the same time to lift the space shuttle against the force of gravity.

◄ The faster the projectile is fired out of the gun, the further it will go. If it could be fired fast enough, it would go into orbit.

▼ Multi-stage rockets are needed to lift loads out of Earth orbit.

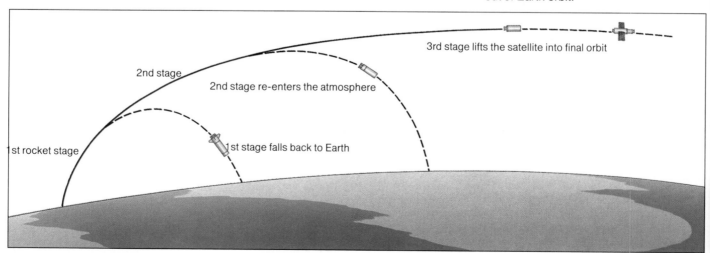

3rd stage lifts the satellite into final orbit

2nd stage

2nd stage re-enters the atmosphere

1st rocket stage

1st stage falls back to Earth

Gravity and orbits

It is the force of gravity that keeps satellites in an orbit. Without this force they would carry on in a straight line and shoot off into space.

172

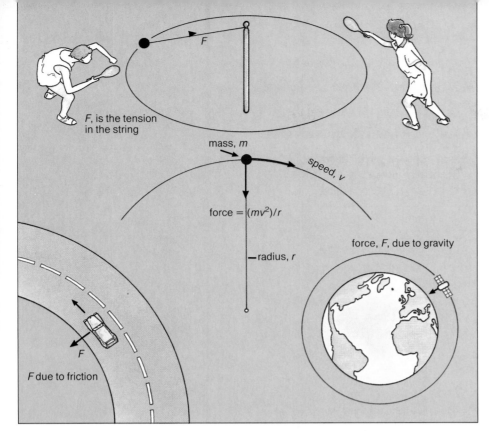

F, is the tension in the string

mass, *m*

speed, *v*

force = $(mv^2)/r$

radius, *r*

force, *F*, due to gravity

F due to friction

◀
Circular motion needs a central force. This is shown as *F* in each diagram.

Anything that moves in a circle needs a force to act on it, pulling it towards the centre of the circle, this is called a *centripetal force*. The diagram shows examples of circular movement, and the forces which are causing them.

What may surprise you is that no force is needed to push objects *along* the circle in space. Of course, on Earth we usually have to counteract some kind of friction force. But there is no friction in empty space. The Earth and the planets will go on circling the Sun for ever.

The Moon will circle the Earth for a very long time. But there is, in fact, a friction force between Earth and Moon – due to the tides. In the distant future the Moon will get nearer to the Earth, break up and fall into it!

Once Earth satellites are in orbit, they can switch off their engines. But most satellites are still inside the Earth's atmosphere. It is very thin, but there is enough frictional drag to bring the satellites back to Earth. At 8000 metres a second they usually burn up due to friction when they get into a denser part of the atmosphere.

Space travel

Human beings first left Earth in 1961, when the Russian Yuri Gagarin circled the Earth in the first manned Earth-satellite. Over the next few years both Russia and U.S.A. sent astronauts around the Earth. They also sent probes to the Moon, Venus and Mars. Satellites were used to help transmit TV and radio messages across the world (see Chapter 6, *Communications*). On 20 July 1969 Neil Armstrong stepped out of a lunar landing capsule and was the first man on the Moon.

It takes about 2½ days to reach the Moon. The space craft leaves an orbit around the Earth at a speed of 11 kilometres per second. As it moves away from the Earth it is always being pulled back by the force of Earth's gravity. The craft slows down until it reaches a point where the gravity pull from the Moon starts to accelerate it 'downwards'. At this point it is moving at less than 1 km/s.

The laws of gravity

The force of gravity from an object decreases rapidly with distance. Measured from the centre of the Earth, when the distance is doubled the force due to gravity decreases to a quarter.

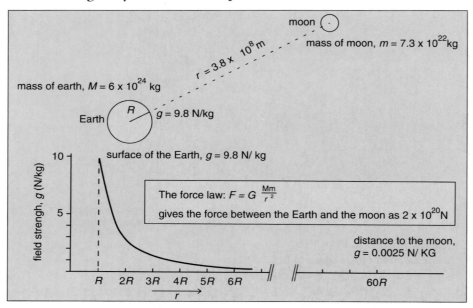

moon

mass of moon, $m = 7.3 \times 10^{22}$ kg

$r = 3.8 \times 10^8$ m

mass of earth, $M = 6 \times 10^{24}$ kg

Earth R $g = 9.8$ N/kg

surface of the Earth, $g = 9.8$ N/ kg

The force law: $F = G \dfrac{Mm}{r^2}$

gives the force between the Earth and the moon as 2×10^{20} N

distance to the moon, $g = 0.0025$ N/ KG

field strengh, g (N/kg)

10

5

R $2R$ $3R$ $4R$ $5R$ $6R$ $60R$

r

◄ The force of gravity between two objects depends on their masses and the distance between them.

The Moon is 60 times as far from the centre of the Earth as you are now. The gravity pull on each kilogram of your body is 9.8 newtons. The Earth pulls on the Moon with a force of less than 3 millinewtons per kilogram. This is enough to keep the Moon in orbit around the Earth.

The force due to gravity also depends on the masses involved. The Earth has a mass of 6×10^{21} tonnes. If it had the same mass as the Moon – but taking up the same volume – the surface gravity field would be 0.12 N/kg. The Moon is 81 times less massive than the Earth. On an 'Earth' like this the high-jump record would be about 200 metres. But such an 'Earth' would have lost its atmosphere, and the space-suit would cramp your jumping style!

The problem with space travel

Getting out of the solar system is not too difficult. The Voyager space probes, launched in 1977, have left the solar system. Voyager 2 swept past Neptune in September 1989. It sent excellent photographs back to Earth. Neptune is the outermost large planet. From then on, Voyager 2 was leaving the solar system, travelling at 10 km/s.

Voyager took 12 years to get to Neptune. Voyager 2 is now moving towards one of our nearest stars – Sirius – the brightest star in the sky. Barring accidents, Voyager will get there in A.D. 296036. If it went to the nearest star of all, Proxima Centauri, it would take just half the time, 'only' 150 000 years. So the problem, using current technology, is the sheer time that it takes to travel these huge distances. We would need to send a whole colony, with renewable food and energy sources, to make sure that anyone was left alive at the end of the journey.

▼ Neptune as seen by the Voyager space craft in 1989.

Stars

A star is a hot glowing mass of material. The Sun is a star. It is a small star, as stars go. It has a mass of 2×10^{27} tonnes, and glows a slightly yellowish white with a surface temperature of about 6000 °C. The largest stars are 400 times as massive as the Sun and give out a million times more energy. The smallest stars have a mass about a tenth of the Sun's and give out a thousandth of its energy.

Massive stars are very bright, and look blue. They give out so much energy that they don't last very long. We expect the Sun to have a lifetime of about 10 billion years. It is now 'middle-aged' at about 5 billion years old. A massive star might exist for only a few million years. Smaller stars last longer, and look red. So how do stars form? Why do they die? Where do they get their energy from?

▲
A hot, blue star, Rigel.

The life of a star

Space is huge. Most of it is empty. What matter there is is mostly hydrogen, the simplest, lightest element. In fact, 73% of the universe is hydrogen, the rest is mostly helium (the second lightest element). Less than 2% is left for all of the other elements.

Stars begin as a very large cloud of hydrogen and helium. The cloud is very cold, perhaps a few degrees above absolute zero.

Slowly, the force of gravity makes the hydrogen and helium atoms fall together. If the cloud is big enough it will become a star. Usually, the cloud is

so big that it breaks up into 'cloudlets', each of which forms into a star. We can see groups of stars of about the same age in many parts of the sky.

As the cloud gets smaller and more concentrated the gas gets hotter. The potential energy due to gravity is being transferred into the energy of movement of the gas atoms. The denser the gas cloud becomes, the stronger is its gravity field. The cloud collapses more quickly. By now it is hot, but not hot enough to glow. It is giving off infrared radiation, which telescopes on Earth can detect.

At some stage the centre of the cloud becomes very dense and very hot. We might not be able to see it yet,

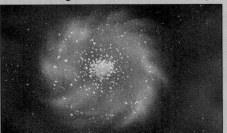

though, because the outer gases and particles may shield it from our sight. Then, if the star has enough mass, it reaches a critical stage.

If the star is massive enough the hydrogen nuclei at its centre will have picked up an immense amount of kinetic energy. When they collide with each other, some of them stick together

in *fusion reactions*. The hydrogen fuses together to make helium. *Nuclear energy* is released. This means that many more hydrogen atoms can fuse together. The small centre becomes a large, hot *core*.

The core sends out fast particles and a lot of visible light and other radiation. The outer layers of cool gas are blown away. Some of these bits may form

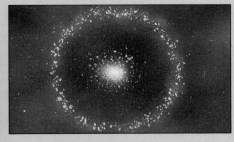

planets round the star. Suddenly the hot surface of the star can be seen: a star is born.

Most dust clouds collapse to form 'double' or even 'triple' stars.

Planets

The outer gas layers may become planets. This is what happened with our Sun. Astronomers have been looking for stars with planets for a long time – there should be millions of them. But stars are so far away any planets would be far too small to see. But a large planet may affect the movement of a star through space, and such movements have been detected for some nearby stars.

Why don't stars last for ever?

A star is in balance. It is so massive that there is a huge gravity force pulling the outer parts towards the centre. If you were on the surface of even a small star like the Sun you would weigh 27 times as much as you do on Earth. Stars are basically made of a gas. They don't collapse because the gases are very hot – at least 10 million °C – and exert a large pressure. This exactly counteracts the inward forces of gravity.

As time goes on, the hydrogen in the core of the star gets used up as it is converted to helium. The star only has to lose 10% of the hydrogen to make the nuclear reaction stop. What happens next depends on the size of the star.

The death of the Sun

For a small star like the Sun the end will be comparatively quiet. When the core reactions stop, the core cools. It starts to contract and the outer layers fall in. This will release potential energy *and the core will get hotter*. The sudden surge of radiation and particles will push away the outer layers and they will expand to reach the orbit of Earth or even Mars. The whole process from collapse to expansion will take just a few hours. The Sun will then be much bigger, and cooler. Instead of being white hot it will be merely red hot. Stars like this are called *red giants*.

The nearest red giant star to the Earth is in the constellation of Orion. It is the top left star in the constellation, and is called Betelgeuse. Becoming a red giant isn't the end of the story. The core of the Sun will still be very hot, and different nuclear reactions may now take place. The Sun could live as a red giant for perhaps billions of years. By now, of course, the inner planets will have become vaporised. But sooner or later the core cools, and so does the huge cloud of warm gas surrounding it. Slowly, the star shrinks to a small, hot ball, about a tenth of the size of today's Sun. It will have become a *white dwarf* star. As it cools further it eventually ends up, lost to sight, as a black dwarf star. It might even become a *black hole*.

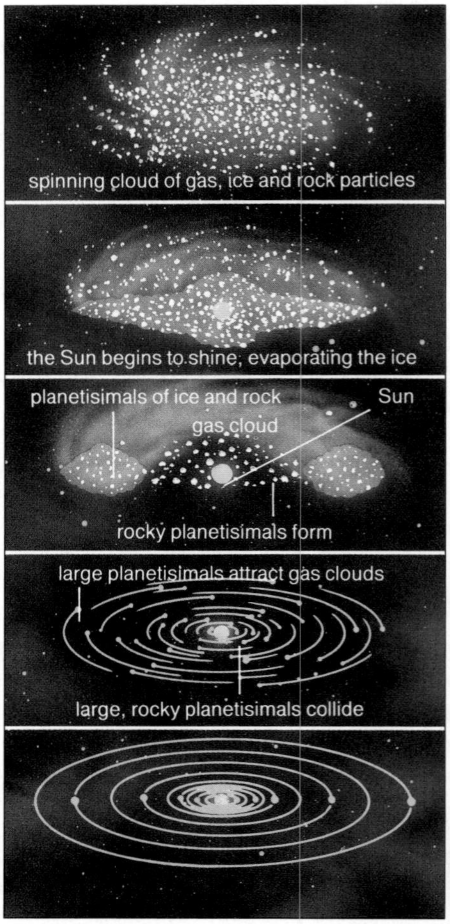
spinning cloud of gas, ice and rock particles
the Sun begins to shine, evaporating the ice
planetisimals of ice and rock
Sun
gas cloud
rocky planetisimals form
large planetisimals attract gas clouds
large, rocky planetisimals collide

▲ Planets are the left-over bits from a star. These were 'sorted' by gravity, the outward pressure of the particles and radiation from the star. The denser materials stayed close to the star, forming the dense, small planets (Mercury, Venus, Earth and Mars). The lightest particles formed the outer 'gas planets', which are mostly hydrogen.

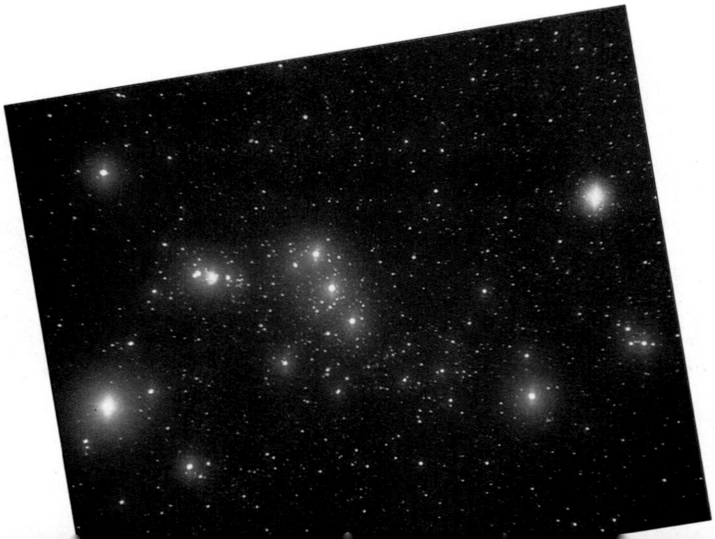

◄ The three stars that form 'Orion's Belt' are some of the clearest in the sky.

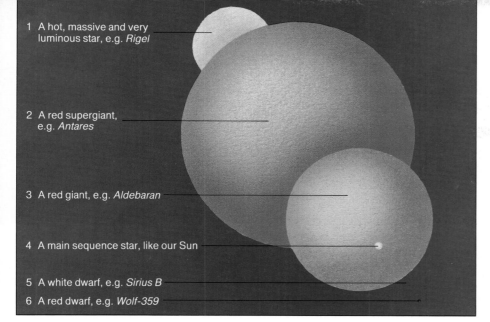

1 A hot, massive and very luminous star, e.g. *Rigel*

2 A red supergiant, e.g. *Antares*

3 A red giant, e.g. *Aldebaran*

4 A main sequence star, like our Sun

5 A white dwarf, e.g. *Sirius B*

6 A red dwarf, e.g. *Wolf-359*

◀
The life-story of a star.

Novae, supernovae and black holes

Large massive stars use up their hydrogen very quickly. When they come to the end of the hydrogen-conversion stage there are other nuclear reactions that could keep them going. They might be able to survive for a few hundreds or thousands of years looking much the same to our telescopes. But the new reactions have produced a much hotter core.

Then, one day, the reactions give out. In a few hours the pressure drops and the star collapses. The outer layers, still rich in hydrogen, fall into the core. This is still very hot, and the fresh hydrogen starts to react immediately. The result is an explosion. What we see in the sky is a 'new star' or *nova*. We can sometimes recognise it as the new state of a star we knew about already. A typical nova gives a burst of energy 100 000 times greater than steady output of the old star. The outburst lasts for a few weeks, gradually dying away.

Astronomers see about 30 novae a year. Once every 400 or 500 years we see a *supernova*.

A supernova is a star that suddenly becomes brighter than a 1000 million Suns (4000 times brighter than an ordinary nova). Luckily, the ones that have been seen are so far away they don't do any harm. But in A.D. 1054 a supernova was so bright that it could be seen in daylight. It was in the constellation Taurus, and is now known as the Crab Nebula.

Supernovae happen when very massive stars collapse. When this happens a huge mass of hydrogen falls into a very, very hot core. The core may be 300 or 400 times hotter than the core of the Sun. The collapse takes just a second or two. The resulting explosion gives off more radiation than a whole galaxy of stars.

Black holes

What is left after the explosion is a rapidly expanding cloud of gas, and a very hot, very dense central core. Matter has been crushed to its densest state: it has become a sea of neutrons. A cubic metre of this sea would have a mass of about 500 000 tonnes. If the Earth were compacted to this density, it would be just 300 metres in diameter.

The neutron star would also be very small, perhaps only 20 kilometres across. Its gravity field would be 70 billion times the gravity field on Earth.

But it doesn't end there, either! As the neutron star cools down, the immense gravity forces make the star collapse even further. When the star

▲
The Crab Nebula is the remnant of a supernova (an exploding star). It is about 6000 light years from Earth.

▼
Astronomers know about the past from data like the Bayeux tapestry. It shows a comet in 1066.

shrinks to be about 5 km in diameter the gravity field becomes so strong that not even light can escape from the star. It has become a *black hole*.

A universe of galaxies

Seen from Earth, most stars are pin-points of light, even when seen with the largest telescopes. But if you look into the piece of sky just below the 'belt' of Orion you can see a small fuzzy patch of light. You can see it better with a small telescope or a pair of binoculars. An object like this is called a *nebula* (or 'cloud').

There are many of these 'nebulae' dotted all over the sky. Some can be seen with the naked eye. Some are clouds of gas, lit up from the inside by radiation from a nearby star. The gas glows like the neon in an advertising sign. Some nebulae are the remains of exploded stars, others are where new stars are being formed.

But not all nebulae are gas clouds. This was proved by the new powerful telescopes just being built about 70 years ago. These telescopes showed that some nebulae were in fact *clouds of stars*, not clouds of atoms! They looked like clouds because they were so much further away than any stars we can see.

We now know that they are huge 'islands of stars', containing as many as *several hundred billion stars*. They are called *galaxies*. The largest telescopes have photographed over a billion of these galaxies, and the deeper we look into space the more we see. (In this book a billion is a thousand million (10^9).)

The Milky Way

We live in a galaxy called the Milky Way. Look up into the sky on a clear night and you will see a broad band which looks brighter than the rest of the sky. A pair of binoculars will show that the brightness is due to thousands of stars, very close together. You are looking along the spiral arms of the galaxy.

▲
You can see the three stars of 'Orion's Belt' at the top, and the Horsehead Nebula between them. Below this is the Orion Nebula.

▼
This telescope at Mount Wilson in California uses a 2.5 m mirror at the bottom of the central tower to gather light. When built, it was the largest in the world. Edwin Hubble used it to measure the distances between galaxies and their velocities. He used the data to prove that the universe is expanding.

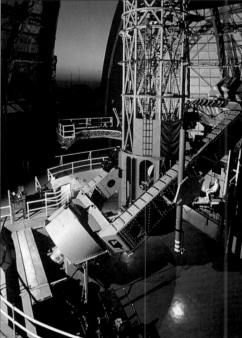

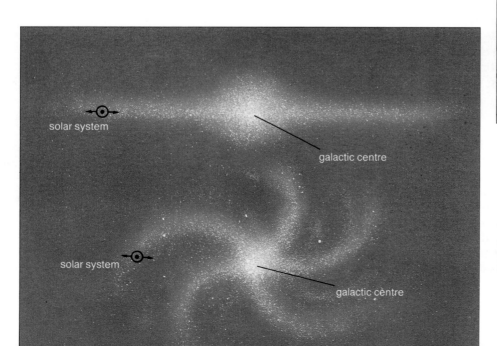

solar system

galactic centre

solar system

galactic cèntre

◄
The solar system is far out along one of the spiral arms of the Milky Way galaxy. When you look from Earth in the directions of the arrows, you see the most stars.

An expanding universe

One of the first astronomers to photograph the distant galaxies and show that they were made of stars was an American called Edwin Hubble. He also photographed the *spectra* of light emitted by the galaxies. Chemists use spectra to find out what chemical elements a substance contains.

Astronomers also use spectra to tell them which elements are in the stars. But the spectra can also give them another important piece of information – the speed at which the star is moving. This relies on the *Doppler* effect.

The Doppler effect

You have already *heard* the Doppler effect. When a police car or ambulance is in a hurry it sounds a siren. As the vehicle comes towards you, you hear the sound rise in pitch. As it goes away the pitch gets lower. This happens because sound is a wave. You hear more or fewer waves per second as the source of sound moves to you or away from you.

Light is also a wave. When a star moves towards us its light changes colour because we see more waves per second than we would if the star was still. The light looks more *blue*. If the star is moving away, we see fewer waves per second and so the light looks *redder*.

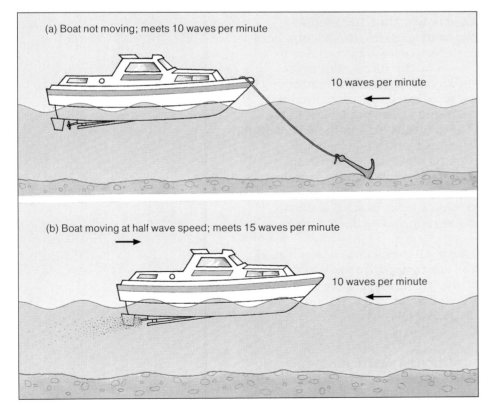

(a) Boat not moving; meets 10 waves per minute

10 waves per minute

(b) Boat moving at half wave speed; meets 15 waves per minute

10 waves per minute

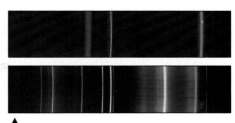

The emission spectra of hydrogen (top) and helium. These show how we can tell the difference between the elements. Light from the elements is split into its component wavelengths. These appear as coloured lines at different places in the spectrum.

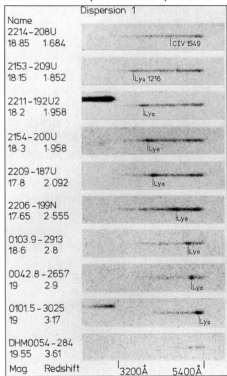

The photograph shows spectra from some quasars. Going from top to bottom, you can see that the same spectrum lines moves towards the red end of the spectrum – 'red shift'. Stars with the largest red shift are thought to be the furthest away. The bigger the red shift, the faster they are moving. This fits in with the theory of the expanding universe.

The Doppler effect. What would happen if the boat moved to the left at the same speed as the waves?

Hubble saw that the spectra of elements in distant galaxies showed a *red shift*. No only that, but the further they were away from us, the more the lines were shifted towards the red end of the spectrum.

It seemed that every one of these huge, distant collections of stars was moving away from us. This could only be explained if the whole universe was getting bigger. And not only that, the galaxies are *accelerating* as they move away. We are living in an *expanding universe*.

How old is the universe?

This can be worked out from the rate of expansion of the galaxies and quasars. If we assume that this expansion has been fairly constant, then everything in the universe was once very close together. It is quite hard to measure the rate of expansion, so astronomers hedge their bets. The accepted value is that the universe is somewhere between 11 billion and 18 billion years old.

The 'big bang'

Scientists who study the universe as a whole are called *cosmologists*. Most cosmologists believe that the universe began as a very small, intense point. All matter, energy, time and space was folded together into this point. It was surrounded by nothing – not even empty space. We cannot imagine what it was like.

Then this point began to expand (no one can imagine why). The first matter was mostly in the form of quarks, electrons and the strange particles called neutrinos, which are like uncharged electrons. When the universe was a few thousandths of a second old, the quarks combined to form protons and neutrons. When the universe was 1 second old, it was at a temperature of 10 billion degrees.

As the new universe got bigger it cooled down. After 100 seconds, there was enough matter to make billions more galaxies than we now see.

But nearly half of the particles were anti-particles – antiprotons and antineutrons, electrons and positrons. When matter meets antimatter, mass turns into radiation. In a few tens of seconds most of the matter in the universe destroyed itself. But there was a slight excess of matter over antimatter. This difference formed the stars and galaxies that exist today.

Some of the protons combined with the neutrons to form the nuclei of helium. No neutrons were left over, so the other protons became hydrogen. This gave us the basic matter of the universe: 75% hydrogen, 25% helium. We now know enough about the way sub-atomic particles 'work' to confirm this ratio by theory as well as by observation.

Nothing much happened for the next million years or so. Then matter became cool enough for the electrons to be captured by the hydrogen and helium nuclei and so form atoms.

Electrons are negative, nuclei are positive. All the electric forces cancel out. Atoms are electrically neutral. So, the most important force in the universe became the very weak force of gravity. Slowly, gravity began its work. At an age of about 3 billion years, stars had formed in their teeming billions, in huge groupings that we see as galaxies.

The microwave background

We can even detect the remains of the radiation formed in the big bang. It started off as very dangerous X-rays, at a temperature of several billion degrees. The universe has expanded so much that this has 'cooled down' to barely detectable microwaves, showing the average temperature of the universe to be just 2.7K (2.7 degrees above absolute zero).

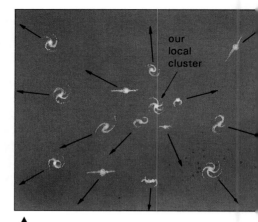

▲
Galaxies are moving away from each other. The further they are from each other, the faster they are moving. One day, will they start to come together again?

THE INDEPENDENT

No 1,722   FRIDAY 24 APRIL 1992   ★★★ Published in London   40p

A Nasa spacecraft has detected echoes of the galaxies' birth fourteen thousand million years ago. The discovery about the formation of the stars after the Big Bang has been hailed by excited scientists as the Holy Grail of cosmology. **Susan Watts** and **Tom Wilkie** report

How the universe began

BACK TO CREATION
How the universe evolved from the Big Bang, through the first three minutes, to the first clusters of matter 300,000 years on. By 15 billion years humanity had emerged from the dust of the stars.

15 billion years
DNA, the molecule of inheritance, and life on Earth emerge   1 billion years

300,000 years
Epoch of recombination: the first ripples of cosmic structure
Discovery announced yesterday

3 minutes

1 second
Stable subnuclear particles, neutrons and protons, are formed

10^{-10} seconds

10^{-34} seconds
The primordial quark soup (only bare fundamental particles exist)

10^{-43} seconds

THE BIG BANG

All matter and energy were condensed to a point

10^{32} degrees
All forces unified and violent increase in expansion (cosmic inflation)

10^{27} degrees

10^{15} degrees
More matter than antimatter in Cosmos

10^{10} degrees

10^9 degrees
Formation of helium and lithium nuclei

6,000 degrees

-255 degrees
Heavy chemical elements produced in gravitational collapse of stars

-270 degrees
Centigrade

GRAPHIC: MICHAEL ROSCOE

FOURTEEN thousand million years ago the universe hiccuped. Yesterday, American scientists announced that they have heard the echo.

A Nasa spacecraft has detected ripples at the edge of the Cosmos which are the fossilised imprint of the birth of the stars and galaxies around us today.

According to Michael Rowan-Robinson, a leading British cosmologist, "What we are seeing here is the moment when the structures we are part of — the stars and galaxies of the universe — first began to form."

The ripples were spotted by the Cosmic Background Explorer (Cobe) satellite and presented to excited astronomers at a meeting of the American Physical Society in Washington yesterday.

"Oh wow . . . you can have no idea how exciting this is," Carlos Frenk, an astronomer at Durham University, said yesterday. "All the world's cosmologists are on the telephone to each other at the moment trying to work out what these numbers mean."

Cobe has provided the answer to a question that has baffled scientists for the past three decades in their attempts to understand the structure of the Cosmos. In the 1960s two American researchers found definitive evidence that a Big Bang had started the whole thing off about 15 billion years ago. But the Big Bang would have spread matter like thin gruel evenly throughout the universe.

the lumps (stars, planets and galaxies) got into the porridge.

"What we have found is evidence for the birth of the universe," said Dr George Smoot, an astrophysicist at the University of California, Berkeley, and the leader of the Cobe team.

Dr Smoot and colleagues at Berkeley joined researchers from several American research organisations to form the Cobe team. These included the Goddard Space Flight Center, Nasa's Jet Propulsion Laboratory, the Massachusetts Institute of Technology and Princeton University. Joel Primack, a physicist at the University of California at Santa Cruz, said that if the research is confirmed, "it's one of the major discoveries of the century. In fact, it's one of the major discoveries of science."

Michael Turner, a University of Chicago physicist, called the discovery "unbelievably important . . . The significance of this cannot be overstated. They have found the Holy Grail of cosmology . . . if it is indeed correct, this certainly would have to be considered for a Nobel Prize."

Since the ripples were created almost 15 billion years ago, their radiation has been travelling toward Earth at the speed of light. By . . . radiation Cobe

able to view the young universe, Dr Smoot said.

A remnant glow from the Big Bang is still around today, in the form of microwave radiation that has bathed the universe for the billions of years since the explosion. Galaxies must have formed by growing gravitational forces bringing matter together. To produce a "lumpy" universe, radiation from the Big Bang should itself show signs of being lumpy.

Cobe, which has been orbiting 500 miles above the Earth since the end of 1989, has instruments on board that are sensitive to this extremely old radiation. The ripples Cobe has found are the first hard evidence of the long-sought lumpiness in the radiation.

Cobe detected almost imperceptible variations in the temperature of the radiation, which measures 270C below zero. Those variations — only about thirty-millionths of a degree — represent slight differences in the density of matter at the edge of the universe, ripples of wispy clouds

matter, the scientists said yesterday. The smallest ripples the satellite picked up stretch across 500 million light years of space.

Cobe has taken a snapshot of the universe just 300,000 years after the Big Bang

diation and matter produced by the explosion cooled down. "The results also show that the idea of a Big Bang model is once again brilliantly successful," Professor Rowan-Robinson, of London University, said.

He described the ripples as similar to the chaotic pattern of waves you might see from an aeroplane window flying over an ocean. "I can be pretty confident now that if we had an even bigger telescope in space we could see the fluctuations that are the early signs of individual galaxies themselves. It's just a matter of technology now," he added.

The point in time of Cobe's snapshot is known as "the epoch of recombination". At this point,

leased from the foggy soup of radiation, was set free to be picked up by modern astronomers with their telescopes.

"Further analysis of Cobe's results will shed light on the identity of the mysterious dark matter that we know contributes most of the mass of the universe," Dr Carlos Frenk, of Durham University, said yesterday. This mystery dark matter is scientists' best guess at explaining why the universe is lumpy.

Astronomers have worked out that, for today's galaxies to have formed, there ought to be far more matter around than they have observed. One of the leading theories to get round this is the Dark Matter theory, which says that about 99 per cent of the matter of the universe is invisible to us. This theory predicts fluctuations in the background radiation of exactly the size Cobe has observed. "Because these had not been seen, the theoreticians were beginning to get worried that they had got it wrong," Professor Rowan-Robinson said.

"If Cobe had found no ripples the theoreticians would have been in disarray; their best shot at understanding how galaxies were formed would have been disproved," he added. "The cold dark matter theory is a very beautiful theory which makes very exact

these fluctuations should be. How big they are depends on how fast they are able to grow. These results are just the size that the theory predicts. People have been looking for this kind of variation since the 1950s."

However, Arnold Wolfendale, the Astronomer Royal, sounded a note of caution. He said the scientific community must examine the results before shouting too loudly about their importance.

"There is no doubt that, if verified, this is a very important result. Detecting these small fluctuations is very difficult. Another group reported having picked up similar fluctuations last year, then later found they were due to cosmic rays. At the frequencies our colleagues in the US are working at, cosmic rays should not be a problem, but there is dust between the stars which can also produce radiation and make you think it is cosmological."

Martin Rees, Professor of Astrophysics at Cambridge University, said: "We needed equipment sensitive enough to pick up these fluctuations. We can expect in the next year or so there will be other observations from the ground corroborating this.

He said the results opened up a whole new area of astronomy. "Now we have seen them we can start analysing them. We can learn a lot about the history of the universe — what happened when. We might find, for example, that there was a second foggy era after

---

What happens next?

When you throw a ball into the air, it falls back down. If you could throw it fast enough it would leave Earth altogether. It would become a space probe, like the Voyager spacecraft that are now on their way to the stars. The Voyagers will escape the gravity field of the Sun as well as that of the Earth. Can the galaxies escape from each other?

There are three possible fates for the universe.

1 If the galaxies are moving fast enough they will escape each other's gravity pulls and the universe will carry on expanding.

2 If the galaxies are moving too slowly, the forces of gravity will slow them down completely. They will stop and then begin to fall back towards each other again. Eventually they will collide and the universe will end in the '*big crunch*'.

3 If the speeds are just right, the galaxies will just stop and stay where they get to, in perfect balance.

▲
Science really hitting the headlines! It was claimed that a special satellite had detected ripples left over from the 'big bang'. This would be like seeing what was happening to the universe only 300 000 years after the big bang happened.

The graph shows these three possibilities. Just in case you are worried by the possible end of the universe, remember that humans have been on Earth for just 2 million years or so. Anything might happen in the next 2 million years, but you will have lost interest in about 70 years or so anyway! In any case, the Sun isn't due to become a red giant for about another 10 billion years.

How do we know all this?

Astromony deals with huge numbers. It describes huge objects, at huge distances that have existed for vast periods of time. It is very hard even to imagine these sizes, distances and times.

The evidence for what you have read in this chapter is mostly based on the everyday physics of the school laboratory. The rest is based on measurements and observations made in laboratories where small, high-energy particles of matter are tested to destruction.

Telescopes

The main instrument of an astronomer is the telescope. The simple astronomical telescope is made from two positive lenses. The front lens is 'weak'. It has a low power and long focal length. As shown in the diagram, it makes a real image of some stars close to the user's eye. The image is upside down. The second lens is simply a magnifying glass, used to magnify this image.

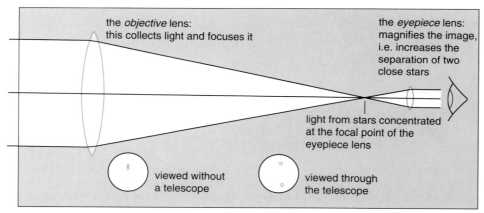

The main use of a telescope is to gather light. Distant objects are very faint, so the more light that we can collect, the further into space we can see. To collect more light we need a wide front lens. This causes problems. Glass lenses are heavy, and it is hard to make sure that such a large piece of glass is perfect all through. Also, a simple lens causes unwanted colour effects due to *dispersion*.

A mirror telescope solves these problems. The *reflecting telescope* was invented by Isaac Newton. As shown in the diagram, a large curved mirror is used instead of the front lens. It can be made a lot lighter than a lens telescope of the same light-gathering power. It doesn't suffer from colour defects and it is easier to make the surface accurate than it is to make perfect glass.

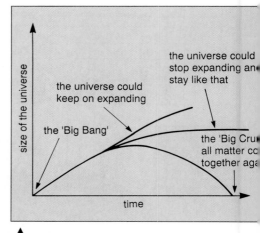

▲ Whether the universe will collapse or go on expanding depends on (a) how fast the galaxies are going and (b) how much matter there is in the universe. The more matter, the bigger the gravitational pull to stop the expansion. Scientists suspect that there is a lot more matter in the universe than we have so far detected. The current favourite theory is for the 'big crunch'.

◀ An astronomical telescope makes the stars seem brighter and separates details (magnifies).

▼ A Newtonian reflector. The main light-gathering and focusing is done by a large concave mirror.

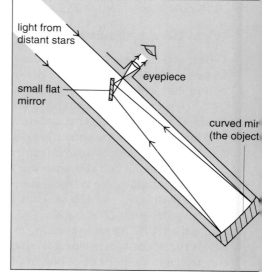

◄
A series of radio-telescope dishes working together.

The largest telescopes are radio telescopes. They are reflecting telescopes. Radio waves can be reflected by wire grids to the 'eyepiece' which is simply a small wire aerial (see Chapter 6, *Communications*).

How we know about stars

Not even the largest telescopes can show us the *surface* of a star. The images that we see are just points of light. Even these are blurred by the effects of the Earth's atmosphere or the effects of diffraction in the telescopes (see Chapter 6). But as explained above, we can analyse the light by spreading it out in a spectrum. These measurements are usually made by taking photographs with an exposure of many hours. But modern telescopes may use the very sensitive electronic charge-coupled devices (CCDs) that are used in video cameras.

Spectra tell us about:

- the temperature of the star: the hotter it is, the bluer the light;
- the elements present in the surface of the star: the light that we see comes from the surface, and each element has a characteristic line spectrum;
- the movement of the star: the lines in the spectrum are shifted in wavelength if the star moves away or towards us (see page 179);
- the total energy emitted by the star (its luminosity), which also helps us to calculate its mass.

Experiments and theories about sub-atomic particles like protons, neutrons, electrons and neutrinos allow scientists to calculate what it must be like deep inside the star. Thus we know how hot the centre of the star must be, and how much energy it should radiate away. This also gives clues about how far away a star is.

How we know how far away the stars are

There are various ways for measuring the distances of stars. Some are good for near stars, others for distant stars and even galaxies. Here are just two simple ways.

Brightness measurements

Take two stars of equal size and real brightness, e.g. two 'suns'. We can tell that they are the same because they will have the same 'colour'. If they are also at the same distance, our instruments would collect the same amount of energy from each. But the energy received gets less the further away the stars are. Light obeys the inverse square law. This means that if one star was twice as far away, we would measure just a quarter of the energy compared with the nearer star. This method is very useful. It works even for whole galaxies – but only if we compare like with like.

Parallax

This is basic trigonometry as used by land surveyors and map-makers on Earth. They start with a measured base line. Then they go to each end of the line and measure the angle of view to an object, like a church spire.

A scale diagram will give an accurate map (as shown). In astronomy you can start with a base line of a few miles (or a few thousand miles if you use the diameter of the Earth). This allows the distances to planets and even the Sun to be measured. The biggest base line is the diameter of the Earth's orbit around the Sun. This means taking measurements six months apart! It was this method that allowed the distance of the nearest stars to be measured. It was first used in 1838.

How do we know the size of the universe?

The distance of the furthest objects that we can detect are measured by using the red shift (see page 179).

(see page 179)

Galaxies are collections of billions of stars and are much further away than the single stars that we see. The universe is expanding, and the further away a galaxy is, the faster it is moving. The red shift tells us the speed, and so we can work out the distance.

Measurements are not very accurate, however. The furthest objects we detect are the very energetic quasars. These are about half-way to the 'edge of the universe'. This may not be the real edge, it's just that at a distance of over about 10 billion light years the light would have to have started out before the universe began. Don't even think about it!

Is there life on other planets?

Life as we know it relies on the chemistry of carbon and water. The water has to be liquid for life forms to be able to use it. This means a temperature of between 0 and 100 °C. There must be millions of stars in the universe with planets at just the right distances for the pressure and temperature to be capable of sustaining life. We haven't discovered any yet. Also, no one knows for certain how life began. It may be a 'one-off' event. One thing that we can say, however, is that it is very unlikely that there is life on any of the other planets in our solar system.

Whistle-stop tour

We now know a great deal about the nine planets in our solar system. There are two planets between the Earth and the Sun. *Mercury* is closest to the Sun. It is small, and does not have a large enough gravity field to

184

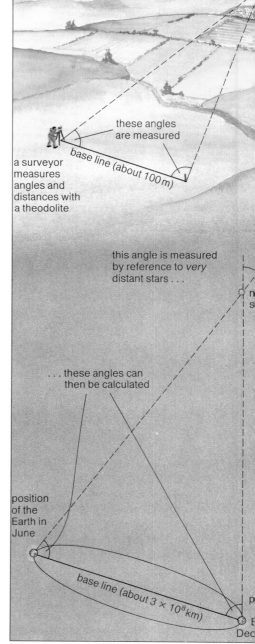

these angles are measured

base line (about 100 m)

a surveyor measures angles and distances with a theodolite

this angle is measured by reference to *very* distant stars . . .

. . . these angles can then be calculated

position of the Earth in June

base line (about 3×10^8 km)

▲ The distances of the nearest stars are measured by using trigonometry – just like a surveyor measuring distances – but the base line is a bit longer!

▼ A composite of photographs of Mercury, taken by Mariner 10 in 1974.

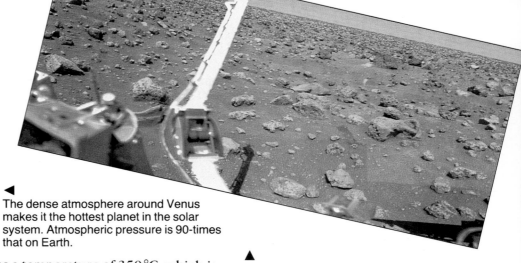

◀
The dense atmosphere around Venus makes it the hottest planet in the solar system. Atmospheric pressure is 90-times that on Earth.

▲
The Viking spacecraft landed on Mars. It sent back pictures and results from sampling experiments.

hold an atmosphere. Its surface reaches a temperature of 350 °C, which is hot enough to melt lead. At night, the temperature falls to −170 °C.

Venus is more promising for possible life. It is about the same size as the Earth. If it had a similar atmosphere, life could exist on it. But the atmosphere of Venus is mostly carbon dioxide, the 'greenhouse gas'. This raises the surface temperature to 485 °C, making it the hottest planet in the solar system. As a result, the surface pressure is 90 times that of Earth.

Mars is further away from the Sun than Earth. It has a very low-pressure atmosphere, again mostly carbon dioxide. Any water is likely to be frozen most of the time. But in the Martian summer the noon temperature at the equator rises to 18 °C – a cool summer's day on Earth. Mars is the only planet that has been probed for life. The Viking space craft visited the planet in 1976 and sent down its Lander module to test for signs of life. None were found.

Jupiter, Saturn, Uranus and *Neptune* are different kinds of planets altogether. They are very much bigger than the inner planets. They receive very little energy from the Sun. None of them have a real 'surface'. They have atmospheres mostly made of hydrogen, with varying amounts of methane and helium.

On Jupiter, for example, the gravity field at the top of the atmosphere is over twice as strong as the Earth's surface field. At a depth of about 1000 km the hydrogen is compressed to a liquid. Here its temperature is 2000 °C.

Pluto is almost a double planet. It has a moon, Charon, nearly as big as itself. From Pluto it would be hard to pick out which star is the Sun, it is so far away. It must be cold enough to freeze any gas solid.

▲
Jupiter and four of its moons.

▼
Saturn as seen by Voyager 1 in 1980.

▶
Neptune. The colours show the height of clouds – white the highest and dark blue the lowest.

▼
Pluto. A drawing made from various data. The moon is almost as big as the planet itself.

▶
Several pictures taken by Voyager 2 have been put together to give this view of Uranus and one if its moons.

Life on Earth began about a billion years after the planet had formed. At that time, the Earth would have been very similar to Venus. As explained in Chapter 8, *Managing the Earth*, it is the presence of this life which has formed the atmosphere as we know it today. It is therefore possible that planets like Venus and Mars could be 'seeded' with simple life forms, and in time become suitable places for the kind of advanced ecosystems that we have on Earth.

Activities

1 This activity takes a few minutes a night for at least a week.
(a) Find out when the Moon rises. You can do this either by looking for it, by looking it up in a good diary or in a good newspaper (usually next to the weather forecast).
(b) Look to see where the Moon is at the same time every night (say 8 p.m.). Draw its shape. Note where it is (e.g. by using a star map) compared to a well-known constellation. If you don't know any constellations, use a tree or a tall building as a fixed marker (if you do this you'll have to observe from exactly the same spot each night).
(c) Write a short description of what happens to the Moon over the period of time you observe it.

2 Star clocks. This activity takes a few minutes every hour for at least three hours on a starry night.

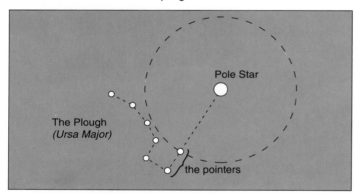

(a) Copy the diagram showing the Pole Star. It includes a dotted outline of the 'Plough' as a guide to what it looks like. As soon as it gets dark enough, find the Plough and sketch where it is on your diagram. Do the same thing every hour until bedtime. Label your sketch with the time.
(b) Use your diagram to work out how many degrees the Plough swings through, on average, in an hour. How long would it take to swing through 360°? Explain your result.
(c) You could use the position of the Plough as the hour hand of a clock. But there's a snag. What is it?

3 Finding your way at night. Find the Pole Star by using the two 'pointers' on the Plough. Design and carry out an experiment to show that the Pole Star is always due north.

4 Depending on the time of the year, find as many of the following constellations as you can. (You will need a star map; see the 'Reference Section'.) You can see the Plough (Ursa

Major) and Cassiopeia on any night in the year. The other constellations to look for depend on the time of year:

Spring	Summer	Autumn	Winter
Leo Virgo Coma Berenices	Lyra Cygnus Hercules Corona Borealis Scorpius Sagittarius	Andromeda Pegasus Aries Capricornus	Gemini Taurus Pleiades Orion Canis Major

You should be able to see the Milky Way on any night in the year. A pair of binoculars will show extra details. The monthly star maps also give interesting information about the things to look for.

5 The newspaper star maps usually mention *nebulae* ('clouds'). Some of these are gas clouds (as in Orion), but often they are clusters of perhaps thousands of stars in our own galaxy or even complete, distant galaxies. The easiest ones to see are listed below (all views are improved by using a pair of binoculars).
   The Great Nebula (M42) in Orion; the Globular Cluster M56 in Lyra; the Globular Cluster M13 in Hercules; as many as seven galaxies in Coma Berenices; many open clusters in Cassiopeia; the Great Nebula (M31 – a galaxy) in Andromeda; lots of nebulae of different types in Sagittarius. (See Activity 4 for the best time of year to see them.)

6 All planets are to be found near the ecliptic. In other words, they will be close to the 'signs of the zodiac' constellations. To find them you need an up-to-date star map. At certain times Jupiter, Mars, Venus and Mercury may be the brightest 'stars' in the sky. Mercury is always close to the Sun and so is hard to see. Try to map the planets on a star map.

7 On your own, or as a group, find out all you can about one of the following topics:
(a) the Hubble Space Telescope;
(b) comets;
(c) the 'big bang' theory;
(d) black holes;
(e) The Apollo Moon missions.
   Prepare a short talk about your topic that you could give to a Year-8 class. Your talk should be illustrated with posters or other visual aids.

Questions

1 Give three main differences between stars and planets.

2 (a) You should *never* try to look at the Sun through a telescope or a pair of binoculars. Explain why.
(b) If you want to see stars or planets well, you must always wait a few minutes in the dark before trying to see them. Explain why.

3 Explain what the following are:
(a) a galaxy;
(b) the Milky Way;
(c) the ecliptic;
(d) signs of the zodiac;
(e) comets.

4 The strength of the Earth's gravity field is about 10 N per kg at its surface.
(a) Calculate the force with which it attracts masses of (i) 5 kg and (ii) 30 kg.
(b) Use the formula $F = ma$ to calculate the acceleration with which the two masses in part (a) would fall freely.
(c) At what speed would the masses be travelling after falling for 6 seconds?

5 Page 169 explains how gravitational potential energy changes to kinetic energy as an object falls. Read this and answer the following questions (you can assume g to be 10 N/kg).
(a) How much potential energy does a 3 kg rock have, if it is at the top of a cliff and can fall 15 metres?
(b) The same rock slips off the cliff. How much kinetic energy would it have just before it hits the ground?
(c) How fast would the rock be going just before hitting the ground?
(d) The rock embeds itself in the sand. What has happened to the energy that the rock had?

6 Design (describe or draw) a space ship that would get human beings to (a) the nearest star; (b) the nearest galaxy.

7 Explain (briefly):
(a) where the Sun and stars get their energy from; (b) how the energy gets to the Earth.

8 This question asks you to analyse the data on planets in the 'Reference section' (pages 246 and 247).
(a) Which is the most massive planet?
(b) Which planet has the shortest 'day'?
(c) One set of planets has, on average, a much higher density than the others. List these planets.
(d) (i) Use a calculator to work out the average distance of these dense planets from the Sun. (ii) Do the same for the other set of less dense planets. (iii) Suggest reasons for these differences (use your imagination, or think about what the planets might be made of).

9 (a) What is the difference between the *mass* of an object and its *weight*?
(b) Use the table of data about the solar system ('Reference section' pages 246 and 247) to: (i) name the planet with the strongest gravity field at its surface; (ii) find the weight of an object of mass 2 kg on Mars and Jupiter.

10 Imagine the force of gravity spreading out in space from a planet. Can you think of a reason why its effect gets smaller, the further from the planet?

Checklist

These are the facts and ideas that you should have learned by studying this topic.

To reach Basic Level you should:

- know that forces are needed to make things move faster
- know that gravity is a force and be able to give two examples of what it does
- be able to describe how the Sun and the Moon appear to move in the sky
- understand that most of these movements are caused by the Earth's movements
- know the difference between stars and planets
- know two useful things that astronomy can do for us (i.e. finding direction, time and seasons)

To succeed at Foundation Level you should:

- know how forces affect an object's movement on Earth and in space
- be able to use what you know about the Earth in space to explain day and night and the lengths of the day and the year
- know how the planets move in the solar system
- know that the Earth is very old compared with the time that humans have lived on it
- know that the Sun is the main source of energy for the Earth
- know what telescopes can tell us about stars and planets

To succeed at Merit Level you should:

- understand how forces cause acceleration
- know the difference between mass and weight
- know that planets and satellites are kept in orbit by gravity force, and about the way this force acts
- know the main features of the solar system, the galaxy and the universe
- know about the theories people have used to explain the origin and nature of the Earth and the solar system
- know that the Sun's energy comes from nuclear fusion
- understand how a simple astronomical telescope works

To succeed at Special Level you should:

- be able to make calculations involving forces and movement in a gravitational field
- understand how weight is related to mass and depends on the gravitational field strength
- know that circular motion requires a central (centripetal) force, and be able to use this idea to explain about Earth satellites
- understand how Earth satellites are put into orbit, and know about geostationary orbits
- be able to use astronomical data to produce ideas about conditions in different parts of the solar system and the universe
- be able to relate our present-day theories about the universe to the experimental and observational evidence
- know about the life-cycle of a typical star
- be able to discuss the possibilities and problems of space travel
- understand the advantages of reflecting telescopes compared with the simple astronomical telescope

CHAPTER TEN

The World System

Life depends on the ability to obtain and control energy. The Sun is the source for all energy on Earth.

The energy to move this train came from the Sun. Where has the energy gone once the train stops?

The Earth is one of the four smallest planets of the nine that spin around the Sun. The Sun is a slightly 'below average' star, one of a hundred thousand million (10^{11}) in an average-sized galaxy that we call The Milky Way. The Earth is the only planet in the Sun's family that has life on it.

Life must obey the same rules as everything else in the universe: the laws of physics and of chemistry. As far as we can tell, these laws are the same everywhere in the universe. We don't know if there is life somewhere else out there in space. If the rules allow life on Earth there probably is some kind of life, somewhere — but that's another story.

Life depends on *energy* and the ability to *control* it. This is what this chapter is about.

The flow of energy

The energy we receive on Earth started as tiny lumps of matter deep inside the Sun. These are mostly *protons*, whirling and colliding at a temperature of 10 million kelvin. In this dance of the protons some (a very tiny fraction) marry. They combine to make a bigger, four-particle lump – a nucleus of the element helium. As they do so the particles get less massive. In accordance with Einstein's theory of relativity, the lost mass appears as energy.

This release of energy takes place deep inside the Sun, and keeps the Sun hot. The Sun doesn't keep on getting hotter because it radiates an equal amount of energy into space. Only a tiny fraction of this radiated energy reaches Earth and the other planets.

The laws of energy state that 'mass-energy' cannot be created or destroyed, but that energy can become less usable. The energy that is radiated into deep space from the Sun seems to be of no use to anyone or anything. It gets more and more diluted as it spreads out, and there is no way of getting it back.

The energy balance of the Earth

The Earth gets energy from the Sun as electromagnetic radiation. The radiation is most intense in the visible region: the radiation that we have become adapted to *see*. But the bulk of the energy is spread out over the infrared wavelengths, which are the ones most easily absorbed by matter (see Chapter 6, *Communications*). The effect of this radiation is to heat whatever absorbs it.

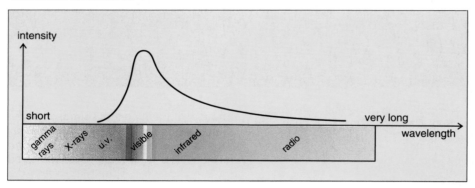

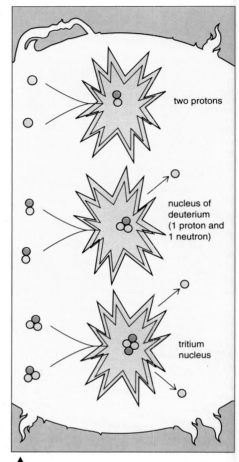

▲
The Sun is powered by the fusion of hydrogen into helium. Each fusion event changes a tiny amount of mass into energy. The Sun converts 4 million tonnes of its mass each *second* into energy by fusion.

◄
The electromagnetic spectrum with solar distribution plotted above it.

But the Earth is quite a good reflector of *radiation*. About 30% of the radiation energy is reflected straight back into space. The Earth is also a good radiator. As it is warmed by the Sun it re-radiates another 47% of this energy back into space. Most of the rest is used to make the weather: winds, clouds and rain. *Of all the energy that the Sun sends towards Earth just 0.02% is trapped by living things.* (See page 215 in the 'Reference section'.)

Of course, the other 99.8% of the energy that reaches the Earth is vital to life. It keeps the place warm. There is a very delicate balance here. If the Earth became more than a few degrees warmer the land would become too dry to support life. If it became even hotter the seas would evaporate and rain would never fall. The Earth would be a hot, cloudy planet just like Venus is today (see page 185 in Chapter 9, *space*).

If the Earth cooled too much, water would freeze. Again, life as we know it now would be impossible.

Strangely enough, it is life which holds the balance. The balance of the world system depends on the two 'life gases': oxygen and carbon dioxide.

Energy transfer

The first law of energy states that energy cannot be created or destroyed. But this law only works if we recognise that *mass* is a form of energy: sometimes a system loses mass which then appears as movement or radiation energy. The best-known example of this is in nuclear decay, fission and fusion. But mass also 'changes' to energy in many everyday chemical changes on a much smaller scale. The reverse can also happen: high-energy radiation can 'lose energy' and form a pair of particles with mass. For example, gamma radiation can produce a pair of oppositely charged electrons.

Apart from these effects, energy has only two 'forms': *potential* and *kinetic*. Potential energy is always due to some kind of force field. The forces may be gravitational, electric, magnetic or the strange new forces discovered deep inside the nuclei of atoms. When these forces cause mass to move they transfer energy from potential into kinetic (movement) energy.

Radiation is a strange mix of kinetic and potential energy. It is a moving wave of alternating electric and magnetic fields. It behaves like a wave in that it can be diffracted and show interference (see pages 97–8). But as an energy carrier it often behaves like a particle. The particles are called *photons*.

In chemical reactions the electric potential energy stored in *chemical bonds* may be released (see below) as radiation or as extra movement of atoms and molecules (kinetic energy). We usually experience the extra energy as a rise in temperature. We say that 'heat is released'. In fact, 'heat' is mostly the energy of motion of particles, or *internal energy*. In the same way, nuclear energy, food energy, solar energy, wind energy, etc. are just handy names for a mix of potential and kinetic energy in different systems.

- work done by a force = force × distance moved in the direction the force acts

- electrical transfer of energy = charge × potential difference (or current × volts × time)

- gravitational potential energy = ½ mgh

- kinetic energy = ½ mv^2

- power = rate of energy transfer
  $P = E/t; P = VI$

▲
You could measure the height of Niagara Falls using a thermometer! Measure difference in temperature between the water at the top and the water at the bottom, *T*. Then let $mgh = msT$, where s is the specific heat capacity of water. Then the height of the falls, $h = sT/g$.

Photosynthesis, life and the atmosphere

The 0.02% of the radiation that life uses is first trapped by plants. They use it for *photosynthesis*. In this process, energy is used to combine together water and carbon dioxide to make a carbohydrate: sugar. Oxygen is a waste product from this reaction:

$$6 H_2O + 6 CO_2 + \text{energy} \xrightarrow{\text{chlorophyll}} C_6H_{12}O_6 + 6 O_2;$$
$$\text{water} + \text{carbon dioxide} + \text{light} \longrightarrow \text{glucose} + \text{oxygen}.$$

Chlorophyll plays a vital part in controlling the reaction. It is a *catalyst*. Like all catalysts, Chlorophyll brings together the reacting particles long enough for them to react. It doesn't get used up itself. Plants change glucose into the polymer starch, and also make other complex molecules like vitamins, proteins and cellulose. The digestive processes in animals can break down these complicated plant chemicals to provide energy, or use them as building blocks for the complex molecules that they need for growth or for making their cells work. But when animals need energy they have to turn these molecules back into glucose. The glucose releases energy when it is broken down (oxidised) by oxygen (see below).

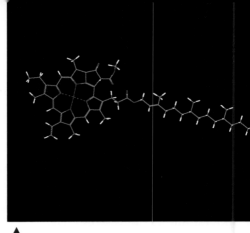

▲
A model of the chlorophyll molecule: this captures the energy in sunlight. An atom of magnesium sits at the centre of the molecule.

▼
Strands of green algae packed with oval chloroplasts (the sites of photosynthesis).

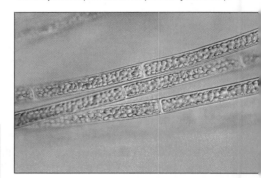

The atmosphere

Without photosynthesis the Earth's atmosphere would contain no oxygen. What we have now has been slowly built up by photosynthesis over the past 500 million years or so.

The Earth's atmosphere

Gas (%)	Mars today	Venus today	Young Earth	Earth today
Carbon dioxide	95	98	98	0.03
Nitrogen	1.7	1.9	1.9	78
Oxygen	0.13	trace	trace	21
Rare gases	2	0.1	0.1	1
Other data				
Surface temperature (°C)	−23	460	300	20
Surface pressure (N/m^2)	6400	9×10^6	60	1×10^5

Originally the Earth's atmosphere was 98% carbon dioxide. The proportion now is just about 0.03%. What happened to all this carbon dioxide gas? It is, in fact, under your feet – in the form of rocks like chalk and limestone. The 'free' oxygen produced by plants allowed new kinds of life: animals. They had no chlorophyll, and got their energy by eating plants. They also ate each other, and so some grew shells to protect themselves. To do this the animals took carbon dioxide dissolved in the seas and combined it with the most common element on the Earth's surface, calcium, to make a hard rock-like substance – calcium carbonate. Calcium is a metal which reacts easily with water to make a solution of calcium hydroxide:

$$\text{calcium} + \text{water} \rightarrow \text{calcium hydroxide} + \text{hydrogen},$$
$$\text{Ca} + 2 H_2O \rightarrow \text{Ca(OH)}_2 + H_2.$$

Calcium hydroxide reacts with carbon dioxide to make calcium carbonate and water:

calcium hydroxide + carbon dioxide → calcium carbonate + water,

$$Ca(OH)_2 \quad + \quad CO_2 \quad \rightarrow \quad CaCO_3 \quad + \quad H_2O.$$

Other reactions helped, but on the whole, life is responsible for the fact that most of the billions of tonnes of carbon dioxide that once floated free in the air are now locked up in rocks. We rely on the *carbon cycle* (page 219) to keep the tiny but vital fraction of carbon dioxide in our atmosphere still there. This cycle involves photosynthesis and combustion.

Respiration and combustion

Life is adapted to an atmosphere that is rich in oxygen and poor in carbon dioxide. Maybe it is the other way around: perhaps life has adapted the atmosphere to its own needs. If so, plants and animals work together to do this. Plants use photosynthesis to build large molecules from smaller ones. The energy in the bonds of these molecules can be used by animals to drive their own life processes. It all happens at the sub-cellular level, in a process called *respiration*.

Respiration breaks up the molecules built by photosynthesis. The cell gets its energy from changing glucose (a sugar) back into water and carbon dioxide. It does this by using the very reactive element oxygen:

glucose + oxygen → carbon dioxide + water + energy,

$$C_6H_{12}O_6 + 6\,O_2 \rightarrow \quad 6\,CO_2 \quad + 6\,H_2O + energy.$$

▲
The white cliffs of Dover. Rocks like these have locked up the carbon dioxide that used to be in the atmosphere.

▼
Carbon dioxide is also locked in animal shells, bones and teeth.

Energy levels and bonds in chemistry

It takes energy to break something up. Think about what happens when you stretch a rubber band until it breaks. It's hard work! This is because the molecules of rubber are held together by forces. The same applies at the level of atoms and molecules. The holding forces are electrical forces.

When forces pull things together energy is *released*. Think about a heavy object falling to the ground – it can cause damage and makes a noise.

In chemical reactions energy has to be *supplied* to break chemical bonds, and some energy is *released* when bonds are made. Most reactions involve breaking some bonds and then making new ones. Take a simple example in combustion: the burning of hydrogen in oxygen to produce water.

First we have to break the bonds between the atoms of oxygen and of hydrogen. This is shown in the diagram.

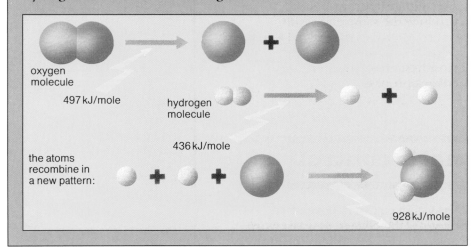

oxygen molecule

497 kJ/mole

hydrogen molecule

436 kJ/mole

the atoms recombine in a new pattern:

928 kJ/mole

◄
Breaking chemical bonds when hydrogen and oxygen react.

When hydrogen burns in oxygen, making the new bonds releases more energy than was needed to break the bonds in the first place. The reaction is said to be *exothermic*.

We can show these energy changes by using *energy-level diagrams*.

The *balanced* equation for the actual reaction is:

$$2 H_2 + O_2 \longrightarrow 2 H_2O.$$

We need two 'lots' (moles) of hydrogen and 1 'lot' (mole) of oxygen to make 2 'lots' (moles) of water.

So, the energy to break bonds: 2 sets of H − H bonds   = 2 × 436 = 872 kJ

1 set of O = O bonds   = 497 kJ

Total   = 1369 joules.

Energy to make bonds: 2 molecules each with 2 bonds = 4 sets of H−O bonds

= 4 × 464 kJ

Total = 1856 kJ.

Net energy release = 1856 − 1369
= 487 kJ.

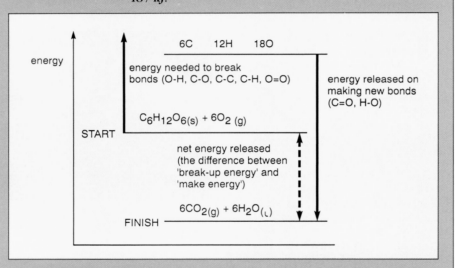

This explains (a) why you need a match to start the burning reaction and (b) why the reaction then keeps on going.

Energy release in the respiration reaction. ◄

Dead plants and animals are broken down either by atmospheric oxygen or with the help of *microbes* to produce the same end result: carbon dioxide is returned to the atmosphere. Microbes play a vital role in this recycling process as *decomposers*.

This natural recycling has kept the atmosphere in balance for many millions of years. It is an example of a feedback process.

Feedback and automatic control

'Feedback' happens when any *change* in a system can somehow act backwards to affect whatever it was that *caused* the change. It was a word first used in electronics. *Negative* feedback tends to keep things the same.

This may be how the oxygen–carbon dioxide ratio is kept constant in the atmosphere.

Imagine a sudden increase in the amount of atmospheric oxygen, perhaps because the plants are doing well! Two things now become possible.

1 More plants lead to more animals – so more plants get eaten (so they stop doing so well, and the oxygen level falls).
2 More oxygen in the atmosphere means a greater risk of fires (due mainly to lightning strikes); plants burn, and the oxygen gets used up. Thus more oxygen means, sooner or later, less oxygen. The balance is maintained.

What might happen if the carbon dioxide level increased dramatically? If you can answer this question you could get a Nobel Prize – because the Earth may now be going through just such an event, which we call the *greenhouse effect* (see page 217). Scientists (and governments) are still arguing about what might happen if this is happening; the latest research suggests that the carbon dioxide level is not rising as fast as people feared that it might.

Natural feedback takes time, perhaps tens of thousands or even millions of years. But at present human beings are burning the plant material that nature took 60 million years to produce (the fossil fuels). At the same time we are cutting down trees all over the world. Both actions are affecting the carbon cycle. The danger here is of *positive* feedback.

In positive feedback the change affects the cause of the change in such a way that the change is made even greater. Some scientists think that if the greenhouse effect does make the Earth warmer, there will be less ice and clouds to reflect infrared radiation away. This will make the Earth hotter still!

Homeostasis

Biologists use the word *homeostasis* to describe the way organisms keep things the same. Your liver and pancreas keep your blood-sugar level constant by using the hormone insulin. Your skin and blood keep you at a steady temperature by using sweat and by changing the blood flow near the skin. This is controlled by signals from the nerve cells that sense temperature. You have studied many other examples of homeostasis in this course. See Chapter 2, *How living things work* for more about homeostasis.

Feedback in chemistry

Many chemical reactions show positive feedback. The most common example is the burning of a fuel. Most fuels just sit there, surrounded by oxygen, until you give them just a little energy. Think of lighting natural gas. This is mostly the hydrocarbon, methane. Like all hydrocarbons it burns in oxygen to form carbon dioxide and water:

methane + oxygen → carbon dioxide + water,

$$CH_4 + 2 O_2 \rightarrow CO_2 + H_2O.$$

As soon as you give enough energy for some bonds to be broken, the reaction just 'runs away'. The reaction is *exothermic* (energy releasing) and the energy released carries on breaking more bonds and releasing more energy to break more bonds . . . We get a flame, a fire, or even an explosion. See Chapter 1, *Chemistry in the home*.

What exactly happens depends upon the *rate* at which the reaction can occur. This is in turn decided by a combination of factors:

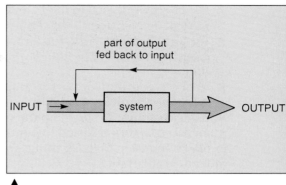

A simple feedback loop.

- the energy released in the reaction (which can raise the temperature, so making collisions between particles more effective);
- the arrangement of the reacting particles (chemicals can react better as gases than as solids or liquids; powders react more quickly than large lumps);
- the concentration of the reacting chemicals (concentrated solutions work more quickly than dilute ones);
- using a catalyst to speed up the reaction.

All of these factors are used to control chemical reactions at home, in industry and even in living things. You should know about *enzymes* as biological catalysts.

There is more about reaction rates in Chapter 4, *Controlling chemical reactions*.

Negative feedback in chemistry is quite rare. Most chemical changes go on until everything is 'used up'. Essentially, this means that the chemicals have reached a state in which all the bonds are at the lowest energy possible. This is another example of the *Second Law of Thermodynamics*: energy spreads out and becomes less usable. For example, left to chemistry alone all the oxygen in the atmosphere would react with other elements or compounds. It takes life to stop this happening, as explained above.

The big picture

The diagram shows the main factors that are involved in the system of the Earth. Most of these have already been mentioned in this chapter, and you have met all of them somewhere in this course.

▼
The world system as you have studied it in this course.

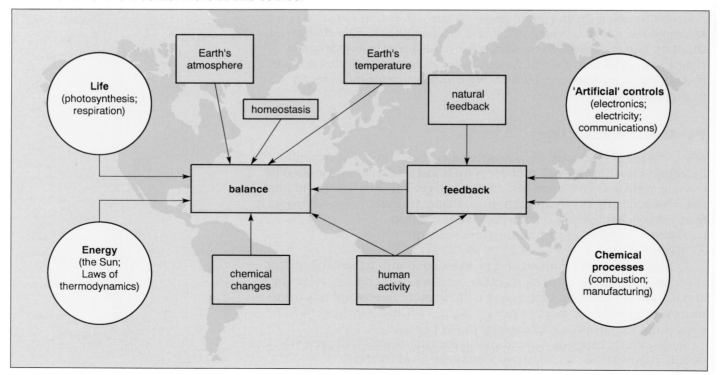

Throughout the course, you have been told about the effect of human beings on this system. Never in the 4.5 billion year history of the world has one species been so dominant.

Humans dominate by using their *intelligence*. Most species become successful by adapting themselves to the world as it is; humans have become successful by adapting the world to themselves. We alter the natural ecosystem into a *managed* ecosystem, by farming and fishing, for example. In the course of millions of years, coal, oil and natural gas have been 'burnt' as part of the natural *rock cycle*. We shall burn most of these reserves up in less than a thousand years at current rates. We alter the water cycle by building dams, cutting down forests, and by covering large areas of land with impermeable concrete. We interfere with 'natural' human population control by using antibiotics (and waste and water treatment). You can probably think of many more examples like these.

Some of these changes are planned, but others are unexpected. No-one foresaw the greenhouse effect, or the hole in the ozone layer. The effect of industrial pollutants on both managed and natural ecosystems has often been very great.

▼

Electrons are arranged in definite patterns around the nucleus. Only the electrons in the outer layer (*shell*) take part in reactions. Lithium and sodium have just one outer electron. This gives them very similar chemical properties.

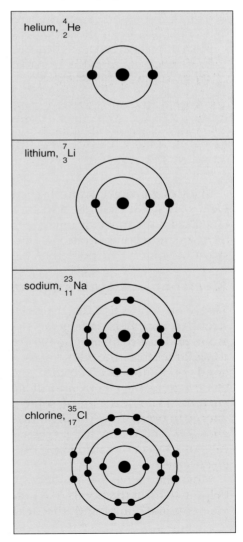

Controlling chemical changes

We rely on chemical changes to provide us with most of our energy and most of the materials we use. See Chapter 7 for more about the chemical industry. Chemistry became a lot more predictable and controllable when the 'secret' behind the Periodic Table of the elements was discovered. At the end of the nineteenth century it was a useful but rather mysterious pattern. The discovery of the *electron* and the *nuclear atom* led to an understanding of how chemistry actually works. It is all to do with electricity: the force that holds molecules together is electrical. It is the force of attraction between the negative electrons and the positive nuclei of atoms.

The best model of the atom says that the electrons are arranged in *shells* around the positive nucleus. The new laws of physics (essentially the quantum theory) are used to decide how many electrons can fit into each shell. The number of electrons in the outermost shell – and how far this shell is away from the nucleus – decide the detailed chemistry of each element. The main difference between electrons in different shells is their different energies.

Electrons can leap from one atom to another, or be shared by the shells of two atoms. These effects produce the *ionic* and *covalent* bonding that you have learned about.

Electrolysis

When ionic compounds are put in water the electric force between the ions gets weaker. The ions may split up and we say the compound has dissolved. The ions stay in solution as charged particles. This solution is called an *electrolyte*. Much everyday chemistry involves reactions between solutions like this: acids and alkalis, salts and precipitation, corrosion and the rusting of iron are all examples of reactions with ionic compounds.

We can use the fact that ions are electrically charged to get them out of solution, by using *electrolysis*. When two charged plates are put in the solution, ions are attracted to the plates (one plate has a positive charge and the other has a negative charge.) The ions lose their charges on contact, and simple ions become ordinary neutral atoms again, as in the electrolysis of dilute hydrochloric acid, shown in the diagram below.

Electrolysis

The anode (positive plate) and cathode (negative plate) are kept charged by the battery. Ions move to the electrodes, so forming a current in the electrolyte. In this example a chloride ion releases its 'extra' electron at the anode, which then flows through to the battery. The ion thus becomes a neutral chlorine atom. The atoms pair up to form chlorine molecules. The reaction may be summarised as:

$$Cl^- + Cl^- \rightarrow Cl_{2\,(g)} + 2\,e^-.$$

A mole of chlorine ions releases a mole of electrons. This many electrons carries a charge of 96 487 coulombs (the *Faraday constant*). It takes 2 faradays to produce one mole of chlorine molecules.

While this is going on at the anode an equal number of electrons flows through the cathode. These electrons are accepted by the hydrogen ions. This turns them into hydrogen atoms which combine to form molecules:

$$H^+ + H^+ + 2\,e^- \rightarrow H_{2\,(g)}.$$

Again, two moles of electrons are involved (2 faradays of charge). The gases bubble off at their electrodes.

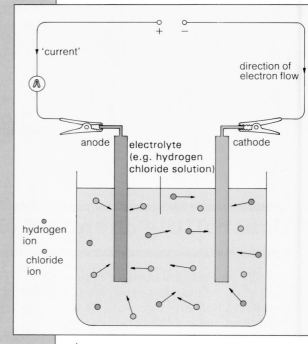

Electrolysis of hydrochloric acid.

Many of the vital chemical reactions in living things involve ions and electrolytes. For example, messages are sent along nerve cells as an electrical pulse made by ions of potassium and sodium. Blood fluid has to have the right concentration of ions, which may be unbalanced if you sweat too much. The body then has to restore the balance of ions.

Electrons in metals and semiconductors

The electron was first discovered by being dragged out of a metal by a strong electric field. In a metal, electrons have broken free of particular atoms and just roam around inside the metal. They are held there by quite weak forces from the whole mass of nuclei. This means that metals are good conductors of electricity – when you apply even a very small electric field, the electrons drift along the metal, forming an electric *current*. If you heat a metal, some electrons are given enough kinetic energy to break away through the surface. This effect is called *thermionic emission*, and is how we get the electron streams used inside the vacuum tube of a TV set or cathode ray oscilloscope. (See Chapter 3, *Using electricity*.)

Most non-metals are insulators, the electrons are firmly trapped, helping to form the bonds that hold atoms together. But there are a few elements and compounds that are in between the good insulators and the metals. These materials have electrons which can be loosened by giving them energy. In fact, even at room temperature there is enough energy for a few electrons to be free. These materials are called *semiconductors*. (See Chapter 3, *using electricity*).

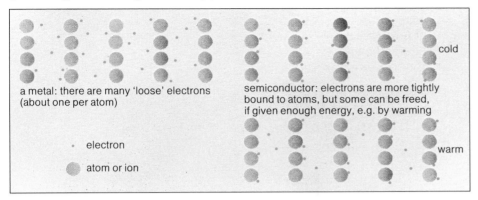

a metal: there are many 'loose' electrons (about one per atom)

semiconductor: electrons are more tightly bound to atoms, but some can be freed, if given enough energy, e.g. by warming

cold

warm

· electron

atom or ion

◄ The electrons in a semiconductor compared with those in a metal.

Perhaps the most important technological developments of the twentieth century have been the use of the vacuum tube and the semiconductor in *microelectronics* (see below).

Controlling and using electrons
Simple circuits use metal conductors to carry the flow of electrons, and we control them with simple make-and-break switches. We use lengths of resistance wire to change the flow (current) and the energy available from them (voltage). You will have seen many simple circuits that use these components.

These applications of electricity are dealt with in Chapter 3. Modern life would be very different without the heating and movement we produce by using electricity as an energy carrier. Bear in mind what electricity does: it is not a source of energy. Electricity *moves* energy, and the energy it carries comes from something else. It usually comes from burning a fuel, or from nuclear energy.

▲ A thermionic valve.

▼ Banks of thousands of valves were needed in the first computers.

Electricity in information and control

In the early days of *electronics* we used the 'free' electron. The electrons were controlled by electric fields, in a glass tube emptied of air. It was possible to make amplifiers, radio transmitters and receivers, and cathode ray tubes for use in oscilloscopes, radar and television. These fields needed quite high voltages. The tubes were made of glass, and the free electrons were produced by hot filaments. The tubes had many disadvantages: they were large, fragile, expensive and used a lot of energy (most of which was ultimately wasted in heating the surroundings).

Microelectronics replaced the vacuum tube with very much smaller devices that used low voltages, needed no heating and were very robust. They were also very cheap to make. Most TV sets and computer monitors still need the vacuum tube, but the tubes are being replaced by 'liquid crystal' screens in some applications where lightness and portability are essential.

▼ A flat-screen LCD display that has none of the 'free-flying' electrons seen in cathode ray tubes.

The *solid-state* circuits used in microelectronics are based on the transistor. This is a simple device in which a current can be controlled – made larger or smaller – by applying a small voltage. Millions of these circuits can be placed on a small square of a semiconductor material and combined to make useful circuits. One of the most useful type of circuit is the *logic gate*.

A logic gate uses the transistor in its simplest form, as an on–off switch. The gates are combined in various ways to produce the variety of complex gates shown on page 111 in Chapter 6, *Communications*.

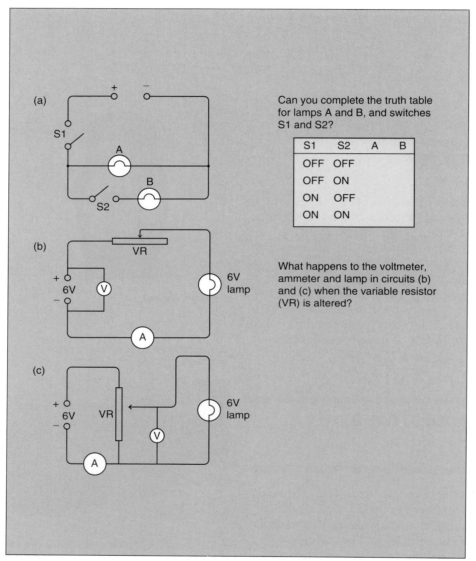

Can you complete the truth table for lamps A and B, and switches S1 and S2?

S1	S2	A	B
OFF	OFF		
OFF	ON		
ON	OFF		
ON	ON		

What happens to the voltmeter, ammeter and lamp in circuits (b) and (c) when the variable resistor (VR) is altered?

◀

Logic gates and truth tables.

Such circuits can make decisions based on complicated instructions and inputs. They can store instructions and data as a set of on–off states by using *binary code*, i.e. they can have a *memory*. They can also be *programmed* to follow instructions exactly and to make decisions.

The devices may be 'ready-programmed' as in cameras, washing machines, microwave cookers, etc. These do the same job every time. But the circuits can also be used more flexibly in programmable devices: *computers*. What the computer does is then decided by what you tell it – the software.

Models and control

The Earth is a complicated place, yet somehow, over thousands of millions of years, conditions on Earth have remained stable enough for life to flourish. It seems to do this by a system of feedback and recycling, as described above. Human beings are making great changes to the Earth. The worry is that these enforced changes are happening faster than natural feedback and recycling processes can cope with.

As well as producing effects that interfere with natural cycles, can human beings *control* the Earth system just like the natural cycles do? Large computers can now be used to produce mathematical models of the Earth's systems, and these can help us to forecast what might happen next. But of course, the forecast is only as good as the *theory* that we have based our model on. How often is the long-range weather forecast really accurate, for example?

One model that is talked about a great deal is that of the greenhouse effect. This theory says that if we continue to burn large amounts of fossil fuels, releasing carbon dioxide into the air, then the Earth will become wrapped in a blanket of gas that stops the planet from cooling down naturally.

The greenhouse effect may be a threat to the world's future, or we may have just got the model wrong. Whatever the case, we have all realised that human activity affects the Earth. Whether it is burning reserves of fossil fuels, damming a river to make electricity, or removing sand from a local beach to use in land-fill, we have to be aware of the possible consequences and be able to change the way that we behave if our activities are likely to upset the balance of the Earth system for ever. We all have a choice.

▲
We must all consider what effect our actions can have on the balance of the Earth's systems – however unimportant they seem – whether it is using an aerosol or cutting down a tree to widen a path or road.

Questions

1 What do the following types of food have in common: bread, rice, pasta, potatoes and maize? List as many things as you can.

2 What parts of the electromagnetic spectrum are responsible (or used) for:
(a) warming the Earth;
(b) causing sun-tan (and snow blindness);
(c) sight;
(d) carrying TV signals;
(e) taking pictures inside the body (of broken bones, for example)?

3 (a) Describe how the human body maintains itself at an internal temperature of 34.5°C:
(i) when it is a hot day; and (ii) on a cold day (other than by using clothes!)
(b) Lizards are called 'cold blooded' animals. What does this mean? How do lizards cope with very hot and very cold weather?

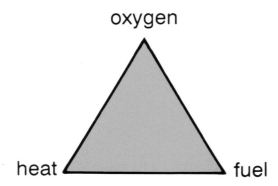

4 The diagram shows the 'fire triangle'.
(a) Explain what it shows.
(b) Use it to explain two ways of putting out fires.
(c) Why are the chemicals made when something burns called 'oxides'?

5 Here is a list of fuels: coal, natural gas, petrol, diesel oil.
(a) Why are they sometimes called *fossil fuels*?
(b) Someone says that these fuels got their energy from the Sun. Is this true? Explain your answer.
(c) The fuels are mostly made of two chemical elements joined together. What two elements are they?

6 (a) Which of these electrical devices uses (i) the most power, (ii) the least power? Pocket calculator; cooker with oven; TV set; hair dryer; electric kettle.
(b) What figure on the label tells you how much power the device uses?

7 The photograph shows an athlete at the end of a race.
(a) What changes have occured during the race to his heart and lung system?
(b) Why have these changes occurred?
(c) Describe in as much detail as you can how the athlete's body has changed so that it gets rid of the 'waste energy' generated during the race.

8 "Photosynthesis and respiration are part of the carbon cycle." Explain what the carbon cycle is and how these two life processes are involved in it.

9 "Energy flows through an ecosystem like water through a landscape; organisms are temporary dams that slow it down for a while". Explain this statement in terms of an ecosystem that you have studied.

10 In what ways are combustion and respiration (a) similar and (b) different?

11 Explain the following, with reference to as many chemical details as possible.
(a) When you cook potatoes you should cut them so that the pieces are all about the same size.
(b) You can make yeast dough rise by warming it — but if it gets too hot it will stop rising altogether.
(c) You can set light to a pile of flour but it doesn't burn very well, but a flour factory has to take very careful precautions to avoid the risk of a dangerous explosion.

12 This question is about crude oil (petroleum). You may need to use the 'Reference section' or some other reference books to answer it.
(a) We can use crude oil to make useful everyday fuels.
(i) From where did the fuels originally get their energy?
(ii) Name three fuels that are made from crude oil. (iii) Explain how the fuels release their energy when used. (iv) What major environmental effect does the use of such 'fossil fuels' have?
(b) Crude oil is also used as a feedstock for making other chemicals (i.e. not fuels). (i) Name some of these other chemicals.

One main use of these chemicals is to make polymers:
(ii) explain what a polymer is (iii) describe as fully as you can how a typical polymer is made from smaller molecules.
(c) In view of the problems we get from using crude oil as a source of fuels, would it be a good idea to reserve it just for making other chemicals, like plastics? Justify your answer.

13 We might solve our energy problems *either* (a) by using a lot less energy, *or* (b) by using a better, non-polluting energy source.
Choose (a) or (b) and write an essay giving the advantages and disadvantages of trying it as a solution.

14 (a) What are the two main 'laws of energy'? (The First and Second Laws of Thermodynamics)?
(b) Explain how these laws apply in either (i) using a motor car or (ii) keeping your home warm.

15 How could you use electricity to:
(a) bend a beam of electrons in a curve;
(b) separate copper from iodine in a solution of copper iodide (CuI_2);
(c) pick up an iron nail;
(d) make a sound;
(e) produce a higher or lower voltage in a separate circuit?

16 The reaction between methane and oxygen is exothermic. The equation for this reaction is:
$CH_4 + 2 O_2 \rightarrow CO_2 + 2 H_2O$.
(a) (i) How many moles of oxygen are needed to react completely with each mole of methane? (ii) How many moles of carbon dioxide are produced?
(b) (i) What is the formula mass of each substance involved in the reaction? (ii) Calculate the mass of oxygen needed to burn 32 g of methane, and how many grams of carbon dioxide that would then be produced.
(c) Energy is needed to break bonds. It is released when bonds are made. The bonds involved in the reaction are shown below:

$$H - \overset{\displaystyle H}{\underset{\displaystyle H}{\overset{|}{\underset{|}{C}}}} - H \qquad O = O \qquad O = C = O \qquad \overset{\displaystyle O}{\underset{\displaystyle H \qquad H}{}}$$

The energy needed to make or form the bonds is given in the table, in terms of the energy per mole of bonds. For example, to break up one mole of oxygen needs 497 kJ.

Bond	H – C	O = O	C = O	O – H
Energy per mole (kJ/mol)	435	497	803	464

(i) How much energy is needed to break up the bonds as 1 mole of methane reacts with oxygen?
(ii) How much energy is released to form the product compounds (water and carbon dioxide)?
(iii) What is the net energy release in the reaction?
(iv) Drawn an energy-level diagram to illustrate your answers.

18 We can show what happens to energy in a system by using Sankey diagrams (see page 245). Draw Sankey diagrams that show (roughly) the energy flow through (a) a human being; (b) a tree; (c) a light bulb; (d) a car engine; (e) a small pond.

19 The photograph shows a crane being used to work a pile-driver. An electric motor lifts a heavy drop-hammer. It is gently lowered into a 'pile case' which guides it to fall down as

accurately as possible on to a foundation pile that is then driven into the ground. This question is about the energy transfers that take place in this system.
You may find the following formulae useful:
- gravitational potential energy = mgh;
- kinetic energy = $\frac{1}{2} mv^2$;
- energy transferred by a force = Fd;
- power = energy/time;
- efficiency = $\dfrac{\text{useful energy output}}{\text{total energy input}}$

- Take g to be 10 N/kg.
(a) The drop hammer has a mass of 4000 kg and is dropped from a distance of 1.5 m above the pile. (i) Show that 60 kJ of gravitational potential energy is available for transfer to the pile. (ii) How much kinetic energy does the hammer have just before it hits the pile?
(b) The aim is to transfer all this energy into sinking the pile further into the ground.
(i) Do you think this aim could be achieved? Suggest how energy could be 'lost'.
(ii) The hammer was able to deliver 90% of its stored energy into the pile. As a result the pile was pushed 0.1 m into the soil. Calculate the frictional force acting against the pile.
(c) The motor used to lift the drop hammmer had in fact to lift it a height of 4 m above the pile. This was to get it into the guide tube.
(i) How much energy did the motor have to supply to do this?
(ii) The motor took 80 seconds to lift the pile. What was the effective power of the motor?
(d) The actual power of the motor was 2.4 kW. Use this fact and the data you have calculated in part b(ii) to show that the overall efficiency of the pile-driving system is just less than 30%.

20 An ecologist collected the following data about the numbers of animals in a National Park over a period of many years.

Year	Number of foxes	Number of rabbits
1950	38	520
1952	36	540
1954	39	530
1956	36	240
1958	20	45
1960	12	2
1962	8	0
1964	6	20
1966	10	330
1968	16	860
1970	28	1260
1972	52	640
1974	44	440
1976	30	310
1978	24	320
1980	22	450
1982	28	860
1984	42	640
1986	36	480
1988	39	560
1990	38	540

(a) Show how the populations change by plotting graphs of fox and rabbit numbers on the same pair of axes (choose different scales for each animal).

(b) Foxes eat rabbits (and other things). Describe the pattern shown by the graph for the years 1950 – 1954 and explain this in ecological terms.

(c) Suggest what was happening between 1954 and 1962 for both populations.

(d) What happened next (up to 1990)?

(e) Describe an (imagined) scenario in which the human population could change in a similar way to that of the rabbits. Alternatively, explain why such a situation could never occur!

Task 1

The wild wood

Read the following passage then answer the questions about it.

There was no Moon, and in the middle of the wood you couldn't see your hand before your face. Silent on a low branch, the tawny owl swivelled her head, using her large eyes to scan the forest floor. It was autumn, and there was a rich smell of decay as the damp leaves rotted. It was the time of year when the tangled underground threads of the fungi colonies began to reproduce. The floor of the clearing was dotted with a variety of toadstools and mushrooms.

The owl ignored the hawk moth fluttering across the clearing – leave that to the bats! She focused her keen eyes on a movement in the layer of dead leaves. A caterpillar arched its way through some newly fallen leaves, and began to munch into a rich and juicy one. The sound – and the scent – attracted the attention of another animal. It lifted its thin nose out of its burrow and sniffed. Sure of the direction, it ran with surprising speed and grabbed the caterpillar in its sharp teeth. The vole used its forepaws to hold the struggling victim and made short work of it. It moved a few steps and then froze. It did this by instinct – and it was just as well. The owl's eyes

lost the vole against the dark background of the dead leaves. They were 'programmed' to sense movement.

But the owl waited patiently. When the vole moved again the owl swooped. The vole neither saw nor heard the silent wings of death. There was a brief flurry as the sharp talons dug into the warm body and the vole screamed until it was torn to pieces by the powerful beak, to be swallowed bones and all.

1 Name one predator and one prey animal named in the passage.

2 Which of the organisms mentioned is a *decomposer*? Explain your answer.

3 The passage describes one small part of an *ecosystem*. What is an ecosystem?

4 All living things need energy, and we can think of energy as *flowing through* an ecosystem. Trace the energy flow that ends up (for a time at least) in the owl.

5 Draw a food web for the organisms mentioned in the passage.

6 Draw a rough pyramid of numbers for caterpillars, voles and owls.

7 One year, a gamekeeper puts down poison which kills off most of the voles and similar small rodents. What might happen to the caterpillars/moths and the owl? You can give the answer in words, or draw a graph showing how the populations of these animals change over the next few years.

Task 2

A mixed bag

1 What do you think about this?

'Genetic scientists patent terminally ill mice.'

'The first genetically engineered animal to be patented in the United States, a new breed of white mouse, will be on sale next year for about $100 each.

Known as the "oncomouse", the genetically altered animal carries human cancer genes called *oncogenes*, and can mimic human cancer. "Oncomice" are guaranteed to develop cancer within 90 days and die soon afterwards.

The medical firm will sell the mice to cancer research laboratories and pharmaceutical companies which wish to study the development of cancer, to test drugs to fight disease or to test products that might cause cancer.

Michael Fox, of the Humane Society of America, is fighting Congress to ban the patenting of genetically engineered animals, he said that this would be "an official endorsement that animals are simply commodities . . . and are not ours in trust".'

(Newspaper report, November 1988.)

2 Here is some data about the planets in the solar system.

Planet	Mercury	Venus	Earth	Mars	Jupiter	Saturn	Uranus	Neptune
Distance from Sun ($\times 10^6$ km)	58	108	150	228	778			
Surface Temperature (K)	623	733	293	250	153			
Surface gravity (N/kg)	3.6	0.9	9.8	3.7	26	11.3	10.4	14
Number of moons	0	0	1	2	16	17	15	8

(a) (i) Plot a graph of the distance from the Sun (horizontal axis) against surface temperature (vertical axis) for the first five planets.
(ii) Comment on any pattern that you find. Can you explain it?
(iii) Do all of the planets fit the pattern? Can you explain why one of them does not?
(b) Draw two bar charts (i) showing the planets' gravity field strength and (ii) showing the number of moons that each planet has.

You can draw both charts on the same axes, if you make them clear. Compare the two bar charts. Describe and explain any pattern that you can see.

3 Copy out the following passage and fill in the missing words. Underline these words, or write them in a different colour ink. Choose from the words listed at the end – but not all of the words are given and some are wrong!

To start with, the energy in coal came from the _____. We can't use this energy unless the coal is burned – this means it combines with _____. This chemical reaction is _____. In a power station, the energy is first transferred to _____ and so increases its pressure so that it can drive _____. As these turn, they spin large coils of wire at high speed. The coils spin in a _____ field, and so generate electricity.

Unfortunately, most of the energy produced by burning the coal is _____. It goes into water in the _____ towers. Eventually this energy just raises the _____ of the surroundings very slightly. In other words, it _____ out. This means that a power station has an _____ of only about 35%

Word list: *energy, efficiency, turbines, armature, Sun, magnetic, electric, temperature, cooling, exothermic, endothermic, steam.*

4 (a) Explain what *rate of reaction* means.
(b) What are the four main factors that decide how quickly a chemical reaction occurs?
(c) Choose *one* factor and explain what effect it has on the rate of reaction.

5 In the next century, human beings may think seriously about sending a space craft with people to the nearest stars. Describe what problems will have to solved to do this, under the headings: *physical, chemical,* and *biological.*

Task 3
Biological recyling

The diagrams on pages 218–219 in the 'Reference section' show the main biological cycles in nature. Choose one of them and write a short description of what happens and why the cycle is important for human life on Earth.

Task 4
Chemicals on the land

Most of the chemicals a plant uses come from the air (carbon dioxide and oxygen) or the soil (water). But to make use of these basic materials, the plants take up other chemicals from the soil, especially nitrates, phosphates, calcium and magnesium. A fertile soil, able to grow good crops, must have a good supply of these minerals.

When a farmer grows crops on the same soil for many years, these essential minerals get used up. In a natural environment, of course, old plants die and rot, so the minerals go back into the soil. On farms, however, the plants are removed for human or animal food, and the minerals are not recycled unless the animal and plant wastes (sewage and manure) are ploughed back into the soil as *natural* fertiliser.

Modern farming rarely ploughs back natural manure because it is expensive to keep and handle, and not easy to get if the farm doesn't keep animals. Instead, *artificial* fertilisers are used. These are chemicals specially made to contain the right balance of essential minerals. The quality of these fertilisers is tightly controlled. They may contain two or more of the following:

Element	Compound	Source
Nitrogen	Ammonium nitrate	Haber process (nitrogen taken from the air)
Phosphorus	Phosphate	Rocks
Potassium	Potash, potassium chloride	Rocks
Calcium	Calcium carbonate, calcium hydroxide (lime)	Rocks
Magnesium	Magnesium carbonate	Rocks

Artificial fertilisers are usually combinations of nitrates, phosphates and potassium salts, so they are called NPK fertilisers. Each plant's need for minerals is different, so there are many different types and proportions of chemicals for the farmer to choose from.

Farmers have to apply these chemicals easily, often to very large fields, so fertilisers are made in grains which will flow freely from machines. The farmer has to choose the right compound for the crop and know the best time to put it on the field. If the fertiliser is put on too soon, it may be washed away by rain (leached); if it is put on too late, the crop may not be able to make use of it, or it will feed weeds rather than crop plants.

Fertilisers are expensive, and misuse will mean a low profit. If a field loses 10% of its nitrates at the critical time (at a fertiliser cost of £10), the farmer might get 1 tonne less wheat (losing £100 worth of wheat). The table shows the costs of producing a wheat crop.

Winter wheat (all figures are per hectare)

Yield Selling price (income)	7.0 tonnes £742
Cost of:	**£**
seed	45
fertiliser	85
sprays (herbicide, pesticide)	75
labour	120
machinery (wear, fuel)	150
Rental value, rates	135
General (overheads)	30
Total costs	604
Net profit	102

Environmental effects

Unfortunately, too much fertiliser can have harmful effects on the environment — and on us.

Nitrates which have leached out of the soil into rivers, ponds and lakes encourage an abnormal growth of algae (green slime!) Their rapid growth can take oxygen out of the water, so that fish and other organisms die. Some trees are affected by too much nitrate in the soil: for example, oak trees tend to die from the top.

Nitrates get into the drinking water. This might be dangerous to people if drunk in large amounts. This is particularly worrying in rich farming areas where a lot of nitrates are used, such as in East Anglia. It isn't easy to remove nitrates from water, although research is going on to find ways of doing it cheaply and efficiently. So we must rely on farmers not to put too much fertiliser on their fields.

1 Write down the names of three types of fertiliser used in farming.

2 What are the main contents of a typical artificial fertiliser?

3 What are the minerals that a good soil should have?

4 What are 'natural' fertilisers?

5 Why do farmers need to put fertilisers on their fields?

6 Give two harmful effects of using fertilisers.

7 What must farmers be careful about when using fertilisers? (Give three points.)

8 What does 'NPK' stand for?

9 What percentage of the cost of growing a crop is spent on fertilisers?

10 How do nitrates get lost from the soil?

11 Suggest how nitrates dissolved in water could be removed from it. Is the method that you describe likely to be cheap enough or practical enough to be used for purifying drinking-water supplies?

12 Design an investigation to find out how much nitrate gets taken out (leached) by rain from a square metre of soil that has been treated with artificial fertiliser.

Task 5

Predicting and planning

Make a plan to tackle one or more of the following practical tests or investigations. Using your scientific knowledge, try to predict the results.

1 Find out the best mix for concrete to use as a beam in a bridge.

2 How do *temperature* and *pH* affect the working of an enzyme?

3 Which brand of washing-up liquid is the 'best buy'?

4 What is the effect of sound (e.g. background music, noise) on how quickly someone can learn? (It could be learning facts, numbers, a poem, how to do a simple physical task, etc.)

5 Find out whether insects are attracted to flowers by their scent or by their colour.

6 What happens to water waves when they
   • collide with each other?
   • bounce off a straight wall?
   • bounce off a curved wall?
   • pass through gaps of different sizes?

7 How much energy is stored in a torch battery (single cell)?

8 Can insects learn?

9 Which fuel (wood, coal or paraffin) contains the most energy *per unit volume*?

10 Do you use more heating energy when you take a bath than when you take a shower?

11 How would you use microelectronics systems to control the temperature in a greenhouse?

12 How could you filter water without using special, artificial materials?

13 How much smoke does a fuel produce when it burns?

14 You discover an unknown type of invisible 'radiation'. How would you test it to see if it consists of waves?

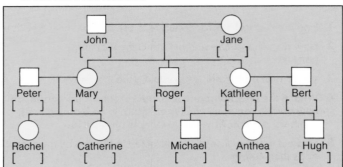

Task 6

Monohybrid crosses in humans

1 Look at the human family tree. The squares show males and the circles show the females.

The shaded squares and circles show people that are *polydactylous*. This means that they have six fingers on each hand. The other squares and circles show people who have the normal five fingers on each hand.

An allele 'D' controlling the polydactylous feature is dominant over the allele 'd' controlling the normal feature.

1 Why it is likely that Jane is heterozygous for the polydactylous feature?

2 Draw out the family tree. Using letters 'D' and 'd', complete the space between the brackets to show which alleles each parent and their children have inherited.

3 Roger is engaged to marry Susan; Susan has the same genotype for finger number as Roger's mother.

Draw up a genetic diagram to show which children of the marriage will have a normal number of fingers.

Help!

(a) *Allele* is a word meaning a pair of genes that have the 'same job'.

(b) *Heterozygous* means having two different alleles, one in each pair of chromosomes.

(c) The *genotype* is a person's pattern of alleles.

2 Modern surgical operations would be impossible without blood transfusions. Blood is easily transfused from one person to another. This is because scientists understand the genetics of the blood cells and how inheritance works. It was in 1900 that a Dr Landsteiner discovered that there were chemicals in the blood that decided whether a person could receive another person's blood.

There are four main blood groups, A, B, AB and O. If *donor* blood group B is given to a *recipient* patient with blood group A by mistake fatal blood clotting will happen. This is just one example of what can occur if the wrong transfusion were to take place.

The blood groups are controlled by three genes, A, B and O. A person will inherit only two of these genes, one from each parent. The genes are alleles. Genes A and B are co-dominant.

If a person inherits gene A from one parent and gene B from another, the blood group will be AB. *Gene O is recessive.*

Use this information to draw a diagram to show how the following parents pass on their blood groups to their four children:

(a) Father is blood group A, and mother, group AB.

(b) Father is blood group O, and mother is group B.

Your diagram could begin with:

	Father	Mother	Child 1	Child 2	Child 3	Child 4
Phenotype	A	AB				

Task 7

Running a race

The following measurements were made on a runner during a 100 metres sprint race. A radar system was used to measure her speed every second.

Speed (m/s)	0	3	6	9	10	10	10	10	10	10	10	10	10	8	6	3	0
Time (s)	0	1	2	3	4	5	6	7	8	9	10	11	12	13	14	15	16

1 Draw a graph of speed against time for the runner.

2 Describe her movement during the race.

3 A well-trained runner can produce a steady force for most of the race. So why did she reach a maximum speed after 4 seconds?

4 Acceleration is 'change in speed per second'. Use the data to calculate the runner's acceleration at the start of the race.

5 The runner had a mass of 50 kg. Calculate the acceleration force she generated at the start of the race.

6 (a) What was the runner's kinetic energy at a time of 8 seconds?

(b) What biological process released this energy?

(c) At the end of the race the runner was sweating. What does this fact tell you about the energy actually generated by the athlete as she ran?

(d) How did the runner get rid of her kinetic energy at the end of the race?

7 (a) You can calculate the distance travelled from a speed-time graph by using the fact that *distance covered = area under the graph*. How far did she get in 12 seconds?

(b) Estimate the time she took to cover 100 metres.

Task 8

Chemical economics

1 In the Bosch–Haber process, nitrogen from the air is combined with hydrogen to make ammonia as the first stage in making agricultural fertilisers. You may remember learning about this earlier in the course: fertilisers are one of the major products of the chemical industry. This question is about some of the economics of the process.

The following table gives the percentage yield of ammonia at different temperatures and pressures.

Pressure (MPa)	2.5	5.0	10	20	40
Temperature (°C)	*Percentage yields*				
100	91.7	94.5	96.7	98.4	99.4
200	63.6	73.5	82.0	89.0	94.6
300	27.4	39.6	53.1	66.7	79.7
400	8.7	15.4	25.4	38.8	55.4
500	2.9	5.6	10.5	18.3	31.9

Part a

(a) From the figures in the table, which of the following describes the most productive combination of pressure and temperature for making ammonia?
- High pressure with high temperature
- High pressure with low temperature
- Low pressure with high temperature
- Low pressure with low temperature
- Medium pressure and temperature

(b) Unfortunately, high-pressure compressors are very expensive to buy and use, so a manufacturer (AMCO) thinks about using a cheaper compressor which can produce 20 MPa only. What percentage yield would they expect to get at a temperature of 100 °C? Is the use of low pressures a serious disadvantage, in your opinion?

(c) AMCO makes the decision to operate at a low pressure — and then the research chemists tell them that at 100 °C the reaction rate is so slow that the production rate wouldn't be economical. They suggest a temperature of 450 °C would be much better. Why is the reaction rate likely to be so much quicker at a higher temperature?

(d) The experts also point out that at 450 °C they could use a catalyst to improve the reaction rate (the only available catalysts don't work below about 400 °C). What is a catalyst?

(e) The manufacturer takes the advice and builds a pilot plant. They find that when they pump the mixture of hydrogen and nitrogen through it at a reasonable rate only about 13 per cent of the gases combine to make ammonia, even with a catalyst present.

(i) What percentage yield does the table say they should have obtained?

(ii) Suggest what the manufacturer could do to improve the yield — without changing the catalyst or the temperature and pressure.

Part b

Another manufacturer (TECO) sets up another ammonia plant in competition with the first, working at higher pressures, lower temperatures and with a different catalyst. The table below gives the comparative costs and outputs of the two plants.

Daily figures	AMCO	TECO
output (tonnes)	500	1000
raw materials cost (£)	1000	2000
labour cost (£)	1000	2000
energy (fuel) cost (£)	2000	1400
plant cost (£)	1200	2600

(a) What is the total cost, for each manufacturer, of their daily outputs?

(b) What is the cost per tonne of the ammonia produced?

(c) What is the cost which makes one manufacturing process more expensive than the other?

(d) What feature of the *chemical* process is responsible for this extra expense?

2 A team of students were making magnesium sulphate by adding sulphuric acid to magnesium oxide. The results from six team members are listed below.

Team member	Mass of magnesium oxide used (g)	Mass of magnesium sulphate produced (g)
A	1.0	1.4
B	3.0	4.3
C	2.0	3.0
D	6.0	6.2
E	5.0	7.5
F	8.0	12.1
G	0	0

(G got it all wrong . . .)

(a) List the practical steps that the students would have to make to get clean, dry magnesium sulphate as a product.

(b) (i) Write down the word equation for the process.

(ii) Write down a balanced formula equation for the process.

(c) Plot these results as crosses (like so: +) on a set of axes (product on y-axis, raw material (oxide) on x-axis). Label them with the correct letters A to G.

(d) Draw the best straight line using these results. Write down two things that you notice about the graph.

(e) Which other student seems to have done something wrong? Suggest what this could have been (assuming that he or she used the weighing balance correctly!).

(f) Use the graph to find out:

(i) how much magnesium sulphate could be produced from 10 grams of magnesium oxide.

(ii) how much magnesium oxide you would need to produce 10 grams of magnesium sulphate.

(iii) (tricky) how much magnesium sulphate you could produce from 18 grams of magnesium oxide.

Task 9

Chemical energy

Answer as many of the following questions as you can.

1 The data gives the quantity of energy given out when 1 kilogram of each substance is burned.

	Petrol	*Sugar*
Energy	42 MJ	17 MJ
Cost	42p	57p

(1 MJ is 1 000 000 joules)

(a) Which substance gives the most energy per penny?

(b) Why is sugar not used as a fuel for cars?

(c) What else must a good fuel be able to do as well as produce a lot of energy?

(d) Suggest two reasons why the body uses sugar (in the form of glucose) as a fuel for muscles and cells.

2 (a) Draw the apparatus you would use to collect a sample of liquid water from the exhaust gases given off by a small petrol engine in the laboratory.

(b) What are the 'contrails' (vapour trails) from a jet airliner cruising high in the sky made of? Where has this substance come from? Why don't the contrails form when the aircraft is flying low?

3 You can lift your arm from waist to shoulder, quite slowly in about a second. The muscle action is fuelled by the reaction between glucose and oxygen in the cells. This reaction is speeded up by a series of enzymes in the cells, which are very good catalysts. In fact, they speed up the reaction by as much as 10 000 000 000 times.

Calculate how long it would take you to lift your arm if these enzymes weren't there. Give your answer to the nearest year.

Data
If using a calculator use:
1 hour is 3600 seconds
1 day is 24 hours
1 year is 365 days
If not using a calculator use the approximations:
1 hour is 3333 seconds
1 day is 25 hours
1 year is 333 days

4 A group of students were investigating fuels and did an experiment to measure how much energy the gas used in camping stoves could supply. Their results are listed below.

Mass of gas container before use	233.5 g
Mass of gas container after use	231.5 g
Mass of water heated	0.4 kg
Temperature of water before heating	20°C
Temperature of water after heating	60°C

(a) Draw a diagram showing the equipment they might have used for this experiment, and how it would be set up.
(b) What mass of gas was used?
(c) What was the rise in temperature of the water?
(d) Use the formula:

$$\text{heating energy} = \text{mass of water} \times \text{rise in temperature} \times 4.2$$

to check that the energy in kilojoules supplied to the water by the burning gas was 67.2 kJ.
(e) This energy was supplied by the mass of gas that you calculated in part (b) above. Scale up your answer to part (d) to calculate how much energy would be supplied by a kilogram (1000 grams) of gas.
(f) The calorific value of the gas (butane) is said to be 50000 kJ per kilogram. Suggest a reason why the students got a different value.

Task 10

Feedback

Feedback is an important idea that is used in many different systems; for example in microelectronic control, in home heating, and in living things. The diagrams show some of these uses.
(a) Describe as fully as you can how each system works and/or what is happening in each case.
(b) Explain in non-technical words what *feedback* means.

1 A thermostat, helped by a heating system can control the temperature of a room.

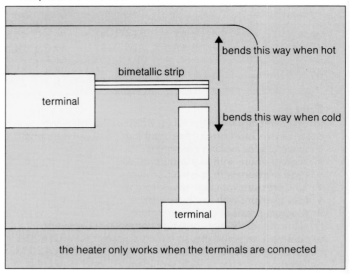

2 The pituitary gland, helped by the brain and the kidneys, can control the water balance in the body. When the brain detects that the blood is too concentrated, the pituitary gland is made to secrete a special hormone (water-keeping hormone). This acts on the kidneys.

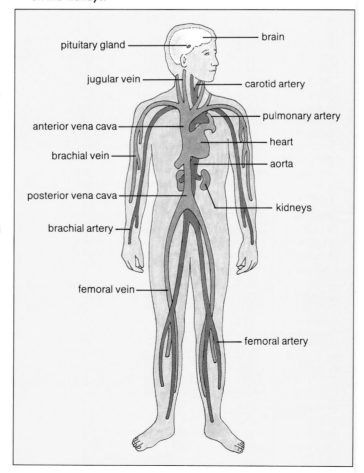

3 A 'governor' is used to keep a steam engine working at a steady speed. The steam going through the pipe turns the drive shaft which makes the engine's wheels turn. The quantity of steam getting through is controlled by a valve. This is connected to the drive shaft as shown. If the shaft turns too fast, the heavy spheres move upwards, closing the valve.

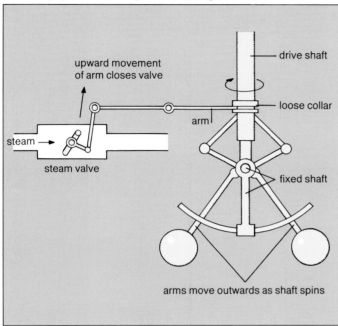

4 In a paper mill, paper is made continuously in a long roll. Before it is rolled up, it has to be dried, but not made too dry.

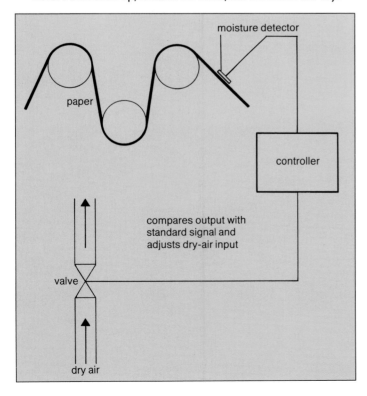

Task 11

Fishing and overfishing

The graph below shows typical data for a population of fish (cod) in the sea. This task is about how catching the fish as a crop – for food – might be managed.

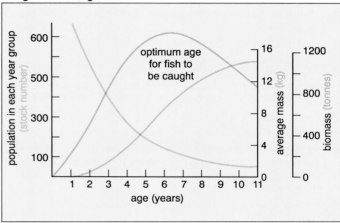

1 A female fish lays a very large number of eggs. Think about what happens to the young fish (called *fry*) as they get older, and explain the shape of the 'stock' graph.

2 Why does the graph of biomass reach a peak and then decline?

3 Haddock roam the sea in huge shoals containing tens of thousands of fish. There are a lot more young fish than old ones. Haddock begin to breed when they are 3 years old. The figures for the total haddock catch in Scotland for the five years 1983–87 are as follows.

Age	Tonnes landed
1	3900
2	116000
3	103000
4	57000
5	13000
6	3300
7	831
8	283
Age 10–12	about 100 tonnes overall

(a) Draw a bar chart of these figures.
(b) Do these figures show a wise fishing policy? What would you say to convince the trawler owners that this is the wrong thing to do?

4 Sketch a graph of the future stock (fish population) that you would expect if the fish were caught in large numbers when they were two years old.

5 (a) The fish are caught by trawlers in large nets. There has been a lot of disputes between European Community officials and fishermen about the smallest size of the holes in the nets used. What difference does the net hole size make?
(b) Haddock are smaller than cod, so small hole sizes are allowed. But cod and haddock often swim together. What problems might this cause?

(The data in this question is taken from information supplied by the Nature Conservancy Council, *Data Support for Education*.)

211

Task 12

Physical processes

The following tasks are about physical processes — or how things work in the world of physics. Do as many as you can. Use the 'Reference section' or a relevant chapter in the book to help you.

1 When you move on Earth it is usually because you apply a force to push against something. Rockets can work in space, where there isn't anything to push against. Explain how they can do this.

2 'When things move in circles they need a centripetal force.' Explain what this means. Give three examples of things moving in circles and say what causes the centripetal force in each case.

3 A car engine, a power station or even a human being can never be 100% efficient. Explain why this is.

4 It is *very* dangerous to put an empty, closed glass bottle on a fire. (The bottle, of course, isn't really empty.) Use the kinetic theory (i.e. that matter is made up of small, moving particles) to explain why it is so dangerous.

5 The following types of radiation are all part of the electromagnetic spectrum:
infrared; ultraviolet; radio waves; X-rays; microwaves; visible light.
(a) Put them in order of wavelength; longest first.
(b) Give one use or effect produced by each type.
(c) Name one everyday source for each type of radiation.
(d) Give two features that all electromagnetic radiations have in common.

6 The following are the main parts of any communication system:
receiver, transducer(s), medium, source, coder, decoder.
    Draw a diagram showing them in the order that you would expect in a telephone system that uses fibre optics. Name the objects that carry out the tasks of each part.

PART 2

Reference section

How to find what you want

This part of the book is arranged in four sections.

- *Biology:* data store
- *Chemistry:* data store
- *Physics:* data store
  All the main facts you need to follow this course are arranged in topics. You can learn a lot by just browsing through this.
- *Index*

But if you want to look something up, think of a key word that is to do with what you want to know. For example, you might want to know about the carbon cycle. The key word would be 'carbon': look this up in the Index on page 253 and it will refer you to the page that describes what you need to know. The key words are listed in alphabetical order. If you know about computer data bases, you may have used key searches already.

Some parts of the *Reference section* are repeated from book 1. This is to help you with revision.

Some details that are given in the topic chapters are not repeated. Just use the Index to find them.

Reference

▽ Useful words in biology

Absorption is the passage of small molecules of digested food through the wall of the intestine into the blood.

Aerobic respiration is the release of energy from food by using oxygen from the external environment (air or water).

Anaerobic respiration is the release of energy from food without using oxygen.

Bacteria are single-celled organisms that are found everywhere. They are adapted to live in almost any environment found on Earth. Most are harmless to other living things, but some cause diseases. Most bacteria live off the chemicals in plant and animal wastes (faeces, dead leaves, etc.) or dead plants and animals. Bacteria play a vital part in the ecological cycles of life on Earth, in which materials are used and re-used (see pages 218 and 219).

Circulation is the movement of fluids such as blood around the body of a living organism.

Clones are exact copies of a living organism. They have exactly the same genetic coding, like identical twins. For example, plant 'cuttings' are clones of the parent plant. Special techniques are used to make sure that clones are free from disease.

Co-ordination means making sure that all of the different organ systems in an organism work together to ensure that the whole organism survives.

Diffusion is the movement of a substance from a region of higher concentration to a region of lower concentration. In living organisms, this often takes place through a membrane. Food is absorbed in the gut by diffusion. In the lungs, oxygen enters the blood and carbon dioxide leaves the blood by diffusion.

Digestion is the breakdown of large food molecules into simple, soluble substances small enough to be absorbed.

Enzymes. These are complicated chemicals produced by living cells, which control chemical reactions that take place in the organism. Enzymes are biological catalysts (they speed up reactions). Some enzymes are used in industry — in biological washing powders for example. Most enzymes are easily damaged by heat, as they are designed for use in living things which can only survive within a small temperature range (e.g. 0 °C–40 °C).

Some examples are:
- insulin — helps to control blood-sugar level in the body;
- maltase — changes one kind of sugar (maltose) into another (glucose);
- protease — types of enzymes that digest proteins (these are the ones used in washing powders, for making meat tender and for removing hair from animal hides, etc.);
- cellulase — breaks down cellulose (the indigestible parts of plants; used to soften vegetables, getting agar jelly out of seaweed, etc.);
- amylase — changes starch into simpler chemicals (used in making syrups, fruit juices, etc.).

Excretion. The removal of waste substances produced as a result of chemical reactions within living cells.

Genes. These are small 'chunks of code' found inside living cells. They carry the information needed by the cell to keep itself alive, to grow and to make chemicals (such as enzymes and other proteins). The genes are found as part of long chains of molecules (called chromosomes) in the nucleus of the cell.

Homeostasis is all about keeping the environment inside the body and around living cells constant.

Organism. A living thing, e.g. an animal or plant.

Specialisation. This is what we call organisms developing different cells, tissues and organs that carry out particular functions in a living body, e.g. digestion and excretion.

Viruses. These are even smaller than bacteria, and even less like plants and animals. They can only grow and reproduce inside the living cells of other organisms. This means that many of them are harmful to other forms of life, e.g. they are the cause of AIDS, the common cold, influenza, polio, and many diseases in plants. Compare viruses with bacteria.

▽ Useful words in ecology

Biomass refers to the total mass of living organisms.
Carnivore. This is a meat-eating animal, or plant.

Consumer. An organism (mostly animals) that gets its energy from biomass.

Decomposers are organisms (usually bacteria and fungi) that break down biomass into simpler chemicals, like proteins and nitrates.

Ecosystem. This is a collection of organisms that live together in the same habitat or environment.

Environment. Describes the whole surroundings of a habitat, including climate, mineral resources, atmosphere and so on.

Habitat is the place where organisms live, e.g. a meadow, hedge or pond.

Herbivores are animals that only eat plants.

Omnivores are animals that eat plants and other animals.

Predators are carnivorous animals that hunt other animals for food.

Prey are the animals hunted by predators.

Producers are plants that make biomass from carbon dioxide and water, using energy from light.

Scavengers are animals that eat dead animals or other wastes.

Reference

214

▽ The flow of energy

The energy from the Sun

Each day the Earth receives 15 thousand million terajoules (1.5×10^{22} J) of energy from that great supplier, the Sun (a terajoule is a million million joules). If this huge amount of energy could be collected and shared out, each person on Earth would get about a 100 thousand joules *every second* (100 kW). Actually, each person (on average) uses only 2 kW. The diagram shows what happens to all this solar energy.

Energy flow in a young woodland

If we imagine that 100% of the Sun's energy is absorbed by a plant, what does the plant do with the energy?

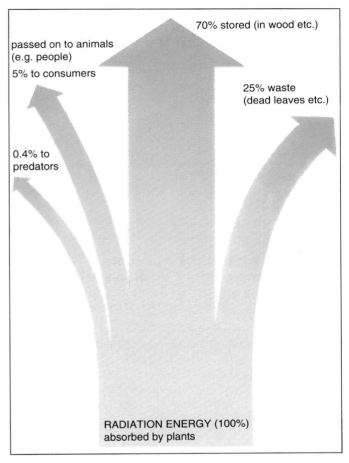

70% stored (in wood etc.)

passed on to animals (e.g. people)
5% to consumers

25% waste (dead leaves etc.)

0.4% to predators

RADIATION ENERGY (100%) absorbed by plants

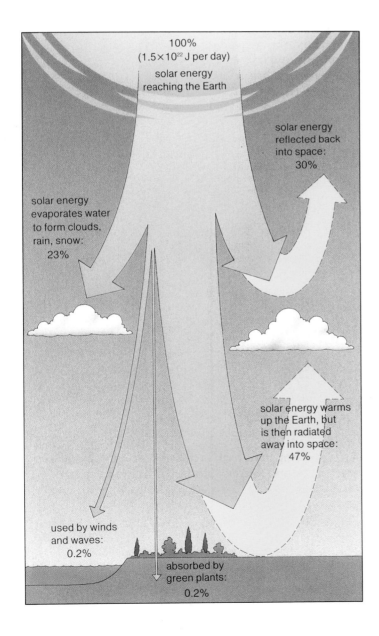

100%
(1.5×10^{22} J per day)
solar energy reaching the Earth

solar energy reflected back into space: 30%

solar energy evaporates water to form clouds, rain, snow: 23%

solar energy warms up the Earth, but is then radiated away into space: 47%

used by winds and waves: 0.2%

absorbed by green plants: 0.2%

Energy flow in a young cow

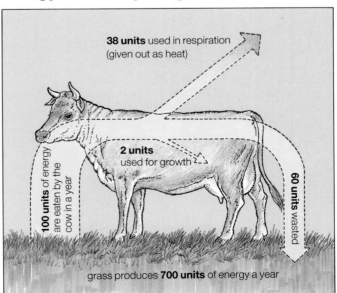

38 units used in respiration (given out as heat)

2 units used for growth

100 units of energy are eaten by the cow in a year

60 units wasted

grass produces 700 units of energy a year

Energy pyramids

The cow only uses 2 units of energy out of 100 for growth. An energy pyramid shows how little energy is transferred through a food chain efficiently.

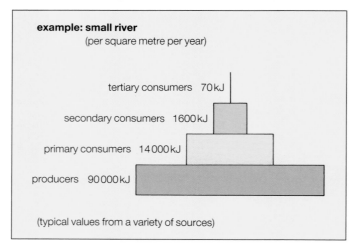

example: small river
(per square metre per year)

tertiary consumers   70 kJ

secondary consumers   1600 kJ

primary consumers   14 000 kJ

producers   90 000 kJ

(typical values from a variety of sources)

The energy needs of a person

An average man needs 12 MJ of energy per day. An average woman needs 10 MJ of energy per day. (A one-bar electric fire uses 3.6 MJ of energy per hour.)

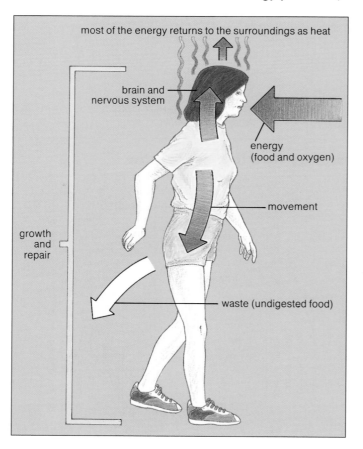

most of the energy returns to the surroundings as heat

brain and nervous system

energy (food and oxygen)

movement

growth and repair

waste (undigested food)

▽ The ozone layer

Oxygen and ozone in the atmosphere cut down dangerous ultraviolet radiation from the Sun.

A photon of ultraviolet radiation (u.v.) approaches the Earth's atmosphere from the Sun.

The u.v. splits oxygen into atoms.

Oxygen atoms (O) combine with oxygen molecules (O_2) to make ozone (O_3).

Ozone molecules absorb the most dangerous (high-energy) u.v. photons, and break up. But, they recombine afterwards — good value!

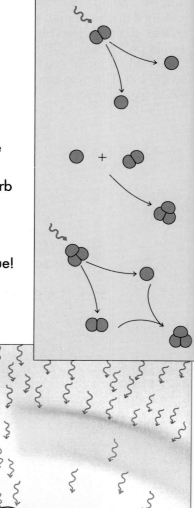

All of this happens high in the atmosphere, forming a layer of ozone. But pollutants (CFCs) stop the ozone molecules reforming, so we get holes in the ozone layer.

▽ The greenhouse effect

Carbon dioxide in the Earth's atmosphere does the same job as the glass in the greenhouse.

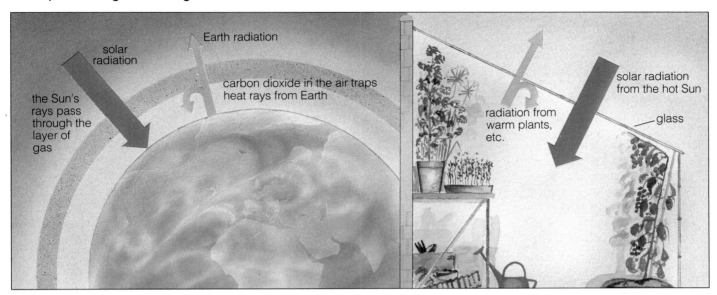

solar radiation

Earth radiation

the Sun's rays pass through the layer of gas

carbon dioxide in the air traps heat rays from Earth

radiation from warm plants, etc.

solar radiation from the hot Sun

glass

▽ Predators and prey

The graph shows the number of animal skins bought from fur trappers by the Hudson Bay Company between 1845 and 1935. The lynx is a large wild cat that eats hares. More hares mean more lynx; but more lynx mean fewer hares, and so on.

lynx (eat hares)

snowshoe hare

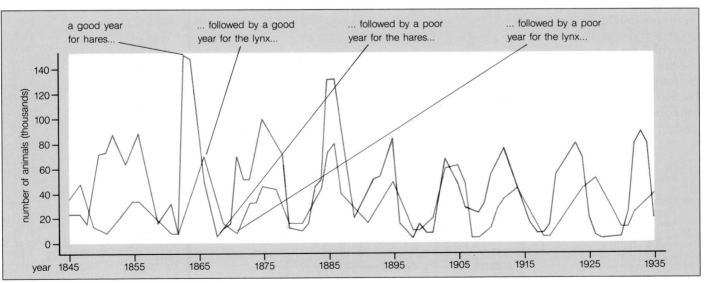

a good year for hares...

... followed by a good year for the lynx...

... followed by a poor year for the hares...

... followed by a poor year for the lynx...

number of animals (thousands)

year 1845 1855 1865 1875 1885 1895 1905 1915 1925 1935

▽ **Biological recycling**

In the natural world, substances are being recycled all the time. The oxygen you breathe in will have come from a plant feeding by photosynthesis. Other plants will take up the carbon dioxide you breathe out.

Human beings and the things they do, may change or interfere with these natural cycles.

- Intensive farming may release all sorts of harmful chemicals into the soil.
- Burning fossil fuels in our power stations puts millions of tonnes of carbon dioxide and other gases into the air every year.
- Cutting down the rain forests at a rate of one hundred acres a minute could change the weather patterns of the world.

It is important to understand exactly how natural recycling works if we are to keep our planet fit to live on. Notice how important microbes are in the cycles.

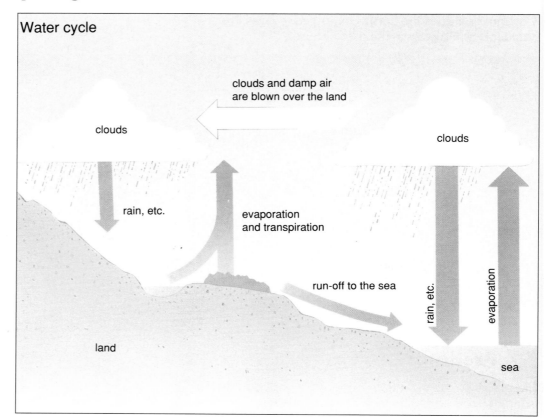

Water cycle

clouds and damp air are blown over the land

clouds

clouds

rain, etc.

evaporation and transpiration

run-off to the sea

rain, etc.

evaporation

land

sea

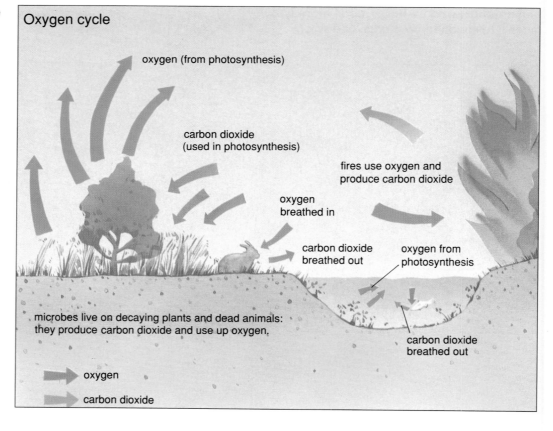

Oxygen cycle

oxygen (from photosynthesis)

carbon dioxide (used in photosynthesis)

fires use oxygen and produce carbon dioxide

oxygen breathed in

carbon dioxide breathed out

oxygen from photosynthesis

carbon dioxide breathed out

microbes live on decaying plants and dead animals: they produce carbon dioxide and use up oxygen.

oxygen

carbon dioxide

Carbon cycle

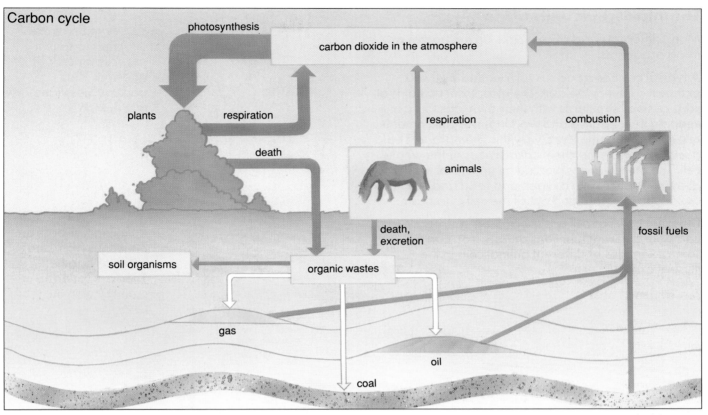

Nitrogen cycle

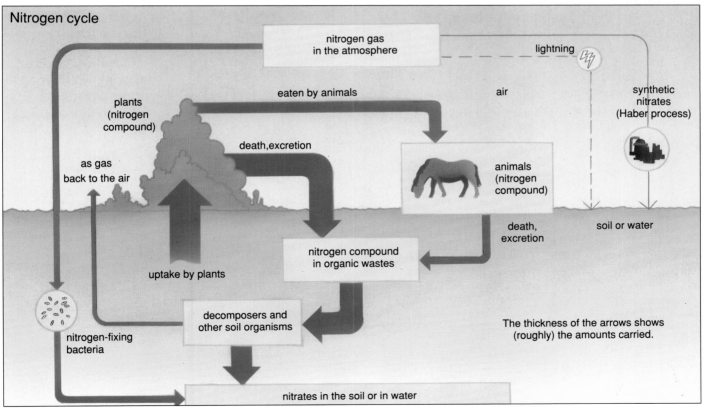

The thickness of the arrows shows (roughly) the amounts carried.

▽ Living cells

The microscopic units of life

Many different types of cell make up the bodies of living organisms.

A typical cell has a nucleus surrounded by living material called *cytoplasm*. The cytoplasm contains all sorts of small structures with their own jobs to do in keeping the cell alive and working. The cell contents are all kept together by a very thin *membrane*. The *nucleus* controls the chemical activities of the whole cell. The membrane is pierced by tiny pores which allow substances like oxygen and food and carbon dioxide to pass into and out of the cell cytoplasm.

Different types of cell are *specialised* in structure to carry out different functions or jobs. You can see some examples of different animal cells in the illustrations.

An animal cell

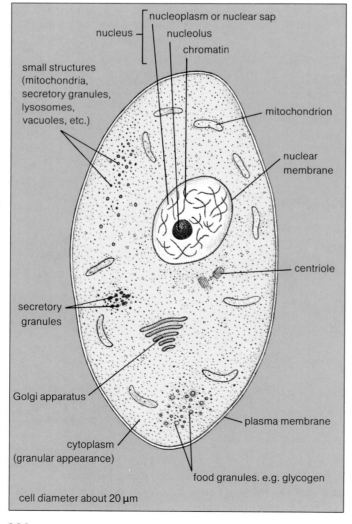

cell diameter about 20 µm

Nerve cells

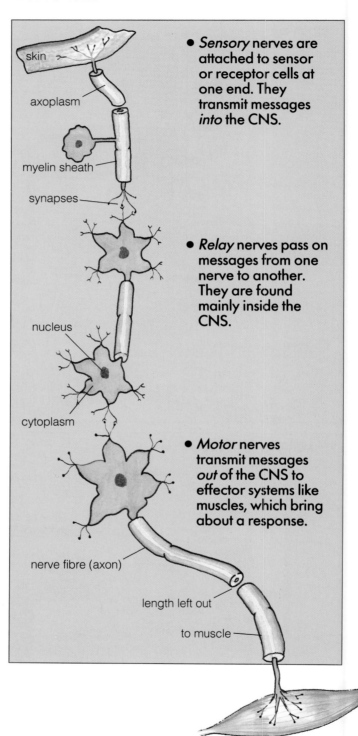

- *Sensory* nerves are attached to sensor or receptor cells at one end. They transmit messages *into* the CNS.

- *Relay* nerves pass on messages from one nerve to another. They are found mainly inside the CNS.

- *Motor* nerves transmit messages *out* of the CNS to effector systems like muscles, which bring about a response.

Cells in the blood

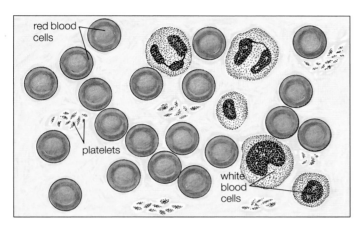

A human sperm cell

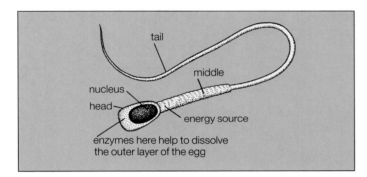

A human egg cell

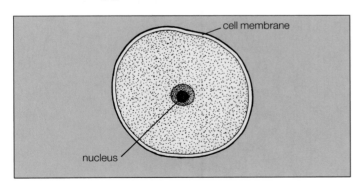

▽ Organs in the human body

When similar cells are grouped together to do a single job, they are called a *tissue*. When different tissues are grouped together, we call this an *organ*. The diagram shows the main organs in the human body.

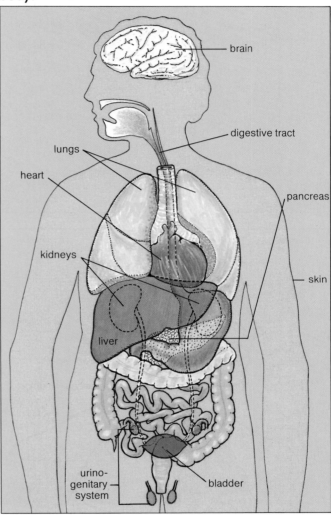

Organs can work together in *systems*. Two important organs that work together are the heart and the lungs.

▽ The heart–lung system

The heart and lungs work together to ensure that cells are kept supplied with the oxygen they need for respiration and that the waste carbon dioxide the cells produce is constantly removed.

The heart is a four-chambered muscular pump that propels the blood around the body, picking up oxygen at the lungs and transporting this vital gas to all the different living tissues. Carbon dioxide is carried back to the lungs for removal.

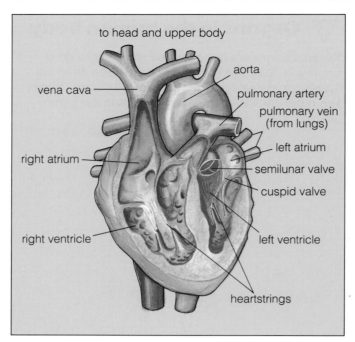

The lungs bring air into the body when we breathe in. Oxygen in the air passes into the blood to be carried off to the cells. Waste carbon dioxide gas passes out of the blood, and out of the body, when we breathe out.

▽ How the lungs work

Air is breathed in through the nose and mouth. Air enters each of the lungs through a large tube called a *bronchus*. Inside the lungs, the tubes divide into smaller and smaller tubes called *bronchioles*. The bronchioles end in tiny clusters of air sacs called *alveoli*. It is here that gaseous exchange takes place. Every alveolus is surrounded with tiny blood vessels that bring blood to the lungs and take it away again. Oxygen diffuses into the blood. The blood then carries the gas to the living cells. Carbon dioxide passes in the opposite direction. It is removed from the lungs by breathing out.

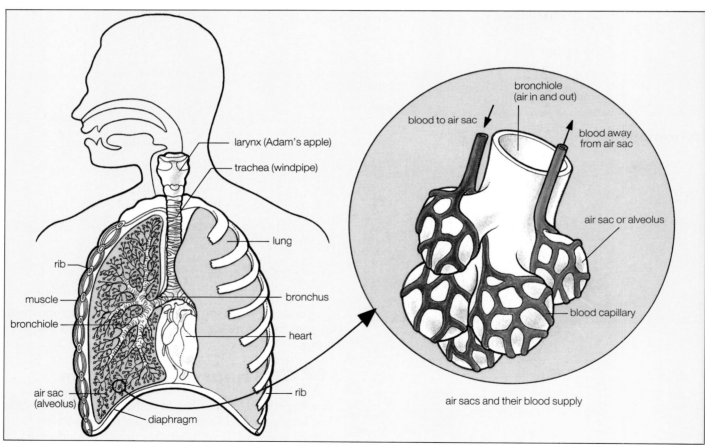

air sacs and their blood supply

▽ The cardiovascular system

The heart is the pump of the cardiovascular system.

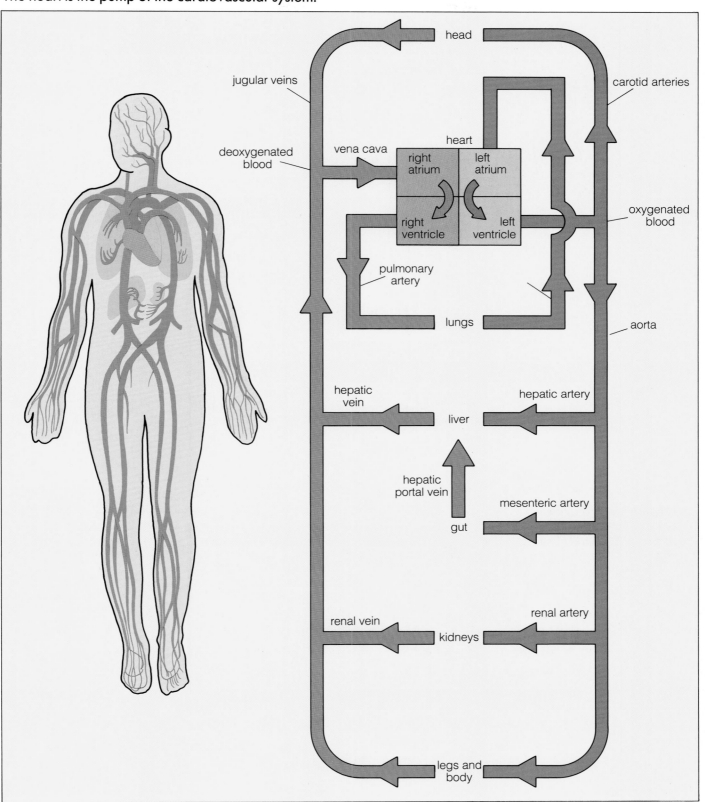

head

jugular veins

carotid arteries

deoxygenated blood

vena cava

heart

right atrium

left atrium

oxygenated blood

right ventricle

left ventricle

pulmonary artery

aorta

lungs

hepatic vein

hepatic artery

liver

hepatic portal vein

mesenteric artery

gut

renal vein

renal artery

kidneys

legs and body

▽ The excretory system

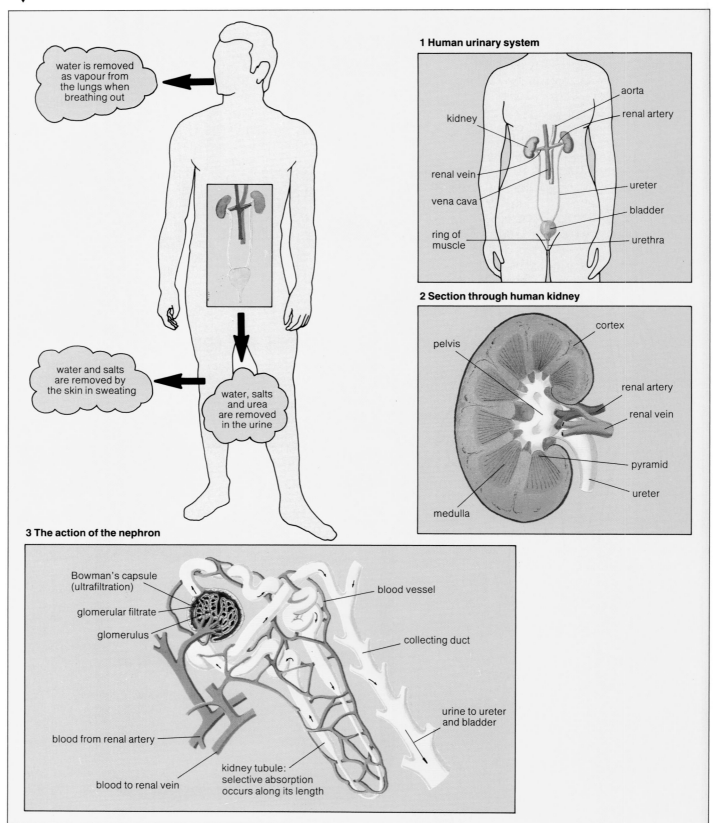

water is removed as vapour from the lungs when breathing out

water and salts are removed by the skin in sweating

water, salts and urea are removed in the urine

1 Human urinary system

- kidney
- aorta
- renal artery
- renal vein
- vena cava
- ureter
- bladder
- ring of muscle
- urethra

2 Section through human kidney

- pelvis
- cortex
- renal artery
- renal vein
- pyramid
- ureter
- medulla

3 The action of the nephron

- Bowman's capsule (ultrafiltration)
- glomerular filtrate
- glomerulus
- blood vessel
- collecting duct
- blood from renal artery
- urine to ureter and bladder
- blood to renal vein
- kidney tubule: selective absorption occurs along its length

How the kidney works

The working unit of the kidney is the *nephron* or kidney tubule. You can see a diagram of the nephron in the illustration opposite.

What happens in the kidney nephron?

1 Blood enters the kidney in the renal artery, which splits into smaller blood vessels.

2 Blood plasma — the liquid part of blood — containing water, salts, glucose sugar, and urea waste, is filtered out of the blood at each *glomerulus*. This is called *ultrafiltration* because it happens at high pressure.

3 The filtered liquid, called the *glomerular filtrate*, enters the kidney tubule at the *Bowman's capsule*.

4 As the liquid flows down the tubule, useful substances such as glucose sugar and some of the salts and water are re-absorbed into the blood. This is called *selective re-absorption* because only *some* of the substances are re-absorbed back into the blood.

5 Harmful wastes like urea, and some water and salts remain inside the kidney tubules. This liquid, called *urine*, flows towards the collecting ducts in the pelvic region of the kidney.

6 The collecting ducts join up to form the *ureter*, which transports urine to the *bladder*.

7 The bladder stores the urine until it can be discharged from the body.

8 Filtered blood, cleansed of urea waste, leaves the kidney via the renal vein.

By changing the amount of water and salts that are re-absorbed along the tubule, the kidneys are able to control the amounts of these substances in the blood and the body.

If the body has excess water we release watery pale yellow urine in large amounts. If the body is suffering from a lack of water, more water is reabsorbed in the kidney tubules. More concentrated, dark yellow urine is produced in smaller amounts.

▽ The nervous system

The human body is controlled, in part, by the central nervous system (CNS). This consists of the brain and spinal cord. Nerves run to all parts of the body carrying information in the form of tiny electrical impulses to and from the CNS.

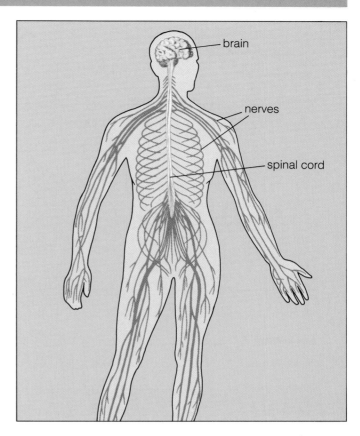

▽ The digestive system

The human alimentary canal or digestive system is a tube, passing through our bodies from mouth to anus. It is about 9 metres long!

How the digestive system works

- Food enters at the *mouth* and is mixed with saliva which softens and lubricates the food for swallowing.
- Saliva contains an *enzyme* called *salivary amylase* which begins the digestion of any starch in the food.
- The *teeth* and *chewing* grind the food into small lumps ready for swallowing.
- The ball of food is swallowed and moves down the *gullet* to the *stomach*.
- The stomach churns and mashes the food and adds *acid* and an enzyme called *pepsin*, which begins the digestion of protein foods.
- Small amounts of partly digested semi-liquid food pass into the *small intestine*.
- The small intestine is a long, narrow tube coiled up inside the lower part of the body. The first part, called the *duodenum*, is where most digestion of the food occurs. The second part, called the *ileum*, is where most absorption of the newly digested food takes place.

Reference

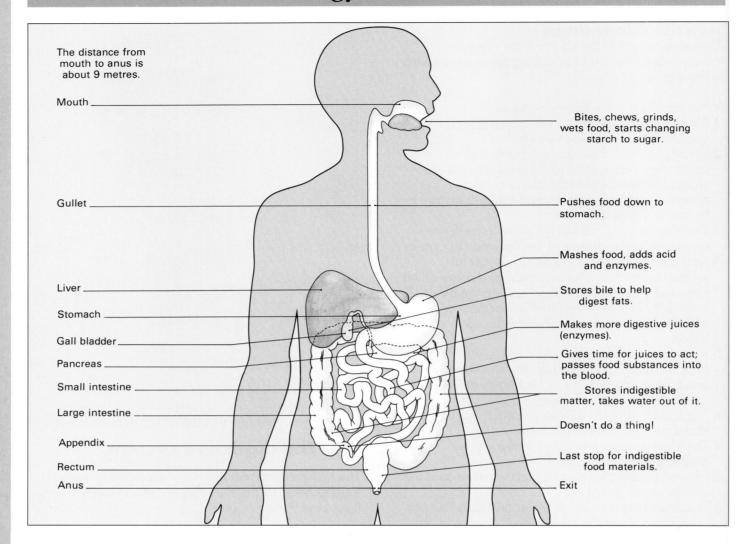

The distance from mouth to anus is about 9 metres.

Mouth — Bites, chews, grinds, wets food, starts changing starch to sugar.

Gullet — Pushes food down to stomach.

Mashes food, adds acid and enzymes.

Liver — Stores bile to help digest fats.

Stomach — Makes more digestive juices (enzymes).

Gall bladder — Gives time for juices to act; passes food substances into the blood.

Pancreas —

Small intestine — Stores indigestible matter, takes water out of it.

Large intestine —

Appendix — Doesn't do a thing!

Rectum — Last stop for indigestible food materials.

Anus — Exit

- The *pancreas gland* releases digestive juices containing more enzymes into the duodenum to mix with the food. *Pancreatic amylase* enzyme continues starch digestion; *lipase* enzyme begins the digestion of fat; *trypsin* enzyme carries on the digestion of proteins in the food.
- The *gall bladder* in the liver releases *bile*, which helps to digest fats.
- By the time the food has reached the ileum, most of it has been digested into simple soluble substances (e.g. glucose sugar from starch. These substances are small enough to be absorbed across the wall of this part of the small intestine and into the blood. This is why the tube must be long: to give time for the digestion and absorption of food as it passes along the gut. The inner lining of the ileum has finger-like small projections called *villi* which increase the surface area for food absorption.
- The indigestible parts of the food (fibre) move into the *large intestine* — the *colon*.
- In the first part of the colon, water is re-absorbed

into the blood from the still liquid food so that drier and harder pellets — faeces — are formed. Faeces consist of indigestible fibre or roughage, minute pieces broken off from the wall of the gut as the food moves along, and millions of dead bacteria from the intestinal wall!
- The faeces are stored in the second part of the large intestine, the *rectum*, until they can be removed from the body through the *anus*.

▽ Enzymes

All of the chemical reactions inside living cells are catalysed and controlled by enzymes. Without enzymes, these reactions would not proceed rapidly enough to maintain the essential processes of life.

Digestive enzymes speed up the chemical digestion, or breakdown, of food inside the gut.

Name of enzyme	Where released	Part of gut releasing enzyme	Type of food digested	Products of digestion
Salivary amylase	mouth	salivary gland	starch	maltose and glucose
Pepsin	stomach	stomach (gastric) glands	protein	amino acids
Pancreatic amylase	small intestine (duodenum)	pancreas gland	starch	maltose and glucose
Trypsin	small intestine (duodenum)	pancreas gland	protein	amino acids
Lipase	small intestine (duodenum)	pancreas gland	fats	fatty acids and glycerol

▽ Different types of food

There are only three main chemical types or classes of food:
- carbohydrates – starch and sugars;
- proteins;
- fats.

Most of the food we actually buy and eat contains a mixture of these three chemical types. For example:
- peanuts contain mainly fat and protein with a little carbohydrate;
- apples contain mainly carbohydrate with a little protein;
- chicken contains mainly protein with some fat. You can find out the exact composition of various common foods in food-value charts.

What are carbohydrates, proteins and fats made of?

Carbohydrates come in three forms:
- complex sugars, e.g. starch, which consist of many single glucose sugars joined together in a long chain;
- double sugars, e.g. maltose sugar, which consists of two glucose molecules joined together;
- single sugars, e.g. single molecules of glucose sugar.

The complex and double sugars in food have to be digested by the gut into single sugars before they can be absorbed through the wall of the intestine and into the blood. Any single sugars taken in as food are small enough to be absorbed straight away.

Proteins are large molecules consisting of many different amino acids joined together in a long chain. Proteins must be digested or broken down into these single amino acid molecules, which are then absorbed into the blood.

Fats consist of three fatty acid molecules joined to a single molecule of glycerol. Fats must be broken down by enzymes into separate fatty acid and glycerol molecules before they can be absorbed by the gut.

Use of foods by the body

Carbohydrates are used to provide energy. Glucose sugar is the main source of energy through respiration for essential life processes. Excess carbohydrate in the diet is stored as glycogen or converted into fat for storage.

Fats are also used to provide energy. They actually provide more energy than carbohydrate, but too much fat is hard to digest and a high-fat diet is thought to be unhealthy. Excess fat is stored under the skin and around large organs like the heart and kidneys.

Proteins are not normally used for energy. Proteins are needed for growth (to make new living tissue). They are also essential for repair of damaged tissue and to replace cells that are constantly being worn away, e.g. skin cells. Only in extreme starvation when no fat or carbohydrate is available are the proteins of the body respired to release energy.

Biology: data store

Food energy – needs

This chart shows the amounts of different kinds of nutrients needed by men and women of different ages in the daily diet. The amounts are called the *recommended daily amounts*.

Recommended daily amounts of nutrients

| | Macronutrients (We need a lot of these) | | Micronutrients (We need a little of these) | | | | | | |
| | | | minerals | | vitamins | | | | |
	energy (MJ)	protein (g)	calcium (mg)	iron (mg)	A (µg)	B1 (mg)	B2 (mg)	niacin (mg)	C (mg)
males									
1 year old	5.0	30	600	7	300	0.5	0.6	7	20
9–11 years	9.5	57	700	12	575	0.9	1.2	14	25
12–14 years	11.0	66	700	12	725	1.1	1.4	16	25
15–17 years	12.0	72	600	12	750	1.2	1.7	19	30
18–34 years									
desk worker	10.5	63	500	10	750	1.0	1.6	18	30
very active	14.0	84	500	10	750	1.3	1.6	18	30
females									
1 year old	4.5	27	600	7	300	0.4	0.6	7	20
9–11 years	8.5	51	700	12	575	0.8	1.2	14	25
12–14 years	9.0	53	700	12	725	0.9	1.4	16	25
15–17 years	9.0	53	600	12	750	0.9	1.7	19	30
18–34 years									
desk worker	9.5	54	500	12	750	0.9	1.3	15	30
very active	10.5	62	500	12	750	1.0	1.3	15	30
pregnant	10.0	60	1200	13	750	1.0	1.6	18	60

Note. The units used in the table are g, gram; mg, milligram (1×10^{-3}g); µg, microgram (1×10^{-6}g); MJ, megajoule (1×10^{6} J).

▽ Nutrients present in 100 gram of food (approximate values)

Food	Energy (kJ)	Protein (g)	Carbohydrate (g)	Fat (g)	Iron (mg)	Vitamin C (g)
bacon grilled	1670	28	0	31	1.3	0
beans, baked	270	5	15	0.5	1.4	0
beef, grilled	930	31	0	11	3.0	0
butter	3050	0.5	0	82	0.2	0
cabbage, boiled	70	1.5	2	0	0.4	20
chapati	1400	8	50	13	2.3	0
chips	1000	3.5	34	10	0.8	10
chocolate	2200	8	59	30	1.6	0
cornflakes	1500	8	82	0.5	7	0
curry, chicken	1000	10.7	2	21	1.8	1
fish, fried	850	20	8	10	0.5	0
hamburger, fried	1100	20	7	17	3.1	0
lettuce	40	1	1	0	0.9	15
margarine	3050	0	0	80	0	0
milk	250	3.3	5	4	0	1
orange juice	170	0.5	9	0	0.3	50
peanuts	2400	24	9	50	2	0
potatoes, boiled	350	1.5	20	0	0.3	11
samosa	2400	6	19	54	1	3
spaghetti	1450	12	74	2	2.1	0
toast, white	1250	10	65	2	2.2	0
yoghurt	200	5	6	1	0.1	0.2

Reference

228

The liver – a living chemical factory

The liver

- is the largest organ in the human body (apart from the skin);
- is located just below the large sheet of muscle (the diaphragm) which separates the heart and lungs from the intestines;
- weighs over a kilogram in an adult;
- is the most chemically active organ of the body;
- produces more heat from chemical reactions than any other organ;
- has a very rich blood supply because it is one of the most important organs of homeostasis in the human body; it regulates and controls the amounts of different substances in the blood.

Functions of the liver

- Regulation of blood-sugar level by storing excess glucose as glycogen or converting glycogen back into glucose and releasing the glucose into the blood when it is needed for energy.
- Amino acids (from the digestion of protein food) not wanted by the body are changed into glycogen and urea.
- Bile is made and stored in the gall bladder; bile is released into the gut to help digest fatty foods.
- Old red blood cells are destroyed and their iron is stored here.
- Some poisons and drugs (e.g. alcohol) are removed from the blood and changed into harmless substances.

The skeletal system

Animal bodies are supported by a *skeleton*.

Insects have an outside skeleton — the *exoskeleton*.

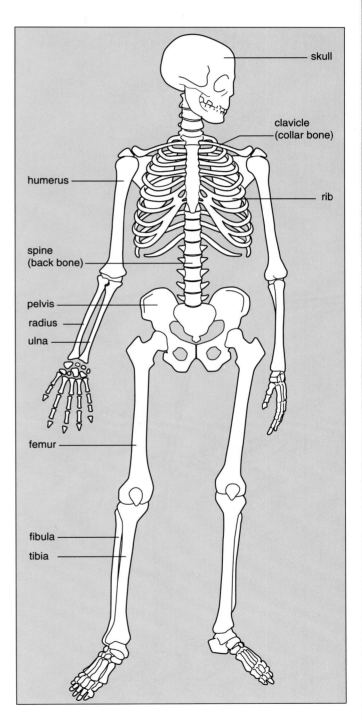

Reference

▽ ## The flowering plant

Flowers contain the reproductive structures of the plant. Most of a plant's food is made and stored in its *leaves.*

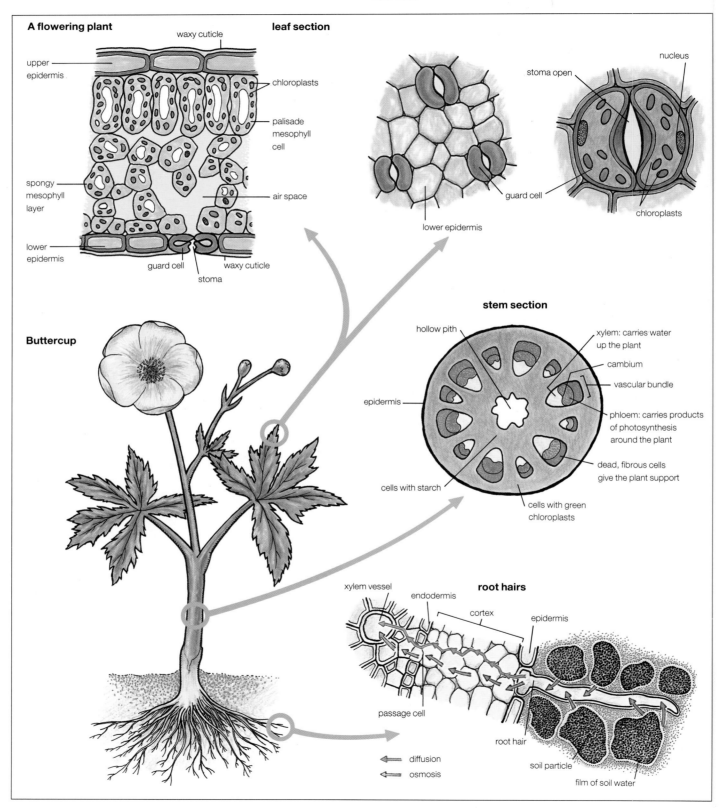

A flowering plant

leaf section

waxy cuticle

upper epidermis

chloroplasts

palisade mesophyll cell

spongy mesophyll layer

air space

lower epidermis

guard cell

waxy cuticle

stoma

nucleus

stoma open

guard cell

chloroplasts

lower epidermis

Buttercup

stem section

hollow pith

xylem: carries water up the plant

cambium

vascular bundle

epidermis

phloem: carries products of photosynthesis around the plant

dead, fibrous cells give the plant support

cells with starch

cells with green chloroplasts

root hairs

xylem vessel

endodermis

cortex

epidermis

passage cell

root hair

soil particle

film of soil water

⇐ diffusion

⇐ osmosis

▽ Photosynthesis

Plants get their food from sugars and other organic chemicals that they make for themselves. They do this by taking in carbon dioxide and water and using these in reactions that use energy from light. These reactions are called photosynthesis.

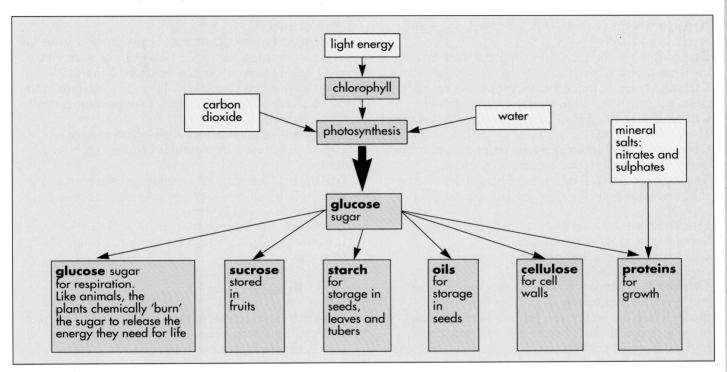

The complete process can be summarised as:

carbon dioxide + water $\xrightarrow[\text{chlorophyll}]{\text{light energy}}$ glucose sugar + oxygen.

Or as a chemical equation:

$6CO_2 + 6H_2O \xrightarrow{\text{light energy}} C_6H_{12}O_6 + 6O_2.$

Useful words and ideas in chemistry

Acids are chemicals that contain hydrogen that can be replaced by a metal. In solution, acids produce H^+ ions, whose concentration is measured on the pH scale.

Alkalis are bases that dissolve in water.

Anode. The positive electrode in electrolysis and electron tubes etc.

Base. This is a chemical that can neutralise an acid to form a salt plus water.

Catalyst. A substance that increases the rate of a chemical reaction without being changed itself.

Cathode. The negative electrode in electrolysis and electron tubes etc.

Compound. A substance containing two or more elements combined together atom by atom.

Concentration. A measure of how much of one substance (the *solute*) is dissolved in another (the *solvent*).

Electrolyte. A liquid that conducts electricity because the liquid contains ions.

Electron. The smallest particle of matter. It is negatively charged.

Element. A substance that can't be broken down into a simpler substance.

Half-life is the time taken for half of a given number of radioactive nuclei (of one type) to break down.

Ion. A charged particle (an atom, molecule or group of atoms that has lost or gained one or more electrons).

Isotope. This term refers to nuclei of the same element which differ in mass, e.g. ^{12}C and ^{14}C.

Mass number. The number of protons plus neutrons in a nucleus.

Neutralisation. A type of chemical reaction between acids and bases in which the pH becomes neutral (pH 7). Essentially, H^+ ions react with OH^- ions to produce water (H_2O).

Neutron. The uncharged (neutral) massive particle in an atomic nucleus.

Nucleus. The central, most massive, part of an atom, containing *neutrons* and *protons*.

Proton. The positively charged, massive particle in an atomic nucleus.

Proton number. The number of protons in a nucleus; this number decides which element the nucleus is.

Radioactive decay. The change in a nucleus due to radioactivity: the nucleus loses mass and/or electric charge to become the nucleus of a different element or isotope.

Radioactivity. The emission of high-speed particles (alpha, α; beta, β) or energetic radiation (gamma, γ) due to breakdown in an unstable nucleus.

Rate of reaction is a measure of how quickly a chemical reaction takes places, e.g. measuring the volume of hydrogen gas produced per second when zinc reacts with an acid.

Relative atomic mass. The average mass of the atoms of an element, compared with the mass of the most common isotope of carbon (^{12}C) taken to have a mass of exactly 12 units.

Relative formula mass. The mass of a molecule or ion compared with ^{12}C (12 units). For example, H_2O has a relative formula mass of 18 units ($2 \times$ hydrogen atoms [1 unit each] plus $1 \times$ oxygen atom of 16 units); SO_4^{2-} has a relative formula mass of 96. Can you see why?

Solute. A substance that is dissolved in a solvent, e.g. copper sulphate is the solute in copper sulphate solution.

Solution. The result of dissolving something in a solvent (e.g. copper sulphate solution — copper sulphate dissolved in water).

Solvent. A substance that can dissolve other substances, e.g. water is a solvent for copper sulphate.

Fuels

Fuels are chemicals which can be used as a source of energy. The energy is usually released when the chemicals are burned with oxygen.

Fossil fuels

These are the remains of living organisms (which may be plants or animals) that lived many millions of years ago. They have been converted into complicated mixtures of *hydrocarbons*, which are compounds of hydrogen, oxygen and carbon.

Renewable fuels

These are fuels made from plants or from animal wastes. Unlike fossil fuels they are not 'used up', but can be made as long as animals and plants live and grow on Earth. Examples include:

Wood: the main cooking fuel of the world. Although it is renewable, in many parts of the world it is being used up faster than it can grow

Biogas: this is methane, CH_4. It is produced by the action of bacteria causing decay on many organic wastes, such as agricultural waste (e.g. sugar cane leaves), animal and human faeces, household waste in rubbish tips, etc. Biogas is widely used in China, and also by some local councils in the U.K., who are burning the methane from decaying rubbish to provide hot water for district heating.

Biological ethanol: ethanol is alcohol, and is produced when yeasts grow in sugar solution. Mixed with petrol it can be used to power car engines, and is made on a large scale in Brazil from sugar cane.

Fuels and pollution

All fuels cause pollution when used. The chemicals produced when hydrocarbon fuels (coal, oil, wood, ethanol) are burned are water and carbon dioxide. If the fuels contain other substances (such as sulphur) then other polluting substances are released (such as sulphur dioxide, which dissolves in water to make sulphuric acid – and so 'acid rain'). Water is harmless, but carbon dioxide is building up in the atmosphere. The result could be a gradual warming up of the Earth due to the *greenhouse effect* (see page 217).

Carbon monoxide is a deadly poisonous gas produced when a fuel is not burned properly. If there is a shortage of oxygen, the hydrocarbon fuel will produce carbon monoxide (CO) instead of carbon dioxide (CO_2).

Nuclear fuels

These are radioactive elements that provide energy in power stations (and nuclear bombs) as a result of physical changes deep inside the atom (in the nucleus). They are not 'fuels' in the ordinary chemical sense; there is no combination with oxygen or any other kind of chemical reaction. The elements used in power stations are plutonium and uranium.

▽ Chemical reactions

In a chemical reaction, chemicals join together or break up so that new chemicals are formed. Energy is always involved when a chemical reaction takes place; it is either released (an *exothermic* reaction) or has to be supplied (*endothermic*).

starting chemicals $\xrightarrow{reaction}$ new substances

reactants $\xrightarrow{reaction}$ products

Some common types of reaction
Oxidation

Burning (combustion) is a typical oxidation reaction, in which oxygen is combined with another substance. For example:

iron + oxygen $\longrightarrow$ iron oxide (rusting),
Fe + O_2 $\longrightarrow$ 2FeO,

copper + oxygen $\rightarrow$ copper oxide,
2Cu + O_2 $\rightarrow$ 2CuO.

Displacement reactions

One element 'pushes' another one out of a compound:

iron + copper sulphate $\longrightarrow$ iron sulphate + copper,
Fe + $CuSO_4$ $\longrightarrow$ $FeSO_4$ + Cu.

The copper has been displaced by the iron.

This is a common reaction with metals and ionic compounds. The more active element displaces the less active element ('more active' = higher in the activity series).

Simple decomposition

Some compounds can be split up simply as a result of the particles colliding with each other (which happens when they are heated) or by the action of light energy.

calcium carbonate (chalk) $\xrightarrow{heating}$ calcium oxide ('quicklime') + carbon dioxide

Double decomposition

In these reactions the reactants exchange parts of themselves. They are usually ionic compounds, e.g.:

barium chloride + copper sulphate $\longrightarrow$ copper chloride + barium sulphate,
$BaCl_2$ + $CuSO_4$ $\longrightarrow$ $CuCl_2$ + $BaSO_4$.

Acid–base reactions

These follow the pattern:
 acid + base $\longrightarrow$ salt + water.

* hydrochloric acid + sodium hydroxide $\longrightarrow$ sodium chloride + water,
HCl + NaOH $\longrightarrow$ NaCl + H_2O;

* hydrochloric acid + magnesium oxide $\longrightarrow$ magnesium chloride + water,
2HCl + MgO $\longrightarrow$ $MgCl_2$ + H_2O.

Sometimes there are other products as well. With acids and carbonates for example, carbon dioxide is always a product:

hydrochloric acid + calcium carbonate $\longrightarrow$ calcium chloride + water + carbon dioxide,
2HCl + $CaCO_3$ $\longrightarrow$ $CaCl_2$ + H_2O + CO_2.

Neutralisation

Bases are alkaline, and when they react with an acid in the correct amounts they 'cancel' each other – the products are *neutral* (pH7, neither acid nor alkali): this is called 'neutralisation'.

Activation energy

Even reactions which give out a great deal of energy (exothermic) need a smaller amount of energy to trigger them off (a fire needs a match or at least a spark, an explosive needs a fuse). This energy is called the *activation energy* of the reaction.

Activity series of common metals

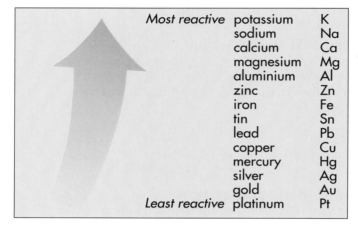

Most reactive	potassium	K
	sodium	Na
	calcium	Ca
	magnesium	Mg
	aluminium	Al
	zinc	Zn
	iron	Fe
	tin	Sn
	lead	Pb
	copper	Cu
	mercury	Hg
	silver	Ag
	gold	Au
Least reactive	platinum	Pt

Measuring reactants and products

Keeping track of the chemicals involved in a reaction can be quite tricky — they are changing all the time. But what doesn't and cannot change is the total amount of each element taking part.

First, we use the masses of the elements to work out the *formula mass* of each substance taking part:

Substance	carbon dioxide
Elements (mass)	carbon (12) oxygen (16)
Formula	CO_2
Sum	$1 \times$ carbon = 12 $2 \times$ oxygen = 32
Formula mass	12 + 32 = 44

So there are 12 grams of carbon in 44 grams of carbon dioxide, or 12 tonnes in 44 tonnes, etc.

Calculating products (yield)

Take the example of making quicklime, which is made from limestone. How much quicklime is produced for a given mass of limestone? This example shows how to calculate the expected *yield* for the process.

The equation for the reaction is:

limestone $\longrightarrow$ quicklime + carbon dioxide,

$$CaCO_3 \longrightarrow CaO + CO_2.$$

Element masses: Ca = 40, C = 12, O = 16.

Formula masses:

$CaCO_3$,	40 + 12 + (3 × 16)	= 100,
CaO,	40 + 16	= 56,
$CO2$,	12 + (2 × 16)	= 44.

The formula mass of the reactant equals the sum of the formula masses of the products. This must always happen, we can't get something for nothing, or lose anything.

Thus the calculation tells us that we need 100 grams of limestone to produce 56 grams of quicklime (or, we get 56 tonnes of quicklime for every 100 tonnes of limestone). This is only true if the limestone is *pure* calcium carbonate — which is rather unlikely.

Percentage yield

The above calculation predicts the mass of product if the process were perfect. In practice, we might get less (we couldn't get *more*).

$$\text{Percentage yield} = \frac{\text{actual yield}}{\text{predicted yield}} \times 100.$$

Chemical economics

Profit = selling price — total production and marketing costs.

$(P = S - C)$

Factors involved in rates of reaction

(What decides how fast chemical changes can take place?)

Concentration is a measure of how much chemical is packed into a solution. By increasing the concentrations of the reactants, the reacting particles are more likely to meet.

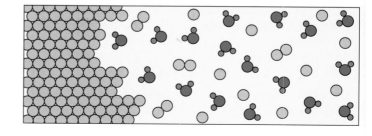

But in a dilute solution, there are fewer particles and they are further apart; so they are less likely to meet.

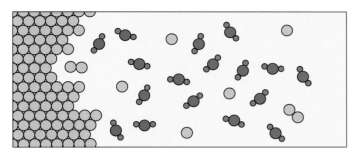

Reaction rates are speeded up by making sure that particles meet more often and/or with enough energy to react. This is done by:

- making the solutions more *concentrated*;
- using *higher temperatures*;
- using a *catalyst*;
- increasing the *surface area* of any solids (e.g. making the solids into fine powders, thin plates or wires).

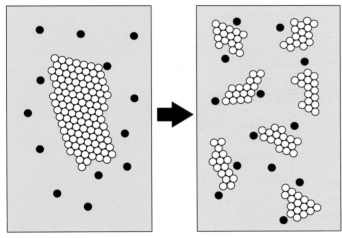

When a lump is broken into smaller pieces, more of its particles are on the 'outside' and so are exposed to a reaction.

Pressure is a measure of the force with which a gas is squeezed. In a gas at high pressure, the particles are closer together and more likely to bump into each other.

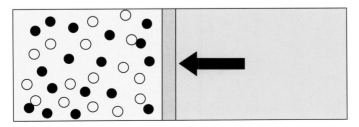

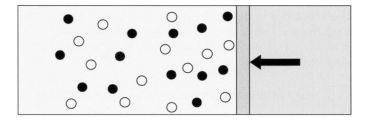

In a gas at lower pressure, the particles are further apart and are less likely to meet.

▽ Electrochemistry

When a salt (sodium chloride, copper sulphate, etc.) dissolves in water, its ions become separated. This produces an *ionic solution*.

When this solution is made part of an electric circuit, the ions move. Positive ions (*cations*) go to the negative plate (*cathode*). Negative ions (*anions*) go to the positive plate (the *anode*). The solution is called an *electrolyte*. This effect is used in electroplating.

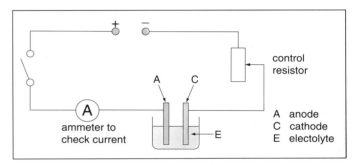

▽ A simple model of an atom

Atoms consist of a central nucleus of protons and neutrons, and a set of electrons that orbit this nucleus.

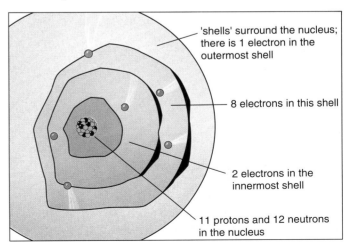

'shells' surround the nucleus; there is 1 electron in the outermost shell

8 electrons in this shell

2 electrons in the innermost shell

11 protons and 12 neutrons in the nucleus

Reference

The electrons in atoms are more like fuzzy clouds than neat points. They do not circle the nucleus in neat orbits, but a drawing of three fuzzy clouds would be very confusing.

▽ **Drawing chemical structure**

Atoms are held together in molecules by bonds. The bonds can be shown in different ways. The drawings show four representations of an ethane molecule (C_2H_4).

Structural formula

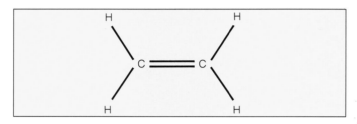

Simple diagram

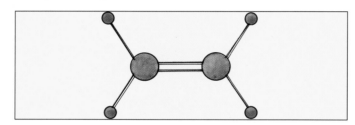

'Ball-and-stick' model

But the sticks don't really exist of course! A more realistic model is 'space filling'.

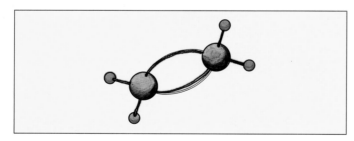

Solid models

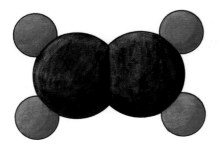

Reference

▽ **Ions**

An electron has a negative charge and a proton has a positive charge. A neutron has no charge at all. If these positive and negative charges are not balanced out in a molecule or atom, it will have extra positive or negative charge(s). This is called an ion. The table shows the charges on some ions.

Positive ions (cations)		Negative ions (anions)	
ammonium	NH_4^+	bromide	Br^-
hydrogen	H^+	chloride	Cl^-
copper (I)	Cu^+	iodide	I^-
potassium	K^+	hydroxide	OH^-
sodium	Na^+	nitrate	NO_3^-
silver	Ag^+	carbonate	CO_3^{2-}
calcium	Ca^{2+}	oxide	O^{2-}
magnesium	Mg^{2+}	sulphate	SO_4^{2-}
copper (II)	Cu^{2+}	sulphite	SO_3^{2-}
iron (II)	Fe^{2+}	sulphide	S^{2-}
zinc	Zn^{2+}	phosphate	PO_4^{3-}
aluminium	Al^{3+}		
iron (III)	Fe^{3+}		

Cations are usually metals and anions are usually non-metals.

▽ **Bonding**

Covalent bonding

The particles are held together by electric forces caused by sharing electrons, e.g. water.

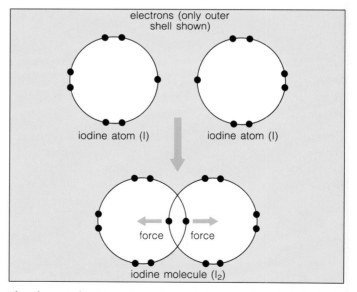

The 'lone' electrons are shared. The molecule is held together by the attraction forces between the shared electrons and the positive nuclei of *both* atoms.

Ionic bonding

Charged particles (the ions) are held together by electric forces caused by transferring electrons, e.g. sodium chloride (NaCl), salt.

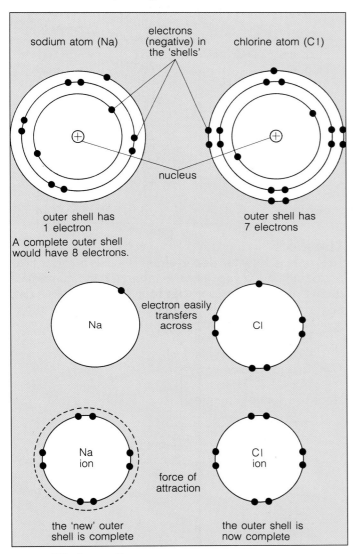

sodium atom (Na)

electrons (negative) in the 'shells'

chlorine atom (Cl)

nucleus

outer shell has 1 electron

outer shell has 7 electrons

A complete outer shell would have 8 electrons.

Na

electron easily transfers across

Cl

Na ion

Cl ion

force of attraction

the 'new' outer shell is complete

the outer shell is now complete

Metallic bonding

Metals are held together by electrical forces between the positive nuclei and a 'mob' of loose electrons that have split away from the metal atoms. These loose electrons make metals good conductors of heat and electricity.

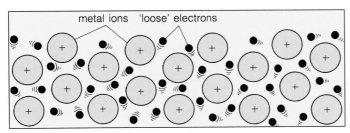

metal ions   'loose' electrons

▽ Solid, liquids, solutions and gases

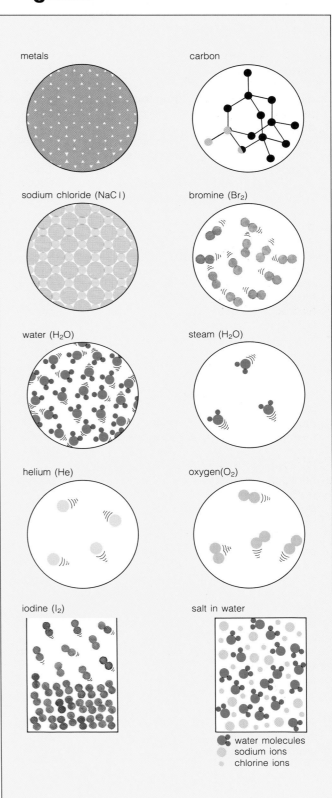

metals

carbon

sodium chloride (NaCl)

bromine (Br_2)

water (H_2O)

steam (H_2O)

helium (He)

oxygen(O_2)

iodine (I_2)

salt in water

water molecules
sodium ions
chlorine ions

Common chemicals

This table shows some commonly found chemical compounds. It gives their 'household' names and their formulae.

Name	Common name	Formula
aluminium oxide	alumina	Al_2O_3
ammonia		NH_3
ammonium chloride		NH_4Cl
ammonium nitrate	'Nitram' (fertiliser)	NH_4NO_3
calcium carbonate	limestone, chalk	$CaCO_3$
calcium chloride		$CaCl_2$
calcium hydroxide	slaked lime	$Ca(OH)_2$
calcium oxide	quicklime	CaO
carbon monoxide		CO
carbon dioxide		CO_2
cobalt (II) chloride		$CoCl_2$
copper (II) chloride		$CuCl_2$
copper (II) oxide		CuO
copper (II) sulphate		$CuSO_4$
hydrogen chloride		HCl
hydrochloric acid		HCl
hydrogen fluoride		HF
hydrogen peroxide		H_2O_2
hydrogen sulphide		H_2S
iron (II) oxide		FeO
iron (III) oxide		Fe_2O_3
magnesium carbonate		$MgCO_3$
magnesium chloride		$MgCl_2$
magnesium oxide	magnesia	MgO
manganese (IV) oxide	manganese dioxide	MnO_2
nitric acid		HNO_3
nitrogen monoxide		NO
nitrogen dioxide		NO_2
potassium chloride		KCl
potassium hydroxide	caustic potash	KOH
potassium manganate (VII)	potassium permanganate	$KMnO_4$
potassium nitrate	saltpetre	KNO_3
silicon (IV) oxide	silicon dioxide, silica	SiO_2
sodium carbonate	soda ash (washing soda)	Na_2CO_3
sodium chloride	salt	$NaCl$
sodium hydrogen-carbonate	sodium bicarbonate	$NaHCO_3$
sodium hydroxide	caustic soda	$NaOH$
sodium nitrate		$NaNO_3$
sodium sulphate		Na_2SO_4
sulphur dioxide		SO_2
sulphur trioxide		SO_3
sulphuric acid		H_2SO_4
zinc oxide		ZnO
water		H_2O

Alkanes

The alkanes are a group of carbon compounds of the general formula C_nH_{2n}.

Name	Formula	Melting point (°C)	Boiling point (°C)
methane	CH_4	−182	−161
ethane	C_2H_6	−183	−88
propane	C_3H_8	−188	−42
butane	C_4H_{10}	−138	−1
pentane	C_5H_{12}	−130	36
hexane	C_6H_{14}	−95	69
heptane	C_7H_{16}	−91	99
octane	C_8H_{18}	−57	126
nonane	C_9H_{20}	−51	151
decane	$C_{10}H_{22}$	−30	174
dodecane	$C_{12}H_{26}$	−10	216
eicosane	$C_{20}H_{42}$	37	344

The mole

The mole is a useful idea in chemistry. It is number (like a 'dozen'), but a very large number. It is the number of atoms, molecules or particles found in a formula mass, in grams. For example, the number of 'particles' in:

12 g of ^{12}C (atoms);
32 g of O_2 (molecules);
44 g of CO_2 (molecules).

A mole is (approximately) 6×10^{23}.

Here are some examples:

Substance	RFM[1] or RAM[2]	Relative masses of different numbers of particles			mass of 6×10^{23} particles (in grams)
		1	100	6×10^{23} particles	
C	12	12	1200	72×10^{23}	12 g
H	1	1	100	6×10^{23}	1 g
O_2	32	32	3200	192×10^{23}	32 g
CH_4	16	16	1600	96×10^{23}	16 g

[1] Relative formula mass.
[2] Relative atomic mass.

▽ How to work out relative formula masses (RFMs)

1 Find the formula, e.g. H_2SO_4.
2 Use the periodic table to find the *mass number*
(which is approximately the relative atomic mass)
for *each* element in the formula:

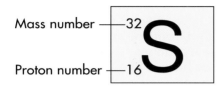

Mass number — 32 **S**

Proton number — 16

3 Add up the mass numbers, taking into account the
number of atoms present:

H_2 S O_4

$1 \times 2 + 32 + 16 \times 4 = 2 + 32 + 64 = 98$

The relative formula mass of H_2SO_4 is 98.

▽ The periodic table

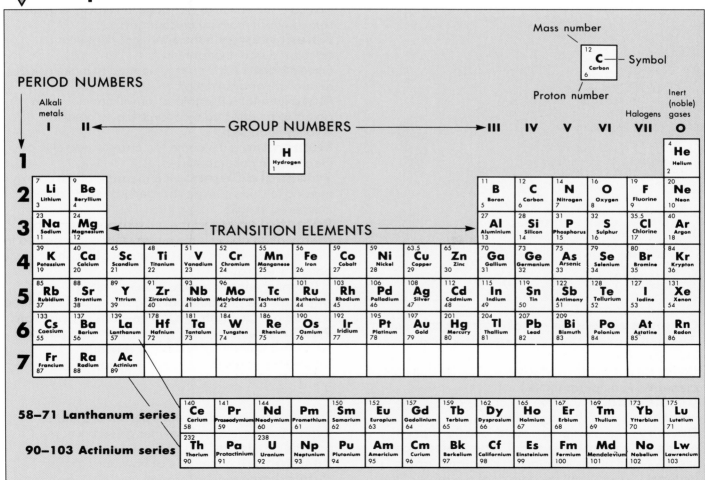

Definitions and explanations

a.c. and **d.c.**: alternating and direct current.

Acceleration is the rate of change of velocity (velocity change per unit time).

Acceleration of free fall is the rate of increase of speed by an object falling freely under gravity.

Braking distance is the distance a vehicle moves before the brakes bring it to a stop, after they have been applied.

Brittle: breaks by shattering into pieces, like glass.

Centre of mass is the 'point of balance' of an object, the place where all of its weight seems to act. This is sometimes called its centre of gravity. See *stability*.

Centripetal force is the force that makes an object move in a circle; it acts towards the centre of the circle.

Compression is a change (decrease) in length.

Conduction, convection and radiation are the three ways by which energy travels from hot objects.

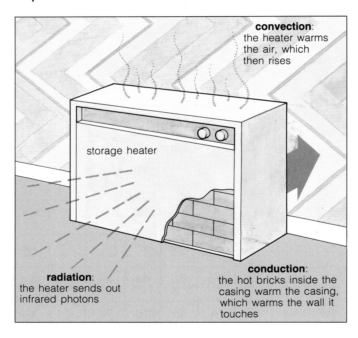

convection: the heater warms the air, which then rises

storage heater

radiation: the heater sends out infrared photons

conduction: the hot bricks inside the casing warm the casing, which warms the wall it touches

Crumple zone is the part of a car that has been designed to protect the passengers. The zone crumples up in an accident.

Current is the rate at which electrical charge flows, measured in amperes (amps).

Deceleration is the rate of change of velocity whilst an object is slowing down.

Density. The density of a material is the mass, in grams, of 1 cm^3 of the material. (Sometimes you will see it worked out as the mass, in kilograms, of 1 m^3 of material.) To work out the density of a sample of the material, divide its mass by its volume.

Efficiency:

$$\text{Percentage efficiency} = \frac{\text{useful energy transferred}}{\text{total energy put in}} \times 100\%$$

$$\left(\text{or } \frac{\text{output}}{\text{input}} \times 100\% \right)$$

No system, machine or process can have an efficiency greater than 100%. That would mean that energy had been created, which is impossible. Energy can only be transferred from one system to another.

Elastic: when a force changes its shape or size, on elastic material will go back to its original shape and size when the force is removed.

Elastic deformation is the change in size or shape of an elastic object caused by a force.

Elastic energy is the energy stored in an object that has been stretched, squashed or twisted by a force.

Evaporation is a liquid changing to a gas (vapour) without actually boiling.

Extension is a change (increase) in length.

Friction is the force between two surfaces that resists movement.

Force is the cause of a change in velocity (equals the rate at which momentum changes).

Kinetic energy is the energy of movement, calculated from the formula $E = \frac{1}{2}mv^2$

Latent heat is the energy needed to make a liquid evaporate or a solid melt.

Mass (inertia) is the natural 'unwillingness' of an object to be affected by a force (i.e. to have its velocity changed).

Momentum is the name for 'mass × velocity'; an idea used in collision studies.

Potential difference is a measure of the energy needed to drive electric charge through an object, measured in volts.

Potential energy: the gravitational potential energy of an object is the energy that is transferred to it from whatever lifts it. It is often just called the potential energy.

Potential energy = mass × height lifted × *g*, where *g* is the gravitational field strength of the planet you are on. On Earth, *g* is 9.8 newtons per kilogram.

Power is the rate of using energy or doing work, measured in watts (or joules per second).

Pressure: pressure = force ÷ area:

$$p = \frac{f}{a}$$

Pressure has units of newtons per square metre (N/m^2) but these are sometimes given the name pascals, Pa. ($1 N/m^2 = 1 Pa$.)

Resistance is a measure of how hard it is for electric charge to flow through an object, measured in ohms.

Specific heat capacity is the heating energy needed to warm 1 kilogram of a material by 1°C.

Speed is the rate of movement (distance per unit time).

Stability is about how easy or difficult it is to knock things over. The two things that decide it are:
- the area of the supporting base,
- the position of the centre of mass ('where the weight is').

The further an object can be tilted before the centre of mass is outside the base, the more stable it is. In all of these diagrams, the centre of mass is shown with a black dot.

Small base — easy to tip over.

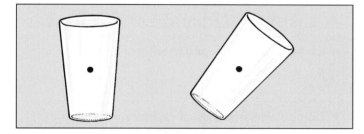

Larger base — harder to tip over.

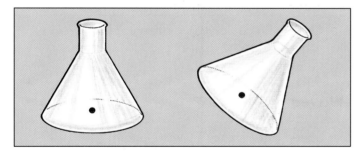

Chair made of light material.

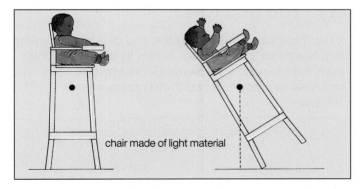

chair made of light material

Chair with the bottom part made of denser material. Note how this lowers the centre of mass.

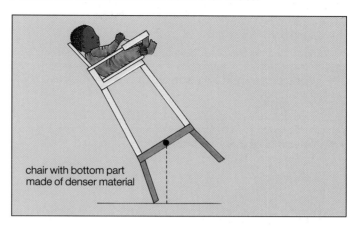

chair with bottom part made of denser material

Stiffness/flexibility is a measure of how much a material changes shape or size when a force is applied.

Thermal capacity is the heating energy needed to warm an object by 1°C.

Thinking distance is the distance a vehicle moves while the driver reacts to a signal to start braking.

Toughness is a measure of how much a material can be deformed by a force, without breaking.

Velocity is the rate of movement in a particular direction.

Work is the energy transferred when a force is applied to move something (work = force × distance moved along the direction of the force).

▽ Physics formulae

Motion
Also see 'Newton's Laws' on page 252.

- Force = mass × acceleration:

$$F = ma$$

- Impulse = change in momentum:

$$Ft = mv - mu$$

$$v = u + at$$
$$d = ut + \tfrac{1}{2}at^2$$

Where v = final velocity; u = starting velocity; a = acceleration; t = time; d = distance travelled.

Physics: data store

Gravity

- Distance fallen from rest:

$h = \frac{1}{2}gt^2$

- Work done in lifting a mass, m, by h metres:

$W = mgh$

- Newton's gravity formula:

$F = G\,\dfrac{m_1 m_2}{r^2}$

Where g is the acceleration of free-fall (9.8 m/s² on Earth); and in the gravity formula, F is the force of attraction between two masses, m_1 and m_2, separated by distance r. G is the 'constant of gravitation' and has the value 6.67×10^{-11} Nm²/kg².

- Centripetal force to keep mass, m, in a circle of radius r at velocity v:

$F = \dfrac{mv^2}{r}$

Energy and power

- Potential energy = mgh (where h = change in height)

- Kinetic energy = $\frac{1}{2}mv^2$ (where v = speed of a mass m)

- Energy transferred to change temperature (T) of a mass (m) of a substance with specific heat capacity s:

$E = msT$

- Energy transferred in time t by current I under potential difference V:

$E = VIt$

- Power = energy/time

- electrical power (in watts):

$P = VI$

- Efficiency $= \dfrac{\text{useful energy transferred}}{\text{energy supplied}} \times 100\%$

Electricity
(See also, Energy and power, above)

- Definition of resistance, R, in ohms

$R = \dfrac{V}{I}$

- Combined resistance of resistors in series:

$R = R_1 + R_2 + R_3 + \ldots$

- Combined resistance of resistors in parallel:

$\dfrac{1}{R} = \dfrac{1}{R_1} + \dfrac{1}{R_2} + \dfrac{1}{R_3} + \ldots$

- Charge (in coulombs) = current, I (amperes) $\times$ time, t (seconds)

$Q = It$

Waves

- Speed = frequency $\times$ wavelength

$V = f\lambda$

▽ The gas laws

If you hold your finger over the end of a bicycle pump that has been 'pulled open' ready to pump, and then push the plunger, the volume of the trapped air is reduced and you can feel that its pressure has increased.

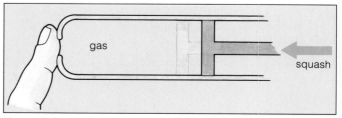

If a volume of gas is heated, the gas expands or its pressure increases.

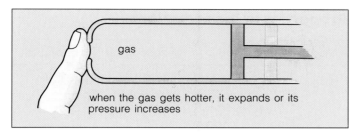

when the gas gets hotter, it expands or its pressure increases

These results are described by the gas formula. It says that for a fixed volume of gas:

$$\frac{PV}{T} = \text{constant}$$

(P is pressure, V, volume and T, temperature in kelvin. Kelvin temperatures start at absolute zero ($-273°C$)).

The pressure, volume and temperature of a gas are inter-related.

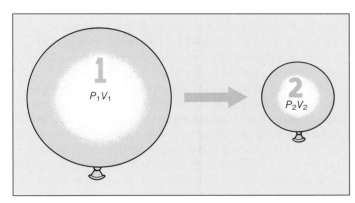

At a *constant temperature*, the volume of a gas is inversely proportional to its pressure. Thus, when changing a gas from condition 1 to condition 2:

$$P_1 \times V_1 = P_2 \times V_2$$

At *constant volume*, the pressure of a gas is proportional to its temperature in K (kelvin).

When changing a gas from condition 1 to condition 2:

$$\frac{P_1}{T_1} = \frac{P_2}{T_2}$$

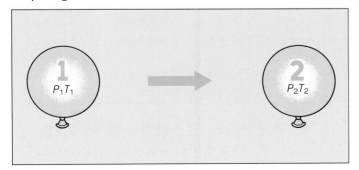

At *constant pressure*, the volume of a gas is proportional to its temperature in kelvin. Now when changing a gas from condition 1 to condition 2:

$$\frac{V_1}{T_1} = \frac{V_2}{T_2}$$

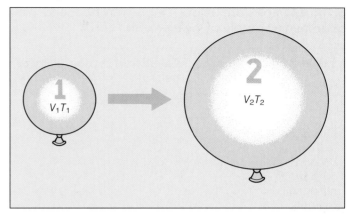

▽ Atoms, nuclei and nuclear energy

Practically all the mass of an atom is in its nucleus. An atom is electrically *neutral* — it has the same number of positive charges (on protons) in the nucleus as there are negative charges surrounding the nucleus (on electrons). The nucleus also contains unchanged (neutral) particles called neutrons, these are as big as the protons.

A model of the atom

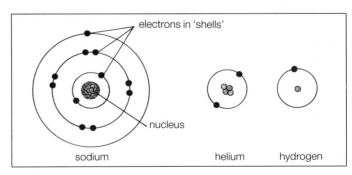

electrons in 'shells'

nucleus

sodium   helium   hydrogen

A model of the nucleus

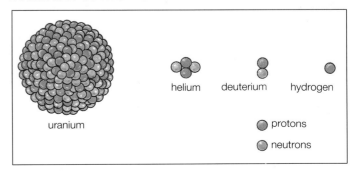

helium   deuterium   hydrogen

uranium

● protons
● neutrons

The number of protons is the same for all atoms of one element, but is different for the different elements. Some nuclei of the *same element* may have *different numbers of neutrons.* They are called *isotopes* of that element.

Some examples are below — more may be found in a good periodic table of the elements.

Element	Number of protons	Number of neutrons	Mass number (total number of neutrons and protons)
hydrogen	1	0	1
helium	2	2	4
carbon*	6	6	12
carbon*	6	8	14
nitrogen	7	7	14
oxygen	8	8	16
chlorine*	17	18	35
chlorine*	17	20	37
uranium	92	146	238
plutonium	94	148	242

* isotopes

Radioactivity

Some nuclei are *unstable,* and there is a chance that they may give out energy by sending out a small part of themselves, either as particles of matter or as electromagnetic radiation. The particles of matter they emit are:

- *alpha particles* — a package of two protons and two neutrons;
- *beta particles* — a single electron.

The electromagnetic radiation is of very short wavelength (high photon energy), called *gamma radiation.* Gamma radiation is even more penetrating and harmful to living cells than X-rays.

Properties of the radiations

Name	Description	Range in air	Stopped by
alpha	very massive (2 protons with 2 neutrons); positive charge	4–10 centimetres	sheet of paper
beta	very light (electrons); negative charge	variable up to about a metre	a few millimetres of aluminium
gamma	photons of electromagnetic radiation; not charged; travel at the speed of light	no limit	several metres of concrete

Half-life

Radioactive elements that give off the radiations described above change into new elements in doing so. This change is called nuclear *decay.* The nuclei do not all change at the same time, they change at random so that it is impossible to predict when a given nucleus will change. But there are so many nuclei in even a very small sample of the element that the laws of chance ensure that for a given radioactive element *half* of the nuclei will have decayed in a certain time. This time is called the *half-life* of that element. Because some elements have isotopes (nuclei with the same number of protons but differing in the number of neutrons) we should use this word rather than 'element' when discussing radioactivity. Some isotopes are radioactive, others are not. For example, carbon can have eight isotopes, only two of which are not radioactive — carbon-12 and carbon-13. Ordinary carbon is a mix of carbon-12 (98.89%), carbon-13 (1.11%) and carbon-14 (a trace).

Examples of radioactive isotopes

Isotope	Radiation emitted	Element it decays to	Half-life of element
carbon-14	beta	nitrogen	5739 years
uranium-235	alpha	thorium	713 million years
caesium-137	beta and gamma	barium	30 years

The half-life of carbon-14 is used in *radiocarbon dating.*

▽ Circuit symbols

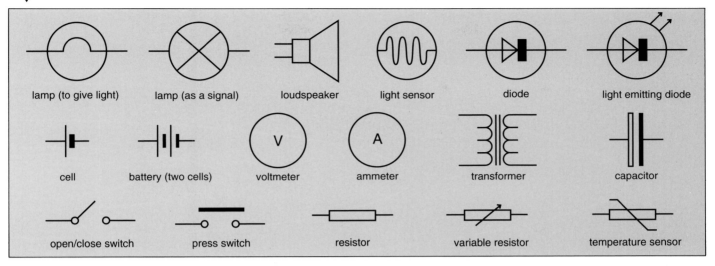

lamp (to give light)	lamp (as a signal)	loudspeaker	light sensor	diode	light emitting diode
cell	battery (two cells)	voltmeter	ammeter	transformer	capacitor
open/close switch	press switch	resistor	variable resistor	temperature sensor	

▽ Energy

Energy is measured in joules (J). A system has energy if it can be used to do work. This means it can exert a force to move something.

Examples of energy systems:
- fuel-oxygen system: can do work in a car engine;
- electric cell: can drive a motor, heat a wire (by moving electrons against a resistance);
- two masses: if separate; can use gravitational force to do work, e.g. a pile-driver forcing steel piles into the ground.

Laws of energy
1 Energy is conserved. This means that it cannot be created from nothing, and it cannot be lost.
2 When energy is used to do work, some of it gets side-tracked: not all of the energy supplied does useful work. The 'missing' energy usually ends up spread out over a large number of particles, i.e. it is lost to the surroundings as 'heat'.

These laws can be illustrated in an energy-flow diagram called Sankey diagram. This one shows the energy transfers through a car engine.

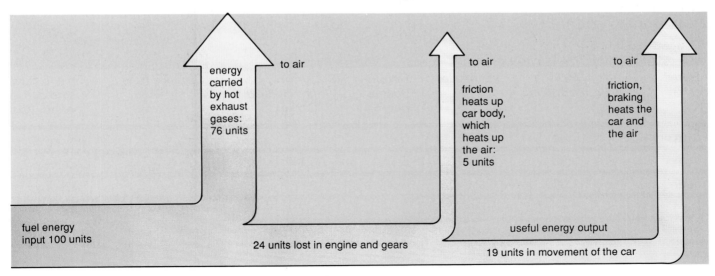

energy carried by hot exhaust gases: 76 units — to air

friction heats up car body, which heats up the air: 5 units — to air

friction, braking heats the car and the air — to air

fuel energy input 100 units

24 units lost in engine and gears

useful energy output

19 units in movement of the car

The output energy equals the input energy from the fuel — oxygen system; but only 19% is used to move the car.

▽ **The planets**

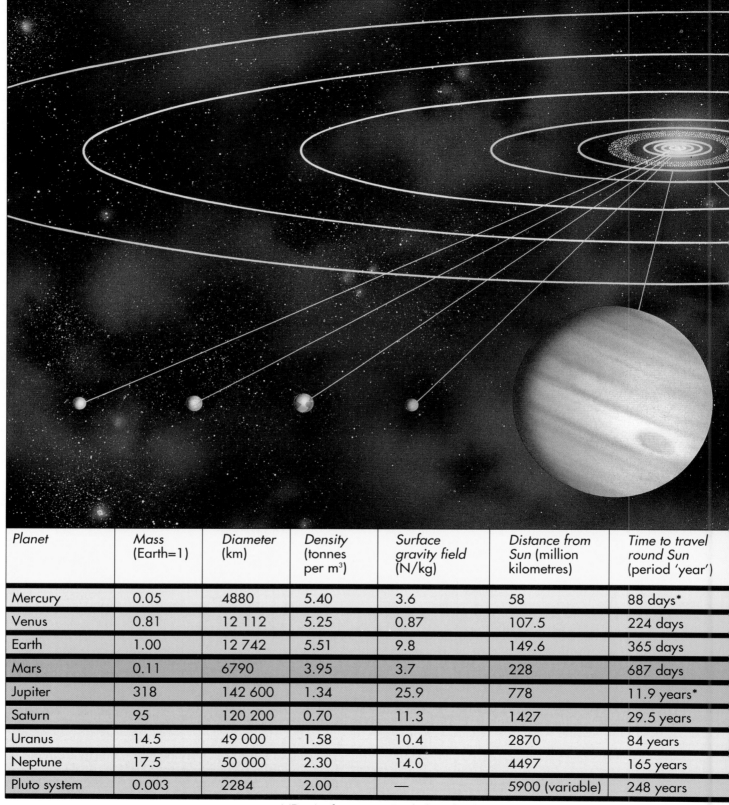

Planet	Mass (Earth=1)	Diameter (km)	Density (tonnes per m³)	Surface gravity field (N/kg)	Distance from Sun (million kilometres)	Time to travel round Sun (period 'year')
Mercury	0.05	4880	5.40	3.6	58	88 days*
Venus	0.81	12 112	5.25	0.87	107.5	224 days
Earth	1.00	12 742	5.51	9.8	149.6	365 days
Mars	0.11	6790	3.95	3.7	228	687 days
Jupiter	318	142 600	1.34	25.9	778	11.9 years*
Saturn	95	120 200	0.70	11.3	1427	29.5 years
Uranus	14.5	49 000	1.58	10.4	2870	84 years
Neptune	17.5	50 000	2.30	14.0	4497	165 years
Pluto system	0.003	2284	2.00	—	5900 (variable)	248 years

* 'Day' refers to one Earth day of 24 hours; 'year' refers to one Earth year of 365 day

Time to spin on axis	Average surface temperature (°C)	Number of moons	Atmosphere	Planet
59 days	350	0	none	Mercury
243 days	460	0	thick; carbon dioxide; sulphuric acid	Venus
23h 56min	20	1	nitrogen and oxygen	Earth
24h 37min	−23	2	thin; carbon dioxide	Mars
9h 50min	−120	16; 1 ring	hydrogen, helium, ammonia, methane	Jupiter
10h 14min	−180	17 plus rings	hydrogen, helium, ammonia, methane	Saturn
10h 49min	−210	15 plus rings	hydrogen, helium, ammonia, methane	Uranus
15h 48min	−220	8	hydrogen, helium, methane	Neptune
6.4 days	−230	1	none – frozen	Pluto system

▽ The stars

The brightest stars have been given names — many of the names date from hundreds of years ago. The stars are grouped into constellations. When you look at the stars from the northern hemisphere, the most prominent constellation is the Great Bear (Ursa Major). If you imagine a line from the two brightest stars in the Great Bear — Dubhe and Merak — it will lead you straight to the Pole Star. This star lies almost directly over the Earth's North Pole and so it was used for simple navigation in the past. The North Pole is gradually drifting away from this star. But we still draw star maps for the northern hemisphere with the Pole Star at the centre.

Constellations around the Pole Star

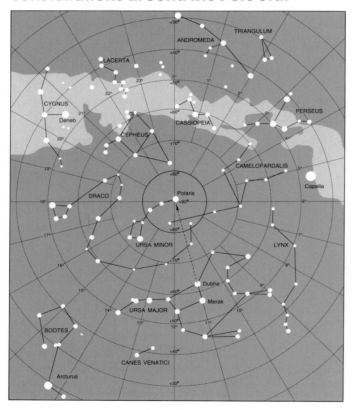

Spring constellations

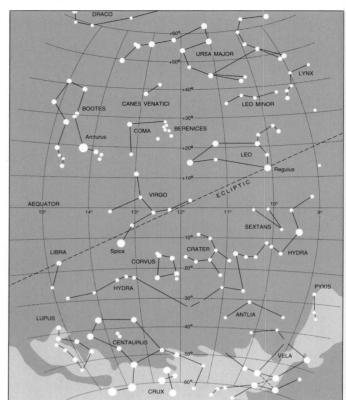

Summer constellations

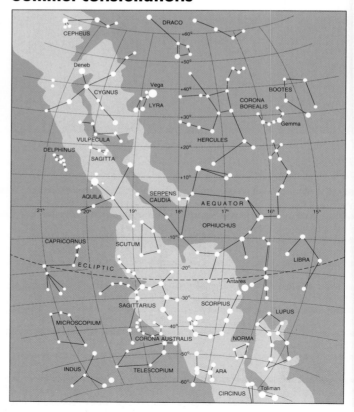

Autumn constellations

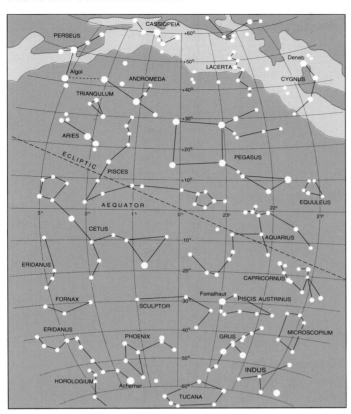

Winter constellations

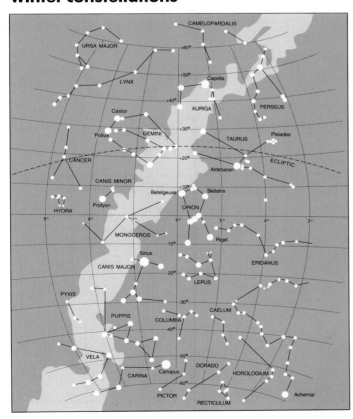

▽ Some useful physical constants

Speed of light, c
3×10^8 m/s

Acceleration of free fall, g
9.8 m/s^2

Strength of Earth's gravitational field at surface
9.8 N/kg

Universal gravitational constant, G
6.7×10^{-11} Nm^2/kg^2

Speed of sound in air (0°C)
330 m/s

Atmospheric pressure (normal)
10^5 N/m^2 (1 bar)

▽ Properties of materials

Material	Density (g/cm³)	Specific heat capacity (J/kg °C)	Melting point (°C)
aluminium	2.7	886	659
copper	8.9	380	1083
iron	7.9	500	1539
lead	11.4	127	328
zinc	7.3	380	420
brick	1.7	—	—
concrete	≈2.2	—	—
glass	2.5	—	varies
Perspex	1.2	1500	—
polythene	0.92–0.96	2300	—
wood	0.2–0.8	—	—
water	1.0	4200	0

Reference

▽ Transducers

Transducers convert a physical quantity (such as light or sound) into an electrical signal, and back again.

Moving-coil microphone

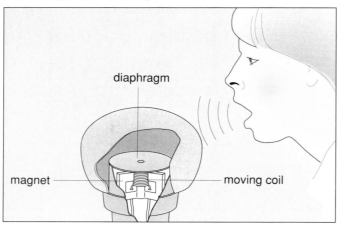

diaphragm

magnet — moving coil

Telephone earpiece

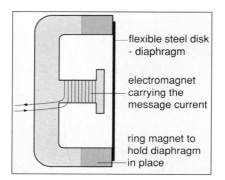

flexible steel disk - diaphragm

electromagnet carrying the message current

ring magnet to hold diaphragm in place

Loudspeaker

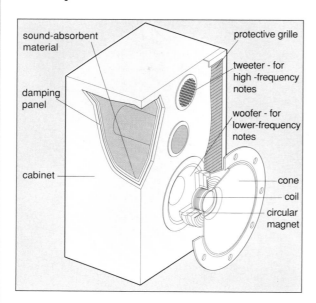

sound-absorbent material

protective grille

tweeter - for high -frequency notes

damping panel

woofer - for lower-frequency notes

cabinet

cone

coil

circular magnet

▽ Lenses and their uses

Weak positive lens

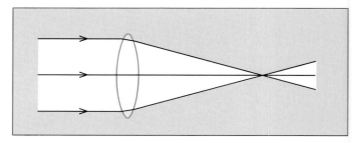

Strong positive lens

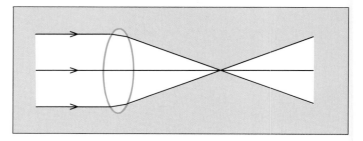

Negative lens

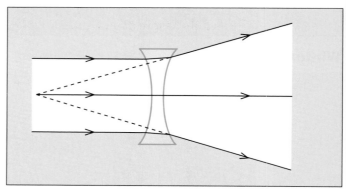

Eye
Light is focused by both the cornea and the eye lens. The eye lens changes shape to alter its strength.

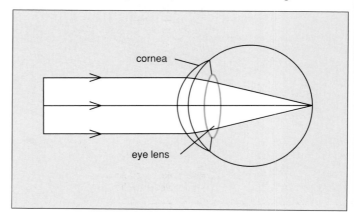

cornea

eye lens

Reference

Camera

The lens can be moved backwards and forwards to focus the image on the film.

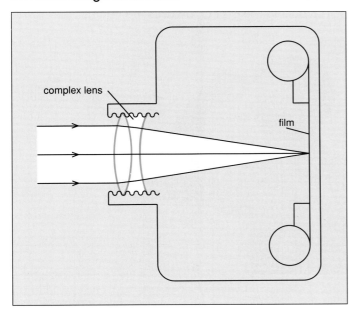

Concave mirror

Torch mirrors make a narrow beam.

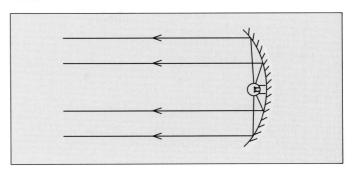

Dentist's mirror

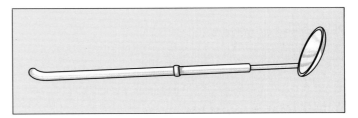

▽ Reflection

When light is reflected, the angle of incidence equals the angle of reflection.

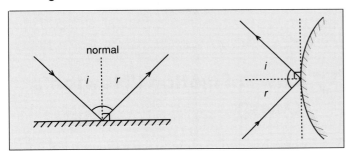

Mirrors and their uses

Convex mirror.

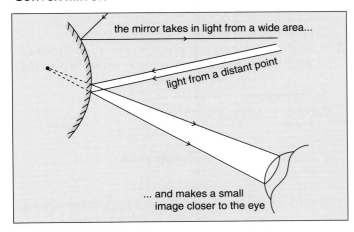

▽ Refraction

Light changes direction when it goes from one material to another if the light does not enter at a right angle to the surface.

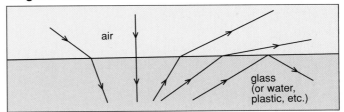

As light goes from a less dense to a more dense material (say, air to glass), its direction changes to make a larger angle to the surface. The reverse happens when light goes the other way (e.g. glass to water). As the angle changes, light leaves closer and closer to the surface. Eventually it cannot leave at all and total internal *reflection* occurs.

Total internal reflection in a light-carrying fibre.

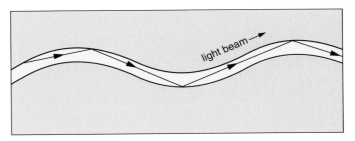

Prism deviating a ray of light.

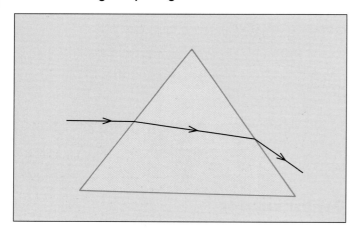

Prisms used as mirrors.

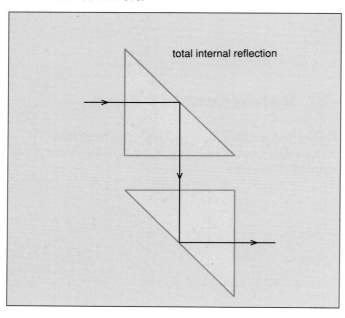

total internal reflection

Real and apparent depth.
An optical illusion caused by refraction.

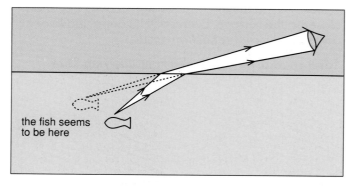

the fish seems
to be here

▽ Circular motion

For an object to move in a circle, there has to be a force pulling the object towards the centre.

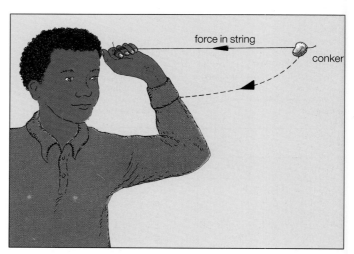

force in string

conker

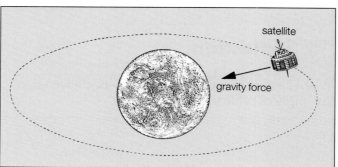

satellite

gravity force

▽ Laws of motion ('Newton's Laws')

1 A force is needed to change the movement of an object; otherwise, the object will keep still or keep moving in a straight line.

2 If an unbalanced force does act on an object, it will make the object accelerate and/or change its direction of movement.

3 At least two objects are always needed to produce a force, and the force acts equally on both objects.

The formulae:
- Force = mass × acceleration
  $F\,ma$

- Impulse = change of momentum
  $Ft = mv$

(F = force (N); t = time (s); a = acceleration (N/kg); m = mass (kg); v = change in velocity (m/s).)

Reference